Domino Games
and
Domino Puzzles

K. W. H. Leeflang

Domino Games and Domino Puzzles

Translated
by Irene Cumming Kleeberg

ST. MARTIN'S PRESS
NEW YORK

Originally published in the Netherlands ©1972
by N. V. Uitgeversmaatschappij Kosmos, Amsterdam

For information, write:
St. Martin's Press, Inc., 175 Fifth Ave., New York, N.Y. 10010
Manufactured in the United States of America
Library of Congress Catalog Card Number: 74-33919

Library of Congress Cataloging in Publication Data

Leeflang, K.W. H.
Domino games and domino puzzles.

Translation of Dominospelen en dominopuzzels.
Bibliography: p.
1. Dominoes. I. Title.
GV1467.L4313 795'.3 74-33919

For Hans, Joost, and Karel

Preface

Everyone is aware of the almost limitless possible ways in which chess pieces can be placed on a board or cards shuffled. It will probably surprise many, however, that there are innumerable possibilities in a simple box of dominoes. A game of dominoes is comparable to a well-integrated mathematical structure which permits a number of possible arrangements. Dominoes can be part of the competition of a domino game or, on a more sophisticated level, give rise to domino puzzles.

The combination of game and discipline is part of a domino puzzle, a union of the kind to which the American mathematician SAWYER referred when he remarked on the charms of certain puzzles, especially for children and mathematicians.

It was a surprise to me when, in the well-known book *Wonderlijke Problemen (Surprising Problems)* by Professor SCHUH, I came upon mathematical applications of the domino figures my father introduced to me as a child. This led me to go somewhat deeper into the quadrilles of LUCAS, toward a more systematic framework built on SCHUH's foundations. Using this framework, it became possible to find a complete solution to the problem of the quadrille with the fewest and that with the most corners. SCHUH considers this puzzle among the most successful. I am delighted to be able to close this section with the splendid 1,000-puzzle of Mr. MINNIGH.

Although the following chapters contain several puzzles which have been known for a long time, most are new and original. In the chapter on magic squares, formulas with wider applications are published for the first time.

It was obvious that this book must have a discussion of domino games. The publications of ARMANINO in the United States and of Mr. BRETHOWER in Holland have laid the groundwork for the establishment of rules for domino games such as "Nossen." I wish to thank Mrs. F. EIJKMAN-BOUMAN for her careful explanation of the Groningen (Netherlands) cross domino. The kind cooperation of Mr. J.R.G. DE VEER, who in one of his puzzle columns roused his readers' interest in the subject quadrilles, enabled me to add some valuable supplementary material to the present edition.

Many of the puzzles in this book are far from simple. From the experience of my predecessors, I realize only too well the possibilities for errors and omissions in my book. I would be grateful to learn of these and of domino puzzles with which I am not familiar.

Overveen, The Netherlands
Summer 1972

K.W.H. LEEFLANG

Table of Contents

Part One: The Stones and the Game

Part Two: Domino Puzzles

Part One

The Stones and the Game

Queer game, dominoes. People go mad about it. They'll play for hours.
Agatha Christie, 'The A.B.C. Murders'

Honore Daumier: . . . Domino! . . . . *Photo: Bibliothèque Nationale, Paris*

I The Development and History of the Game

La simplicité des dispositions de ce jeu porte facilement à croire qu'il doit être, en effet, contemporain des premiers ages de la civilisation.
——Edouard Lucas, 'Récréations mathématiques', Volume II

1. Origin and History

The European game of dominoes is played with twenty-eight rectangular bones (or stones) which are twice as long as they are wide. Previously, they were made in two layers: a black bottom layer of ebony or black-colored bone and a white upper layer of bone or ivory. Today they are usually plastic.

The white top is divided into two ends, each of which has a number of dots. This number varies from zero to six; ends having no dots are called blanks. All combinations that can be formed by the numbers from one to six or, in other words, all the throws possible with a pair of dice, are represented on twenty-one bones. Of the seven remaining bones, six have a blank end combined with one of the numbers and the seventh has two blanks.

Bones which have the same number of dots on both halves are called doublets. They run from doublet blank to doublet six.

The game is of fairly recent date in this form. It first appeared in Italy in the beginning of the eighteenth century and then spread throughout Europe. Toward the end of the eighteenth century, it was brought to England, apparently by French prisoners of war, and spread to both North and South America.

It's interesting that a game with such a simple form developed so late. A similar game was played in ancient Egypt. For centuries, the Chinese played a game differing from ours in that, in addition to the twenty-one bones representing the possible throws of a pair of dice, it included eleven duplicates. It is not known if the Western and Eastern forms of this game have a common origin, as is the case with chess and certain card games. Perhaps it is best to say that, in contrast to these highly developed games, a game of the simplicity of dominoes is reinvented whenever it is forgotten.

The origin of the name dominoes is also obscure. The word *domino* as the name of the game as well as of the bones was accepted in 1798 by the Académié Française. Some etymologists suggest the name comes from a clerical winter hooded cape that was black with a white lining and called a domino. This is no more than a guess, however.

The game of dominoes became extremely popular during the eighteenth and nineteenth centuries. It was so popular in coffee houses that it was even worth the trouble of cheating! In 1820 C. VAN GREEVEN in The Hague published a curious little book titled 'Het Bedrog, hetwelk men met het zogenaamde Domino-spel pleegt, ontmaskerd' *(The Deceits Which People Commit at the So-Called Game of Dominoes, Unmasked).* The writer, who hid behind the initials J.K., gave his readers a list of practices of which he had been the victim:

"Being by nature company loving and having learned that man's spirit cannot always be striving but also needs some diversion and not belonging, also, to that unbearable group of people who avoid all lawful amusement, I was often accustomed, when my business was finished and I had little inclination to read, to go to one or another coffee house. Having read the newspaper, I would spend a little time at a game of dominoes, a game at which people judged me a good player. Nevertheless, I found that I could seldom win a game from certain Gentlemen; many times I noticed that whenever they played a bone they would talk and laugh while playing it. The reader shall, from the proofs I shall offer, perceive that in this way bones were named which they had not yet played. This might have continued a long time without being discovered by me were it not that a friend of mine warned me in their presence that their attentiveness in getting to know me was for the purpose of playing dominoes in a way which was not upright, and that when they produced each bone they also told each other all the bones which were in their hands."

After this windy introduction the methods of cheating were exposed.

The great interest to which more difficult intellectual games such as checkers, chess, and especially bridge have fallen heir in our century has relegated the game of dominoes to the family circle. It is especially suitable for playing there as, in its simplest form, it can be played even by extremely young children. This does not, however, detract from the value of more complicated forms of dominoes for other groups. In the western part of the United States, the domino game called "Five-Up" has many practitioners. In the Netherlands, Nossen, which has perhaps the most right to be called an intellectual game, also has many enthusiasts.

2. Characteristics

Before discussing the various ways in which the game of dominoes can be played, we shall give some general characteristics of any game.

A set of dominoes has a mathematical structure. It is the collection of all pairs that can be formed from a set of natural numbers, beginning with zero and ending with a certain maximum and including combinations of two of the same numbers. The maximum number is usually six, but there are domino sets available with the doublet nine as the highest stone and some sets which go to doublet twelve. As far as this book is concerned, sets that have doublet six as the highest stone are the best choice. The set is manageable and permits many not-too-difficult mathematical puzzles; we shall limit ourselves to it for the most part. This is not to suggest that the set going up to double nine has no value; it is especially useful in large families. See also the domino cross in II under 2.5.

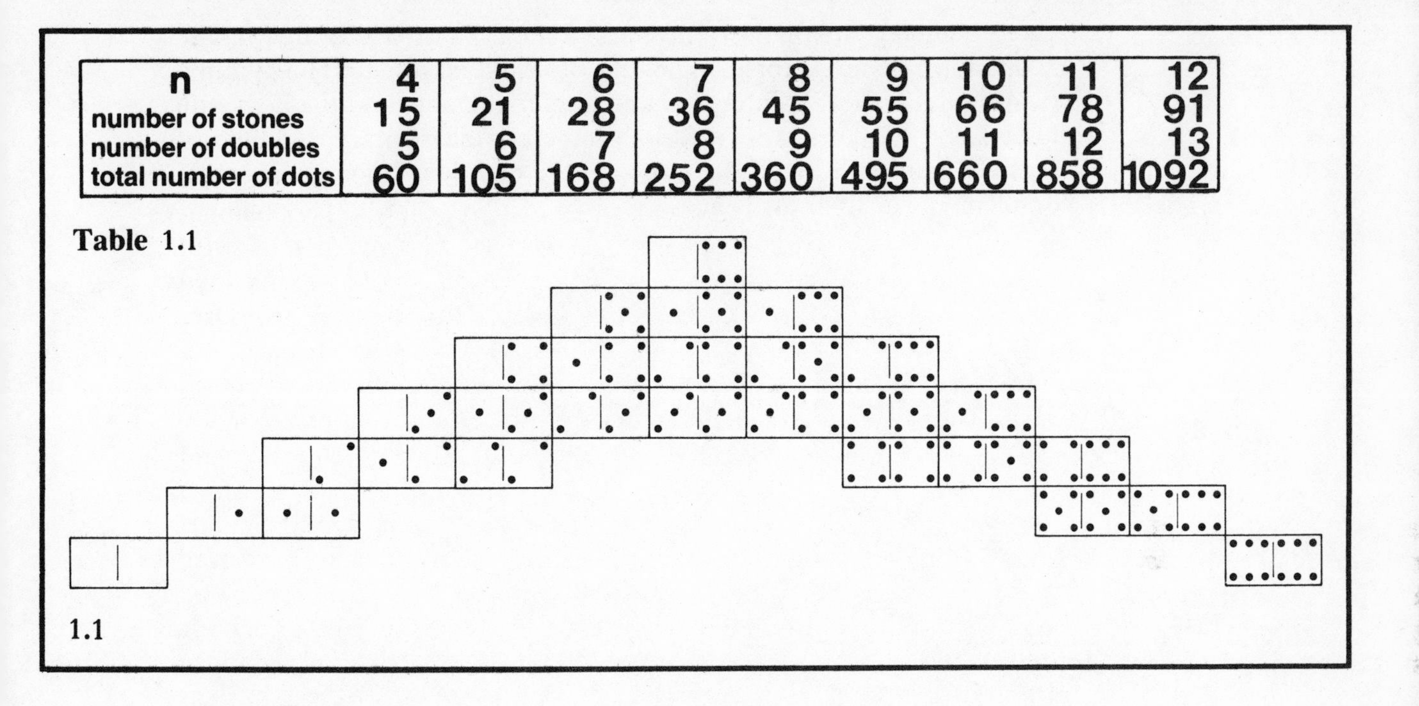

n	4	5	6	7	8	9	10	11	12
number of stones	15	21	28	36	45	55	66	78	91
number of doubles	5	6	7	8	9	10	11	12	13
total number of dots	60	105	168	252	360	495	660	858	1092

Table 1.1

1.1

If n-n is the highest stone of a set, then it follows that:

a. the number of bones of a game consists of $\frac{(n + 1)(n + 2)}{2}$;
b. the number of doubles is n + 1;
c. the number of ends with the same number of dots is n + 2;
d. the sum of all the dots is $S = \frac{n(n + 1)(n + 2)}{2}$, from which it follows that the average number of dots on a bone is equal to n. For sets of differing sizes, this leads to table 1.1.

A set includes n + 1 stones with the same number of spots. On one stone, the double, the same number of dots appears twice; on the remaining stones, the number is combined with another number.
A set in which n is equal to 1 or an even number can be laid out with the same number of dots against each other in a single chain. This is possible for no other value of n. If n is an even number, the number of dots on both ends of this chain is the same. Such a set can, therefore, be arranged in a closed "ring."
Still another interesting characteristic is apparent from the table. If the doubles are removed in a game in which n-n is the highest stone, there remain just as many stones as doubles in the set.

In a set in which n is even there are $\frac{n + 2}{2}$ and in a set in which n is uneven, $\frac{n+ 1}{2}$ dominoes on which both halves have a total of n spots. The number of spots on their ends are called complementary. The remaining stones can be paired so that the number of dots on their ends form repeated complementaries—in the normal game the 0-5 and the 6-1, the 1-2 and the 5-4 and so forth. When the stones are arranged in a pyramid (example 1.1), another interesting characteristic appears: the bones on either side of a vertical center line have complementary numbers of spots on their ends, with the bones in the middle column having their complements on their own ends.

II Domino Games

Of all common games, dominoes is certainly one of the least standardized.
——M. Kraitchic, 'Mathematical Recreations'

1. General Rules

A game like dominoes, in which the pieces or bones are all of the same type and which is not limited by a game board, inevitably has a great many different rules. There are not only many ways to play the game, but also many variations in the secondary rules of the game. The game is codified only in cases where it is played regularly in a club or social group. ARMANINO has explained the rules by which Five-Up and other games are played in certain American clubs, while BRETHOUWER has laid out the rules by which the Dutch game Nossen is played at the "Witte Societeit" (White Club) in The Hague, as well as the way in which games based on Nossen are played.
These codifications are shown below. This section begins with an overview of the most general rules from which, except in the case of the codified games, a choice can be made.

A half stone which is either blank or has a certain number of eyes is called an *end.* Bones which have ends with the same number of eyes are called stones of the same *suit.* With the exception of the doubles, all bones belong to two suits.

A. Number of players

1. Two to six persons can take part in the ordinary game played with twenty-eight bones. Each plays for himself.
2. A few games are played by four players, with the two players sitting across from each other forming a team that plays against the other team.
3. More involved games permit additional players.

B. Shuffling

Before the game begins, the stones are shuffled by moving them around with the spots face downward. In cases where it is known which players shall make the first move, the player on the right shuffles or, when two players are playing, the one who is not making the first move shuffles.

C. The Number of Stones with Which the Players Begin

1. Usually two players take seven stones each, three to four players five each, and more players three each.
2. A better rule is for each player to take the number of bones equal to eight minus the number of players.
   That is, in a case where S persons are taking part in the game, each one takes 8–S stones.

3. The bones are dealt at the beginning of each hand.
4. In the playing of games with larger than ordinary sets, the participants take proportionately more bones.
5. Each player places his bones on edge in front of him, with their backs to the other players. All the players must be able to see how many bones each has. At the beginning of a hand, the participants should make sure all players have taken the same number of bones. Excess bones may not be returned.

D. The Player "On Set"

The player who sets the first stone on the table is called the player *on set*. During the course of a game, he is generally the one who has lost most heavily in the previous hand. In American point games, the player on set rotates in a clockwise direction among the participants. At the beginning of a game, it must be determined who shall be the player on set. This can be done:

1. By drawing from the group of shuffled stones. Each player takes one stone with the one who draws the stone with the highest total number of spots becoming the player on set. In case of a tie, it is decided by the stone with the highest number on one end: for example, 5–2 takes precedence over 4–3. The drawn stones are returned and shuffled again.
2. By a player calling out doubles, starting with the highest after each player has taken his stone. The player who has the first of these stones in his hand is the player on set, and he plays this stone. A double blank is considered the lowest double.

E. The Set

The set is the playing of the first stone. The particular game being played determines whether the first stone is a double or other particular stone or one chosen at will by the player on set.

F. Subsequent Plays

The players play in turns following a clockwise direction. Usually each player plays no more than one stone at his turn. Once he has let go of the stone, he may not change it.

G. The Boneyard

1. Stones remaining on the table after each player has taken his allotted number form the *boneyard*, from which players can draw. The boneyard may become exhausted in only a few cases; usually two stones must remain in the boneyard.
2. In the United States the custom is that when two players play, two stones must stay in the boneyard; with three or more players, only one must remain.

H. Drawing

1. A player with one or more playable stones is obliged to play. If he has none, he must draw from the boneyard. In most games he must continue drawing until he has found a suitable stone, though in some he may draw only a certain number.

2. In Russian dominoes a player may draw when he wishes even when he has a playable bone in his hand. Players may draw only when it is their turn.

I. Passing

A player who can neither play what is in his hand nor draw additional dominoes passes. His turn goes to the next player.

K. Winner and Loser

1. The first player to get rid of all his stones is *domino* and winner of the game. The *largest loser* is the player who has the greatest number of spots on the bones remaining in front of him.
   A game is *closed* when a stone is played that prevents the other players from making further moves. The winner is then the player with the smallest number of spots on his remaining stones. If two players have the same number, they must each draw a stone. The winner is the one who draws the stone having the lowest number of spots.

2. When two players are partners, they have won when one of them has played all his stones. In closed games they win when they have, together, fewer spots on the dominoes they have left than their opponents do.

L. Scoring

People usually play a number of hands one after the other; together these form a game. The results of each hand should be totaled during the course of the game.

1. The simplest method of doing this is to note after every hand how many spots each player—except the domino or winning couple—still has. When one of the players or pairs reaches a certain previously arranged number of points—for example 100 or 150—the game is ended. The game is therefore won by the person(s) with the lowest number of points.
2. Another method is for the winner or the winning pair to be awarded the total number of spots in the hands of the opponents. The game is won by those who first reach the arranged number.
   In the case of a closed game, the scoring can be done in the same way or:
3. The number of dots in each hand can be counted.
4. The first method of scoring cannot be used if, during the hands, points were earned in another way (see under Point Games). In hands played according to L3, it is sometimes agreed by two or more losers (or pairs) to settle among themselves the same way the winner settled with them.

The ways in which games of dominoes are played fall into two types: *block games* and *point games*.

In block games the object is to play so that your opponent has as little chance as possible to set and must draw as often as possible, while at the same time creating conditions favorable for yourself.

In point games the object is to play so that the total number of spots on

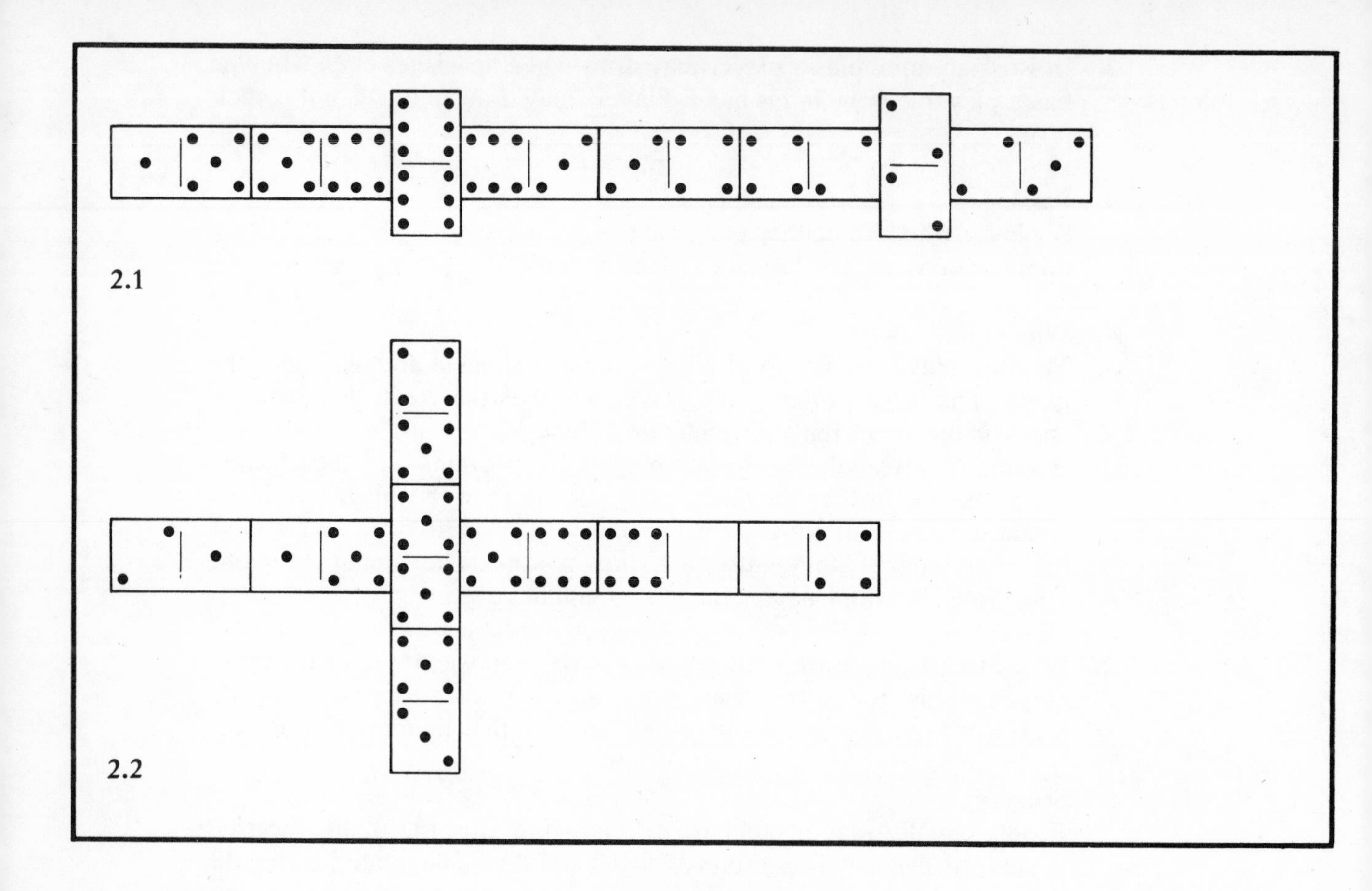

the open ends of the played series is a multiple of a certain number, usually five.

2. Block Games

1. The Ordinary Game of Dominoes

In the ordinary game of dominoes, stones that are not doubles are placed end to end so that ends with the same number of spots are against one another. Doubles are placed crosswise and the ends of doubles may not be played against (example 2.1).

1.1 *Ordinary Dominoes*

Every player takes from the shuffled deck his number of stones: that is, eight less the number of players. The first hand of a game is begun by the player with the highest double. If no one has a double, then the dominoes are reshuffled.

In subsequent hands the largest loser of the previous hand makes the first set. He must set a double. If he has more than one double, the choice is up to him.

If he has no doubles, then he must draw a bone and play that.

If this stone is not a double, any player may, even though it is not his turn, set a suitable double against it. Such a player must then let his turn

pass, by saying, "I wait," rather than playing. If a player sets two doubles, he must give up two turns.
A player who has no suitable stones in his hand must draw until he obtains such a stone. Two stones must remain in the boneyard. If a player can't play and there are no more stones which can be drawn, he says, "I pass."
In scoring, a double blank counts as fourteen spots. Scoring can be done according to any of the methods under L.

1.2 There is a rule in Germany that the player on set who plays a double may immediately play a second suitable stone without losing a turn.

1.3 There are a number of other variations in the usual way of playing. In Anglo-Saxon countries the following rules are often followed.
For the first hand of a game the player on set is often decided by drawing. In following hands the largest loser is the first player on set. When there are two players, each of them takes seven stones, and so forth as under C 1. Any stone may be set.
A player with no suitable stone must continue drawing until he gets one. Two stones must remain in the boneyard. Scoring follows one of the methods under L, with the double blank scored as zero.

1.4 *Dominoes without Drawing*
Four players deal the stones among themselves, each therefore receiving seven. Those players opposite each other are partners against the other pair. The rules of 1.3 are followed.
Partnerships can be determined by drawing, the two players with the highest number of spots playing against the two others.

2. Cross Domino
In cross domino, the first stone set must be a double. For the first hand in the game, the player on set is the player with the highest double in his hand; for subsequent games the player on set is the largest loser. If the latter has no doubles, he must draw.
Suitable stones must be placed first on the four sides of the domino so that a cross is built. Unless decided otherwise, the game is played according to the rules of 1.1.

2.1 *Ordinary Cross* (example 2.2)
Once the four arms of the cross are arranged, the game is played in the usual way.

2.2 *Double Cross* (example 2.3)
The suitable double must be placed on an arm before other dominoes may be played.

2.3 *Four Double Cross* (example 2.4)
A double must be laid at each of the four arms before other stones may be played. If a double belonging on an arm is one of the remaining stones that must stay in the boneyard, then the incomplete arm is reversed.

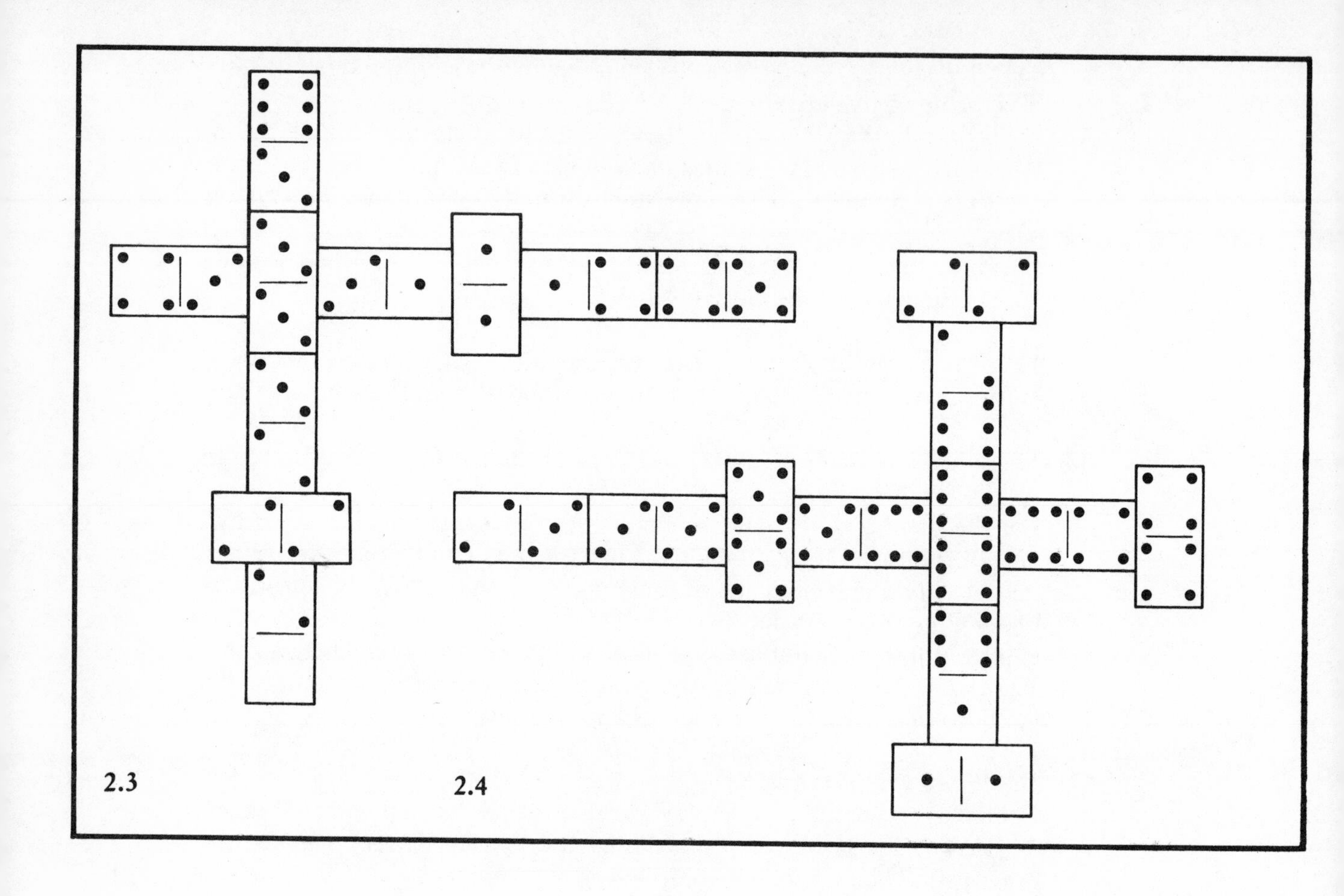

This is the most difficult form of cross domino, and in the beginning of the game the players usually must draw a great deal. The game is more attractive if each player takes no more than four stones (with more than four players, three stones each) and the player who, after drawing two stones, still cannot play, passes. Otherwise the rules as given in 1.1 are followed.

2.4 *Sebastopol* is an American game. The twenty eight stones are divided among four players, each one playing for himself. Once the cross is formed, stones may be placed on any arm. Scoring is according to L 2, with double blank counting for zero.

2.5 An exceptionally good form of cross domino is found in Groningen, the Netherlands. This is a good family game that can keep a large group in suspense for some hours before the final winner is determined. It is played with the set of fifty-five stones running to double nine. Each participant takes five stones, unless there are no more than three players or the number of players has dwindled to no more than three; then each player takes seven stones.

For the first hand, the player with the highest double makes the first set. Four stones must be placed on this, played double. Once the stones are added to the arm in the usual manner, either ordinary stones or doubles, play continues. Players may draw on their turns but not more than two stones; a player with no playable stone must draw. If, after drawing two stones, he is still unable to play, he passes. Two stones must remain in the boneyard.

The player who has played his last stone leaves the game, which continues with the remaining players. In playing his last stone, a player must place it so that the game remains as open as possible. This not only means that he may not close the game, but also puts upon him added responsibilities. If he can set on two open ends, even without danger of closing the game, he must play so that he makes a new open end of a kind that will be valuable for the stones remaining in the hands of the other players or in the boneyard. For example, if his final stone is 6–8, which he can set against a free end with six or one with eight, then he must determine whether more of the six or eight pieces lie on the table. If more sixes than eights already have been played, he must play to the six, thereby making a second free end with eight spots. If he has the choice between two numbers of spots that have been played equally, he may use his own judgement.

One player after the other plays out his last stone until finally one remains; he is the loser. If the hand is closed, the player with the highest number of spots remaining loses. Double blank is scored as thirteen when it is the only remaining stone in a player's hand, otherwise as zero. If two players have the same number of dots remaining and that number is higher than those of the others, the loser is the one with the most stones. If this number is the same, the hand is considered a draw and no score is kept.

The only notation is a penalty mark for the loser. In the next hand this losing player is the first on set, and he must start with a double. If he has more than one double, he can make his own choice; if he has none he must draw. If he fails to draw a double, the lead goes to the next player. Whoever has a previously determined number of penalty marks—usually five—is out of the game. The lead in the following hand again goes to the player with the highest double.

In this way, the number of players becomes smaller as they reach the predetermined number of penalty marks. The final hand between the two remaining players determines the winner of the entire game.

Since spot counting in this form of cross domino has only a subordinate importance to playing out the stones as quickly as possible, it is generally more important to play a double, no matter how low, rather than a stone with a high spot count.

3. The Austrian Game

In Austria a game is played with double eight as the highest stone and a total of forty-five stones. Usually the doubles are omitted in play, reducing the number of bones to thirty-six. The bones are not placed with their ends against each other but side by side, forming a double row (example 2.5).

Players either draw to determine the first player on set for the first hand, or the lead falls to the player with the highest stone in sequence—7–8,

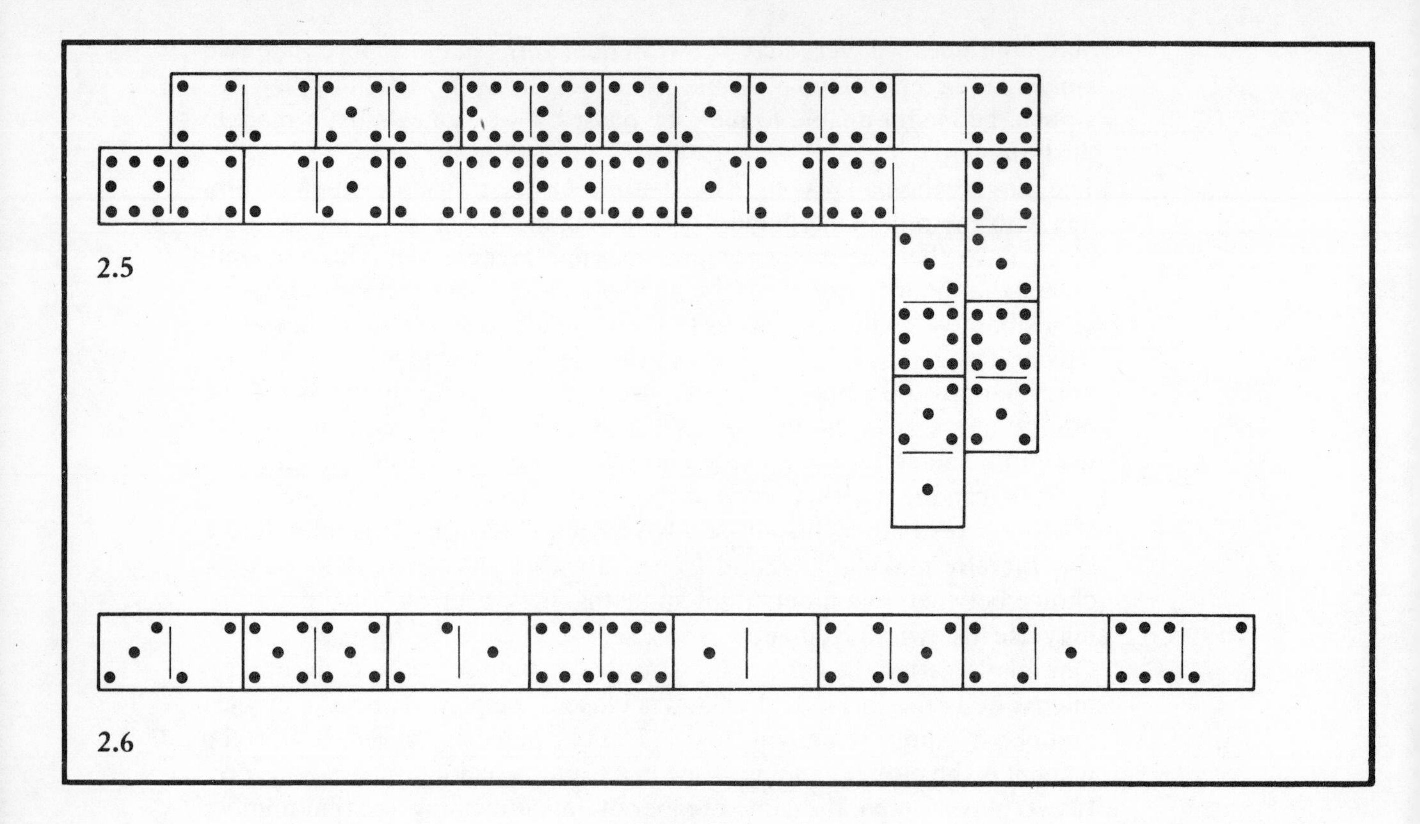
2.5

2.6

6–8, 5–8, and so forth. In subsequent hands the winner rather than the loser of the previous hand is the first player on set. If the earlier game was closed with two players having equal spots remaining (and with more than two participants having fewer spots than their opponents), the lead goes to the person who closed.

3.1 *Austrian Dominoes with Drawing* is played by two or three participants. Two players take eight to nine stones each, three players seven each. Drawing continues until a suitable stone is selected, or it may be decided in advance that, in turn, the highest three stones are drawn. There is no rule about leaving a certain number of stones in the boneyard.

3.2 *Austrian Dominoes without Drawing* is played by two participants with eleven or twelve stones and by three with eight or nine stones. Four participants always play the game without doubles and without drawing; they each take eight stones, leaving four in the boneyard, or, perhaps, seven stones each, with eight in the boneyard.

4. Blind Dominoes or Billiton

Blind dominoes is similar in its method of play to the ordinary game, except that this is a game of pure chance, in which calculation has no part. It begins with the determining of the first player. Afterward the twenty-eight stones are divided as follows:

with two players, each receives fourteen stones;
with three players, each receives nine stones, with the remaining stone placed to start play;
with four players, each receives seven stones;
with five players, each receives five stones, with the three remaining stones going to the player on first set and the players immediately following him.
The players place their stones spots downward with the long sides flush in a stack in front of themselves.
The player on first set turns the top stone of his column over and places it on the table or, in a case where three players are playing, on the previously set stone if possible. Next he turns his second bone and sees if he can play this, continuing until he can play no more. An unuseable stone is placed at the bottom of the stack, blind (with the number of spots hidden) if it is an ordinary stone, open if it is a double. The next player then takes his turn.
If a player turns over a stone which can be played on both ends of the row, he may, before playing it, turn over the following stone in his column to see which place is the more suitable.
The winner is the player who has played all his stones first.

5. Russian Dominoes or Matador

In Russian dominoes the stones must be placed so that ends placed together have a total of seven spots. This game can only be played with the ordinary set.
In the game there are four special stones, called *matadors.* These are the stones having seven eyes in total, the 6–1, the 5–2, and 4–3 and, in addition, the double blank. A matador may be played against any stone. On a blank end only a matador may be used because there are no stones in the game that would total seven spots when combined with a blank.
A player whose turn it is may draw even if he has a suitable stone in his possession. A player with no suitable stone draws until he obtains one or the boneyard is exhausted. Two stones must always remain in the boneyard.

5.1 Doubles as well as matadors are arranged in a straight line. Therefore a player playing a matador may choose which of the two ends shall be an open end. Otherwise the rules of ordinary dominoes are in force as in 1.1, including the method of scoring (example 2.6).

5.2 In a variation of matador played in Anglo-Saxon countries, the doubles are placed in a straight line, but the matadors are placed crosswise next to a blank half. Another blank half must be played against this matador, after which the game proceeds (example 2.7).
A player is free to draw when it is his turn. Otherwise the game is played according to the rules listed under 1.3, although the rule that the highest double must be the first stone set is also occasionally followed.

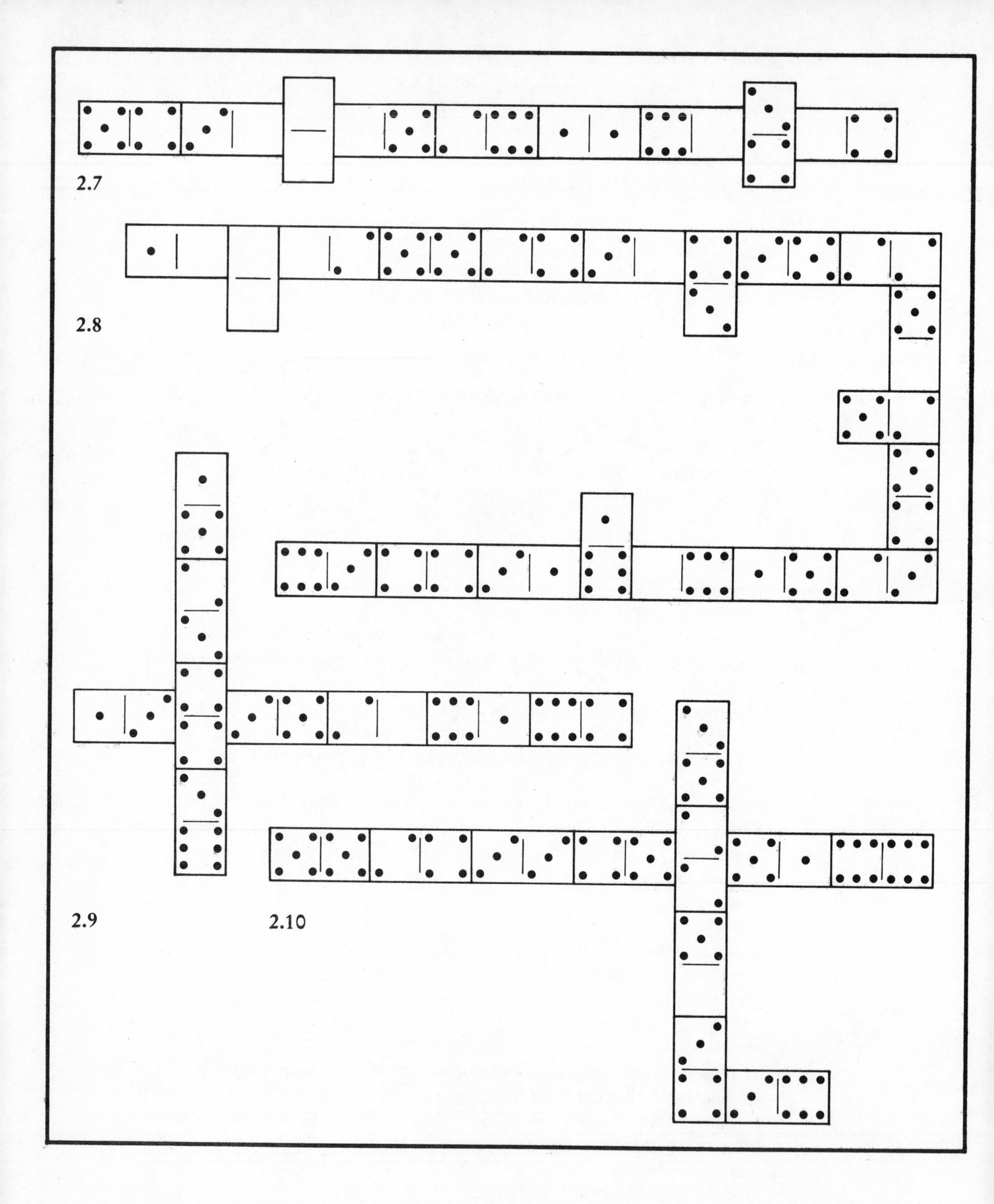
2.7
2.8
2.9
2.10

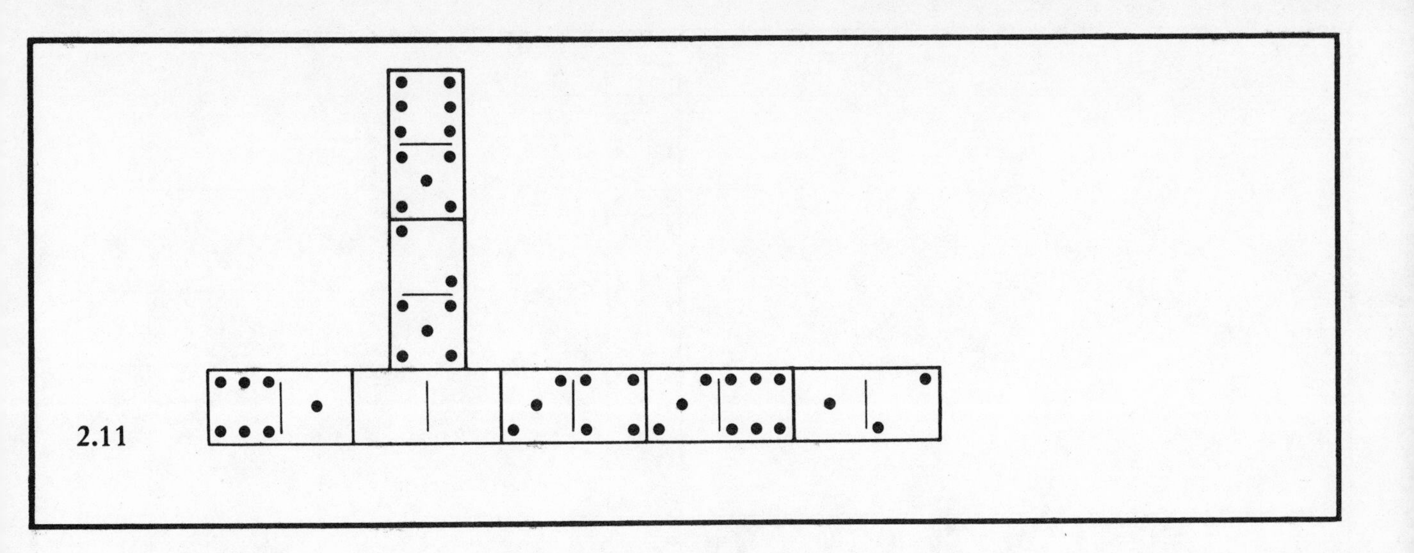
2.11

5.3 A form that is a cross between these two versions is played in Central Europe. The matadors are placed with one end in the line and the other half sticking out from the line. If a double blank is set against the blank end, the game proceeds with a blank end. The other matadors must be placed against the half that lies in the line. The player who plays a matador again has a choice of which suit shall lie in that line (example 2.8). The player of the first set is decided in the first game by drawing. A player may draw freely when it is his turn.

6. Russian Cross Domino

Like ordinary dominoes, the Russian game can begin with the formation of a cross. Otherwise the rules of 5.1 are followed in the manner described below.

6.1 *Russian Cross* (example 2.9)
A double but not a double blank must be played as the first stone. Suitable Russian matadors are placed against this double to form four arms, after which the game continues.

6.2 *Russian Double Cross* (example 2.10)
This also begins with the setting of any double except double blank, against which four suitable Russians are placed forming arms. An arm may be played first when a double or a matador is placed. These doubles or matadors are not placed crosswise.

6.3 *Triangle or Colonel Cross* (example 2.11)
The first stone played must be the double blank. From that, three matadors must be placed, after which the game continues.

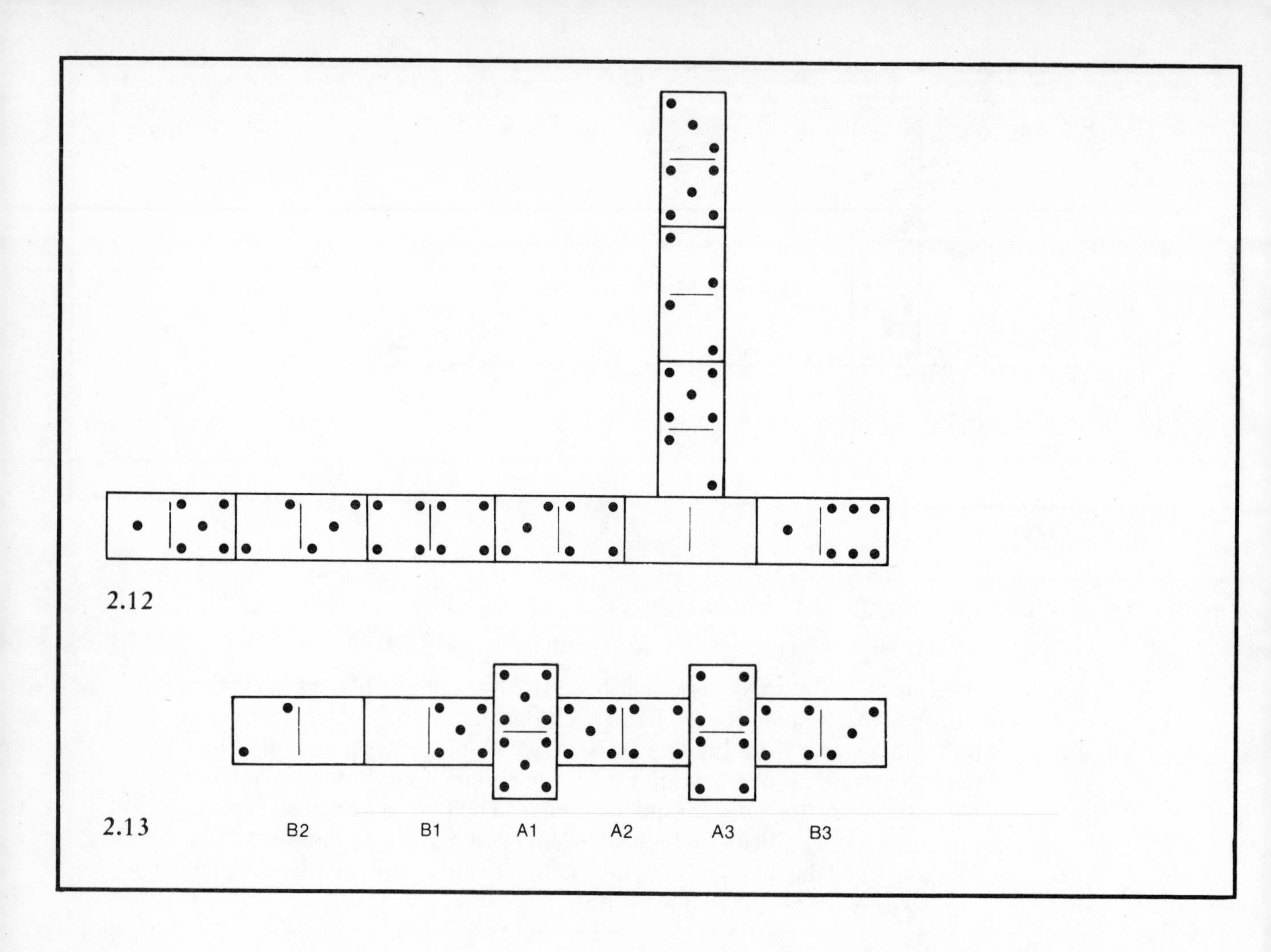

6.4 *Triangle Double Cross or General Cross* (example 2.12)
This is played as described under 6.3, but a suitable Russian double must be placed after the matadors are set. A complete arm may be played even if all the arms are not yet provided with a double.

3. Point Games

Scoring in point games does not depend only on the number of spots remaining in the hands of the losers. During the game points are earned by placing the stones so that the total number of eyes on the free ends of the chain is a multiple of a certain number, usually five. This method of playing has many adherents, especially in the United States.
In these games the stones are set in a normal way with ends of the same sort against each other. Doubles are placed crosswise. In some games the ends of the double that was set first are played, in others all the ends of all the doubles.
Point games are always played with the normal set of twenty-eight stones. The number of players may be two, three, or four, with four players playing as individuals or as two sets of partners.

For the first hand of a game, the player on set is decided by drawing. When the game is played in partners, the players drawing the two highest stones play against the players drawing the two lowest. For the following hands, the on-set designation rotates in clockwise fashion among the players. The player on set may begin with any stone.
Anyone who has one or more suitable stones when his turn comes is obliged to play. If he has no suitable stones, he must draw until he can play; or he must pass when no more bones can be drawn. With two players two stones remain in the boneyard, with three or four players one stone. The rules are different for Decimal and Sniff.

ARMANINO has extensively written about and analyzed this type of game. The following general view of the rules of the game are borrowed mostly from his work.

7. Stones may be placed against the long side of a double.

7.1 *All Fives or Muggins*

This game originated in Europe and is the simplest point game. It can be played by two to four people. Two people take seven stones each, three or four players five stones each.
When a player succeeds in bringing the total number of spots on the free ends of the stones to a multiple of five, he gets that number of points divided by five. The number of eyes on both halves of a played double are counted, but once a second stone is placed against it, the double counts no longer.
As an example see the demonstration game (example 2.13) between two players, A and B. A has placed a double five, which has given him two points. B can earn two points by playing 5–0. A now places 5–4 and earns nothing, as the sum on the spots of the end is $0 + 4 = 4$. B places the 0–2, which also is worth nothing. A follows with the double four and receives $\frac{2 \times 4 + 2}{5} = 2$ points. By playing the 4–3, B earns $\frac{2 + 3}{5} = 1$ point, and so forth. The winner is the "domino" or, when the game is played in pairs, the one who plays his last stone first. The winning score is the total number of dots in the hands of the opponent rounded off to the nearest multiple of five and divided by five. A total of 21 or 22 spots, therefore, counts as 4 points, a total of 23 or 24 spots as 5. These points are also earned in closed games. The number of spots in the winning hand is not subtracted (L 2). If two players have the same number of spots left over and that number is also the lowest, no points are awarded. Double zero counts as nothing.
A game is over when one of the players or pairs reaches a certain number of points, 61 or 100 for example. If this occurs during a hand the hand must be played out. If there are additional players who have reached the required number of points, the winner is the first one over that number.

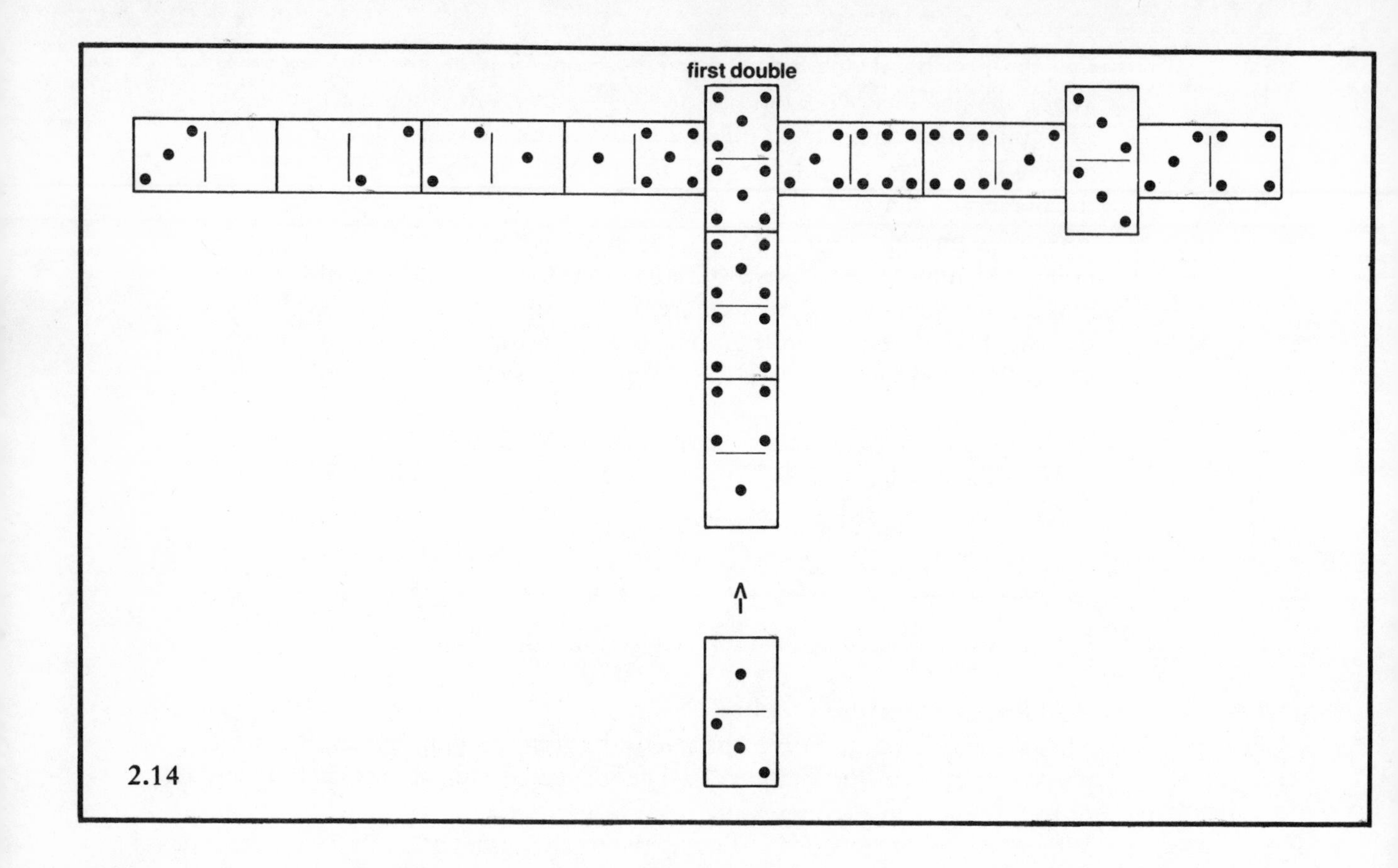

7.2 *All Threes*

This game follows the same rules as All Fives, but a multiple of three is used rather than multiple of five.

7.3 *Threes and Fives*

In this game a player receives points for bringing the ends not only to a multiple of five but also to a multiple of three (one point for each five and each three). If the number of spots is a multiple of five and a multiple of three, it counts as both. A player who can bring the sum of the dots to fifteen receives 15 + 15 = 8 points. Otherwise the rules are the same as for the ordinary game of All Fives.

8. In the second type of point games, there is only one double against which stones may be placed on all four sides. This is the first double played.

8.1 *Decimal*

This is the English name of a game popular in the southern part of the United States and in Latin America. It is played by two, three, or four players, each of whom draws seven stones. Four players may play as individuals or in two pairs, in which case there is no boneyard. When the game is played by two or three participants, a player unable to play must draw until he obtains a suitable stone. No stones remain in the boneyard.

Any stone may be used as the first set. As soon as stones are played against both long sides of the first double, the short sides of this double may also be played. Such a double is called a "spinner."
Scoring is figured as in All Fives. The player first bringing the number of spots on the free ends to a multiple of five wins one point for each five spots. The spinner is treated as any other double. The total number of spots on a double are counted only as long as these lie at a free end. In case something is placed against the short side of the spinner, a new free end is established and scored. In example 2.14, the free ends score as 3 + 4 + 1 = 8 spots. When 1–3 is set the number is brought to ten. The totaling of points at the end of the game is as in All Fives. A game is 250 points.

8.2 *Sniff*

Of European origin, this game is also popular in the United States. Sniff is played by two, three, or four people; four players play in pairs. Two players take seven stones each, three players six each, and four players five each. Any stone may be used for the first set.
A player unable to play must draw, but no more than two stones. If he draws no usable stone he passes. When there are three or four participants, all stones in the boneyard may be drawn; with two players two stones must remain in the boneyard.
Just as in the previous game stones may be set on both short sides of the double first played—called the "Sniff" in this game—as soon as stones have been played on both its long sides, making it a spinner. However, scoring is different. The spots on an end of the spinner are counted as long as the end is free, that is, provided no stone is placed against it. In other words, as soon as the sniff becomes a spinner, there are four free ends.
Suppose the above example is played by the rules of Sniff. Before the playing of the 1–3, there are four free ends with a total of 13 spots, namely 3 + 5 + 4 + 1. The playing of the 1–3 brings the total to 15 dots, a multiple of five. A multiple of five earns one point for each dot, so 15 points are earned. As long as a double lies on a free end, the dots on both sides are counted in scoring. During the scoring at the end of a game, the winner or winning pair receives the total number of spots that their opponents have left over, rounded to the nearest multiple of five. In the case of a closed game with two players or two pairs, if both have the same number of spots, there is no score. If two of only three players tie for victory with the lowest number of spots remaining, they divide the loser's number rounded to the nearest multiple of five. The game is 250 points.

9. The third category of point games contains those in which each double becomes a spinner once a stone is set on its long side.

9.1 Five-Up

To this group belongs one of the best of the point games, Five-Up. It developed in the beginning of the twentieth century in San Francisco, was

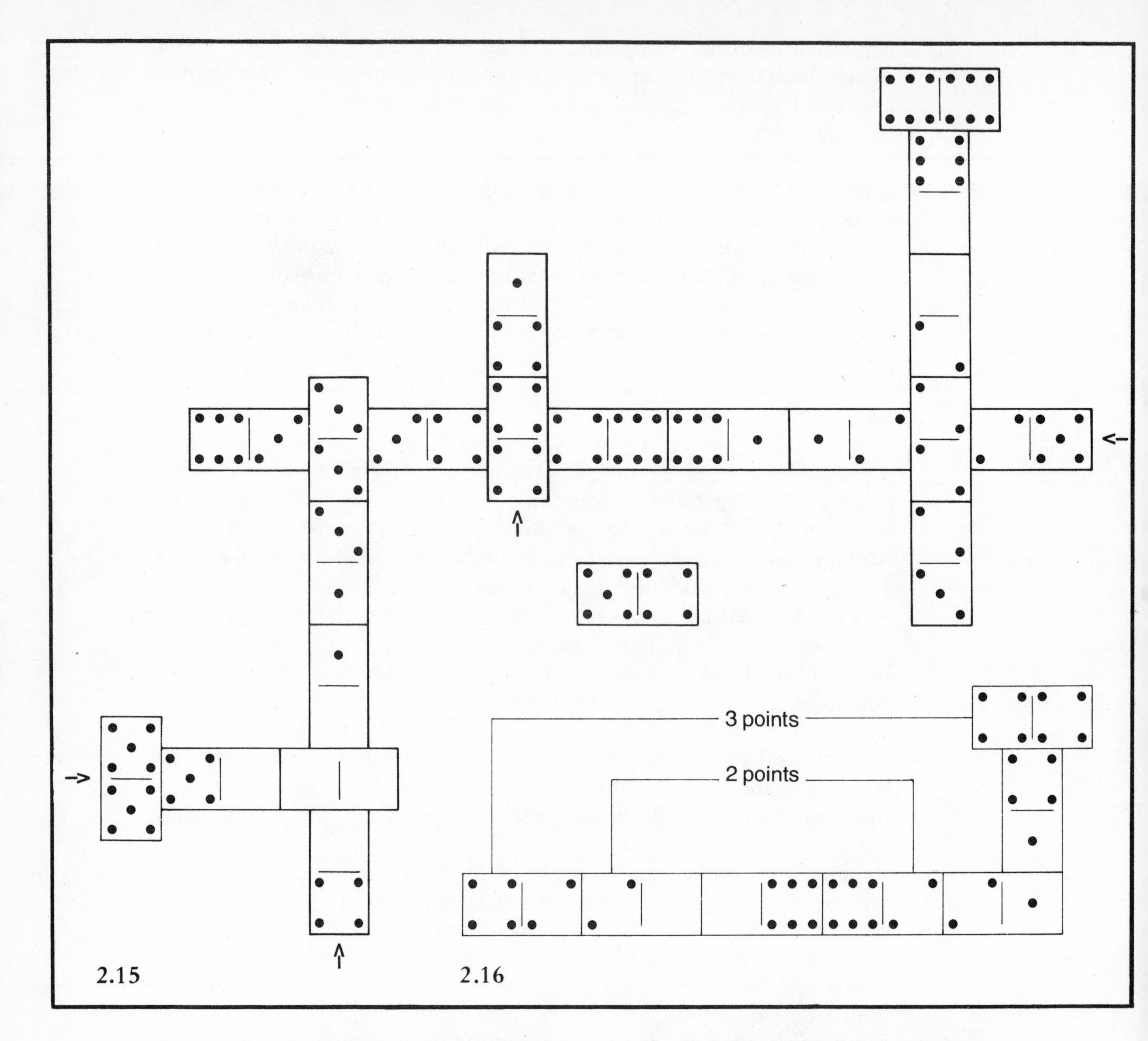

played a great deal in Northern California, and is now also popular elsewhere. It is played with two, three, or four players. Four players form two pairs, which play against each other. Every player takes five stones, and any stone may be set first. A player without a suitable stone must draw. With two players two stones must remain in the boneyard, with more players one stone.

The player bringing the sum of the spots on the free ends to a multiple of five earns one point for every five spots. A double placed against a free end counts for its total number of spots. When a stone is placed against the still free long side of this double, however, its spots no longer count. The reason for this, of course, is that the double has now become a spinner, and stones may be set against its short sides. This applies to all doubles, not only those first set.

In the example (2.15), there are seven free ends on the played stones, which together bear 41 spots—4 + (2 × 5) + 6 + 1 + (2 × 6) + 5 + 3.

The next player has the 4–5. He can place this stone in four different spots, which are:
at the 0–4, bringing the sum of the dots to 42. No points.
at the 4–4, bringing the sum of the dots to 46. No points.
at the 5–5, bringing the sum of the spots to 35 and earning seven points.
at the 2–5, bringing the sum of the spots to 40 and earning the player eight points.
From this example it should not be inferred that a player must always try to make as many points as possible. He will be contented with fewer points if in that way he can hinder his opponents or enable himself or his partner to make a better set. This gives the game its fascination.
At the end of a hand between two or four persons, the winner (or winning pair) receives one point for every five spots in the hands of the opponent or opponents, rounded off to the nearest multiple of five. At the end of the hand, any spots left over in the winning hand are not subtracted.
No points are awarded when both participants have the same number of spots.
With three players, the winner receives points according to the number of spots that both opponents still have in their hands. These two settle their score together. The one with the smallest number of spots left over receives a number of points corresponding to the difference in the rounded-off number of spots that they still hold. This last regulation is not always adhered to. As the two players who are losing realize this, they may be inclined to play together against the apparent winner to heighten the tension of the game.
When a game between three players is closed, the winner receives a score only of the difference in rounded off spots remaining between him and his opponents.
The game is 61 points. The last hand of the game must be played out.

9.2 Some players prefer to play with more stones to the hand. Two players take, for example, seven each, three players nine stones each.

9.3 Seven-Toed Pete

This is played in the same way as Five-Up, with three variations. Each player takes seven stones; with four players there is therefore no boneyard. The first set must be a double or a stone that earns points. The player on first set must draw as necessary if the boneyard permits. Whoever—the first player included—plays a double during the game or makes a play that earns him points plays an additional turn and draws if necessary to do that. If there are no more stones from which to draw, he passes.
This last rule has an especially important influence on the game. The player who places his last stone—it may be a double; it may earn him points, but if that is possible, he must so place it that he earns points—is still not the winner. In a game between four players he is forced to pass, but remains in the game. The other three continue to play until one of them succeeds in placing his last (not a double) stone without making a multiple of five. If no players succeed, the game is considered closed.

In a game between two or three players, the player who plays his last stone must draw to play again if it is a double or one that earns points. If the boneyard is empty except for the required stones, he passes but remains in the game until one of the participants ends it by going out on neither a double nor a point-earning stone.
In all games of the All Fives type, some stones have exceptional value for a player whose turn comes after his predecessor has made a multiple of five. He can earn points if he can play:

a. double zero or double five or one of the stones having five more spots on one of its ends than on the other: the 0–5 and the 1–6;
b. by placing against the long side of a double a stone of a different suit carrying the same number of dots as the total on the double or that number plus or minus a multiple of five. These stones are the 1–2, 2–4, 3–1, 3–6, 4–3, 5–0, and the 6–2;
c. against a spinner a stone with an open end either blank or bearing five spots. This does not apply to Sniff.

10. Bergen

This is a point game of an entirely different character. The object is to give both ends of the domino chain the same number of spots.
There are two, three, or four players, each playing for himself. To begin, each draws six stones. Stones of the same suit are placed together with the doubles crosswise. A player who plays a double receives 2 points, as does a player who places on one end the same number of spots as showing on the other. If he places a double on an already identical end or places on the other end a suitable double, he receives 3 points (example 2.16).
A player with no suitable stone must draw. Two stones remain in the boneyard. The player who becomes domino earns one point. If the game is closed the player holding the fewest spots earns a point unless another player has no doubles. This latter, then, always takes precedence. If more than one player have no doubles, then it is decided by the number of spots they have remaining. If all players have one double, the winner is the one with the lowest double. A game is 15 points.

The games codified in America have a number of rules, rewards, and penalties. In club play these are essential, but for our purposes they are not necessary. Those interested in them should see the publications of Armanino.

4. Nossen

Nossen is an involved and absorbing game that combines ordinary and Russian dominoes. It can be played by three to five players. The number of stones with which the game begins, the player on first set, and the first play are all according to the rules of ordinary dominoes (1.1). In the first round, doubles that fit the lead stone may be played by a player out of his turn.
A player may draw from the boneyard during his turn. If he can't play,

he may not pass as long as there are still stones to draw. Two stones must remain in the boneyard. The player first on set decides after the set which games shall be played. He thereby has a choice not only of:

1. ordinary dominoes (1.1)
2. cross dominoes (2.1)
3. double cross (2.2)
4. Russian dominoes (5.1)
5. Russian cross (6.1)
6. Russian double cross (6.2)
7. Triangle (6.3) or
8. Triangle double cross (6.4),

but may in addition to these eight possibilities also choose from the following:

9. ordinary cross (the first five stones)
10. ordinary cross and then Russian double cross
11. Russian cross (the first five stones) and then ordinary dominoes
12. Russian cross and then ordinary double cross
13. ordinary or Russian construction, with conditions given by the player on first set. These can be:
    a. "first here and then there," which means that the player first on set determines on which side of the first stone each of the next two stones must be placed;
    b. the number of times (but not more than four) the players must set stones on the same side of the first stone.

    After the setting of a number of stones in either the ordinary or the Russian manner, as determined by the player first on set, the game continues in the other manner.
14. Volapuk-construction, cross or double cross. In this construction ordinary dominoes is played on one side of the first stone and Russian on the other side. In a cross or double cross, Russian and ordinary dominoes are played on the two arms opposite each other. In announcing this method of play, the player on first set must decide which side shall be ordinary and which Russian, and how many times each must be played on one side before the other side may be played;
15. Triangle and afterward (after the placing of the three matadors) ordinary dominoes;
16. Triangle and afterward ordinary cross dominoes. After the three matadors are placed on the double blank, a blank must be played as the fourth stone. Once the cross is completed in this manner, the game continues as ordinary dominoes;
17. After the setting of a double: a Russian construction, "first here and then there," and after that an ordinary cross or ordinary double cross.

The player who first plays out his stones wins the "nos."

The game is continued by the remaining players until:

a. if only one player has stones, he may not play again after his predecessor has played his last stone.
b. whether or not this has been declared, the game is closed.

Nossen is enlivened by a system of declarations and penalties that are an essential element of the game. The most significant of these rules are:

1. Before the start of the game, each participant receives 500 units in chips.
2. The first player to play a double receives from each fellow player a number of chips equal to the number of spots on one half. If he plays double blank, he receives 7 chips from each player. He receives a double reward if the first double is a stone just drawn.
   If the lead stone is not a double, then he pays to each fellow player the same number of chips as the total of spots on the lead stone.
3. A player who plays a double on a stone laid by his immediate predecessor receives from his predecessor—assuming he doesn't have the nos—a number of chips equal to the number of spots on one end of his double (7 chips for double blank). This rule applies for the player who places a double on the lead stone even if the player on first set is not his immediate predecessor.
4. Once the player on first set has decided the manner of playing, any player holding all or all but one double declares these by laying them openly on the table. They remain lying open throughout further play. He receives from each of his fellow players 50 chips if he has three doubles out of three stones; 25 chips for three out of four; 250 for four out of four; 200 for four out of five and 250 for five doubles out of five stones.
5. The player who declares the nos receives 5 chips from each fellow player.
6. The player who sees that he can close the game can announce this by saying "I close." He receives 20 chips from each fellow player if his opinion is correct, but pays to each 40 chips if he has made a mistake. If he has rightly closed, his follower must draw all the bones except two still in the boneyard unless he is the only remaining player.
   Moreover, there exists a penalty of 40 chips for violation of the normal rules, such as taking too few stones or more than two stones too many, playing out of turn, passing when a stone may still be drawn, playing an unsuitable stone, and the like. The penalty is 80 chips in cases where it appears from the play of a player that he reneged in his previous turn.
   Following the game, the players pay in chips the differences in the number of spots on their remaining stones.
   For a more detailed description of the rules of the game, game examples, and further discussion, see the work of BRETHOUWER.

Part Two

Domino Puzzles

A good puzzle, like virtue, is its own reward.
——H.E. Dudeney, 'The Canterbury Puzzles'

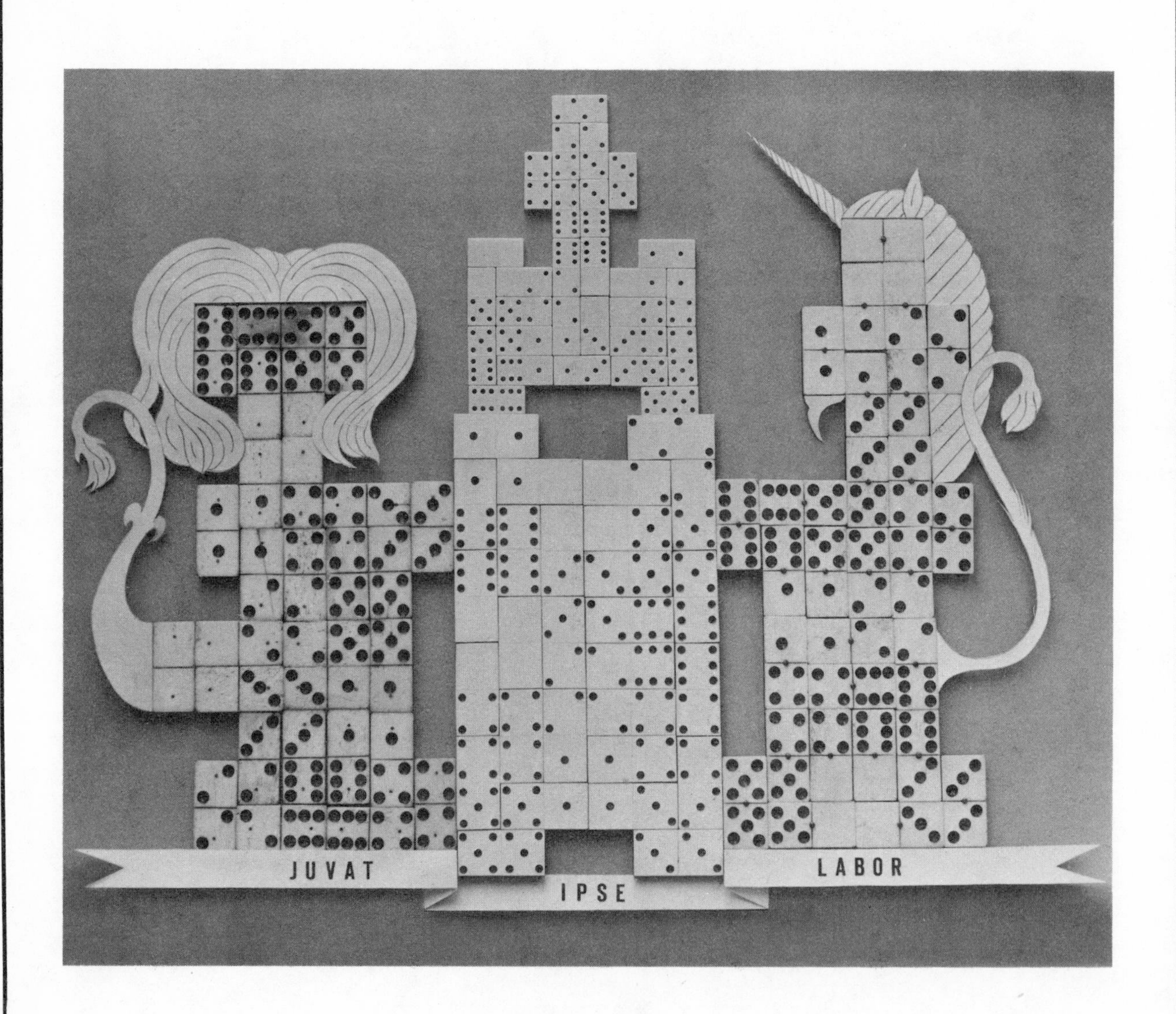

Juvat ipse labor: Work is its own reward *Photo: C.P. Helwes*

III General Remarks about Pure Puzzles

The true puzzle lover is never satisfied with mere haphazard trials.
——H.E. DUDENEY, 'Amusements in Mathematics'

1. Introduction and Examples

In view of the mathematical structure of a set of dominoes, it is not surprising that many kinds of mathematically colored puzzles can be formed with them. In order for the mathematical structure to be maintained, most of these puzzles require the use of the complete set of dominoes. Occasionally, however, a strictly limited group of dominoes is employed.

A mathematically colored puzzle is not a mathematical problem, although the line between the two is difficult to draw. The question of the number of ways in which the bones of an ordinary domino game can be placed one behind the other with ends of the same number meeting is, in fact, a mathematical problem and was solved by TARRY by way of a geometrical model. For mathematics, however, the problem has as good as no significance, and the greatest value of the solution is in its simplicity and elegance. This is the sign of a good mathematical puzzle.

In the course of the solution of a purely mathematical puzzle, there is generally an attempt to test things to see if they fit, but no testing in a wild sense. On the contrary, a good puzzle encourages the person working it to find all possible solutions and, therefore, to work systematically. He should first try by a reasoning that often has the character of a sorting to examine all possible methods of solution in order to limit them as much as possible. After that he must try systematic evaluation, carefully keeping notes on the examined and yet to be examined possibilities. It is in this method of solution, in the bringing into order of an apparently randomly arranged problem, that the great charm of mathematical puzzles lies.

As an example here is given a solution for one of the oldest puzzles in the world, a simple magic square. Magic squares have their roots in ancient Mesopotamia and in India. They are found in the writing of TABIT IBN KORRA (826–901), who worked in Baghdad. In China, the simplest magic square was described by LO SHU in the twelfth century, but it must have been known much longer. Legend said that the puzzle was carved on the back of a turtle that appeared to Emperor YU (ca. 2200 B.C.) while sailing on the Yellow River.

This simplest square is divided into 3×3 boxes into which the numbers from 1 to 9 must be placed so that the sum of the number is the same in each row, each column, and on both diagonal lines. This sum (S) is called the magic sum.

	5	

	1	
	5	
	9	

8	1	6
	5	
	9	

8	1	6
3	5	7
4	9	2

3.1

p	q	r
s	c	t
u	v	w

3.2

c + a	c-(a+b)	c + b
c-(a-b)	c	c+(a-b)
c - b	c+(a+b)	c - a

3.3

c-(a+b)	c-b	c+(a-b)
c-a	c	c+a
c-(a-b)	c+b	c+(a+b)

3.4

Because the nine numbers can be placed in the boxes in about 360,000 ways, no one should feel himself called upon to solve this puzzle by trial and error. One may simplify the problem by determining the magic sum. Since the sum of nine numbers to be placed in the boxes is 45 and this must be divided into three rows, $S = \frac{45}{3} = 15$. A row, a column, and two diagonals intersect in the middle box. Therefore the number placed in this space must be able to form the sum of 15 with two other numbers of each of the four intersecting groups. Not much trial and error is needed to discover that only the number 5 meets these criteria, in the combinations 1–5–9, 2–5–8, 3–5–7, and 4–5–6.

In addition to 5 and 9, the number 1 can be used only with 6 and 8 (example 3.1). It therefore can stand only in a middle box, at one of the edges, where it can be part both of a row and a column. Because of the symmetry of the figure, which can be turned and reversed, the placing of the numbers on one side or the other is a matter of indifference (this will be further discussed later). We place the 1 in the middle of the top row. Then the 9 is placed in the bottom row.

The top row is completed by 8 and 6. It is again a matter of indifference whether the 8 lies to the right or the left of the 1. The further filling in of the boxes gives us the sum of 15 without further difficulty.

In this way the solution is found for the given series of nine sequential natural numbers.

It is also possible to consider this problem in a general sense by asking what requirements the nine different numbers must meet in order to comprise a magic square.
To answer this question we again begin with the central box. Let the number placed there = c and let the square be filled in further as shown in example 3.2.
The sum of the middle row, the middle column, and the two diagonals is $4S = 3c + (p + q + r + s + c + t + u + v + w) = 3c + 3s$, from which it follows that $c = \frac{1}{3}S$.

It further appears that $p + w = r + u = q + v = s + t = 2c$. Therefore these number pairs are complementary: the one number is as much larger than c as the other is smaller.
Armed with this knowledge we may write the simplest magic square, in its most usual form, as in example 3.3. There is therefore only one magic square of nine boxes whose numbers are filled in. These numbers always form three arithmetical series of three terms of which the first terms form a further arithmetical series (example 3.4).
As a second example of a mathematical puzzle, consider the following: determine the magic square of 3×3 boxes composed of nine unlike indivisible numbers with the smallest possible magic sum. An indivisible or prime number is, by definition, a number larger than one that cannot be divided by any other number between 1 and the number itself. The list of the thirty prime numbers smaller than 125 follows:
2, 3, 5, 7, 11, 13, 17, 19, 23, 29, 31, 37, 41, 43, 47, 53, 59, 61, 67, 71, 73, 79, 83, 89, 97, 101, 103, 107, 109, 113.

The prime number 2 is unusable for this square because it is the only even prime number.
Let us, as above, call the difference in three arithmetical series a and the difference in the series formed by the three first terms b. Since the square must consist exclusively of uneven numbers, a as well as b is even.
The smallest number that can be filled in would be 3, but not a multiple of 3. Therefore, it must be 3 or a multiple of 3 + 1 or a multiple of 3 + 2.
If the smallest number is three, a and b cannot be multiples of 3. Neither can they be multiples of 3 + 1 or multiples of 3 + 2, since then inevitably in such an arithmetical series numbers exist that are divisible by 3 and are therefore no longer primes. The number 3 is therefore dropped.
If the smallest number is a multiple of 3 + 1 or a multiple of 3+ 2, a and b must both be multiples of 3 in order to avoid numbers divisible by 3. They must likewise be even, in view of the values: 6, 12, 18, 24 . . . and so forth.
For which value the smallest sum S will result must still be determined.
The series of at least three numbers with as small as possible a di-

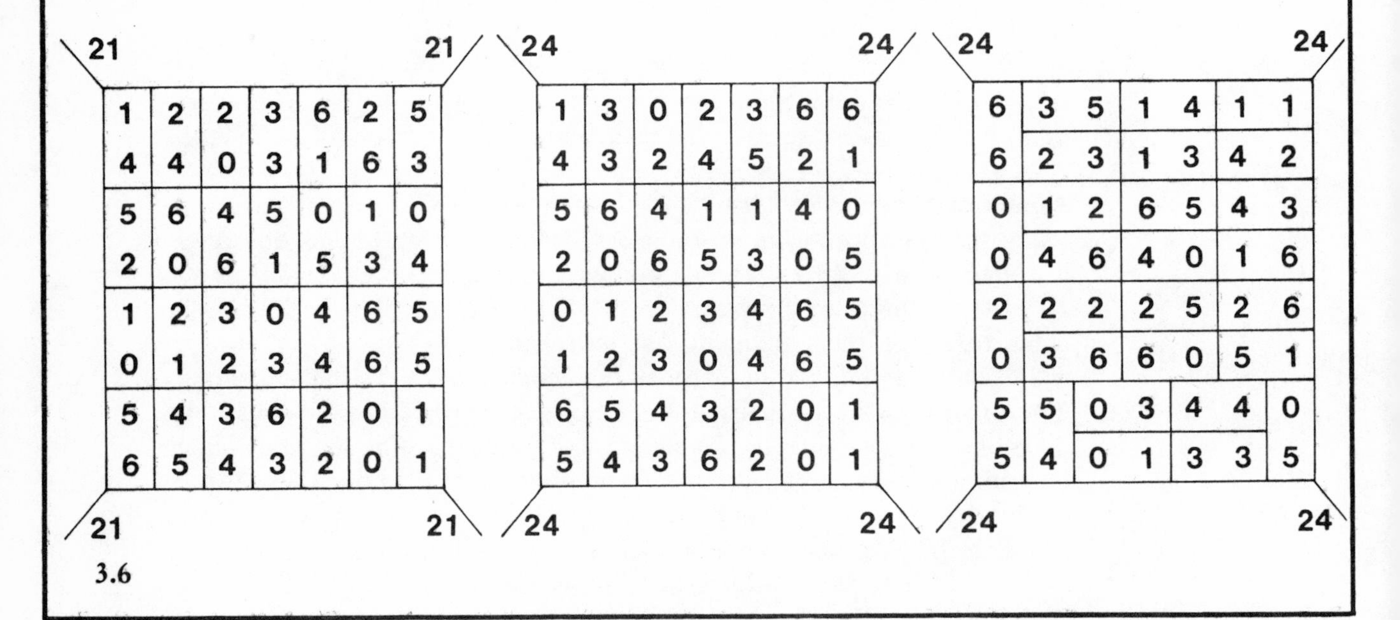

71	5	101
89	59	29
17	113	47

3.5

1	2	2	3	6	2	5
4	4	0	3	1	6	3
5	6	4	5	0	1	0
2	0	6	1	5	3	4
1	2	3	0	4	6	5
0	1	2	3	4	6	5
5	4	3	6	2	0	1
6	5	4	3	2	0	1

1	3	0	2	3	6	6
4	3	2	4	5	2	1
5	6	4	1	1	4	0
2	0	6	5	3	0	5
0	1	2	3	4	6	5
1	2	3	0	4	6	5
6	5	4	3	2	0	1
5	4	3	6	2	0	1

6	3	5	1	4	1	1
6	2	3	1	3	4	2
0	1	2	6	5	4	3
0	4	6	4	0	1	6
2	2	2	2	5	2	6
0	3	6	6	0	5	1
5	5	0	3	4	4	0
5	4	0	1	3	3	5

3.6

fference a = 6 are, from the group of the first thirty prime numbers, the following:
5–11–17–23–29, 7–13–19, 31–37–43, 41–47–53–59, 61–67–73–79, 97–103–109, 101–107–113.
They give no suitable value for b, but the series with a = 12 does:
5–17–29–41–53, 7–19–31–43, 47–59–71–83 and 89–101–113 from which by b = 42 come the series of three which are suitable for the base of the square:
5–17–29
47–59–71
89–101–113
and for b = 30 the trio:
29–41–53
59–71–83
89–101–113.
The first trio gives the square with the smallest magic sum $S = 3 \times 59 = 177$, which is reproduced in example 3.5.

2. The Number of Solutions

In both of the above examples—the square with successive natural numbers and the square using prime numbers—there is only a single solution possible. Most mathematical puzzles have several solutions. However, the ideal puzzle should not have so many solutions to the whole or to any part that the total becomes incalculable and one's confidence in the completeness of the solution is sacrificed.

In a problem asking for the arrangement of the twenty-eight bones of a domino set in a rectangle of seven by eight ends, so that four ends with the same number of spots lie in one row (see Chapter VII), thirteen possible arrangements are immediately apparent, of which ten can be very quickly eliminated. The remaining three possibilities can be quickly seen to have, respectively, zero, three, and thirty-three solutions. A similar puzzle worked out with a domino set in which doublet four is the highest bone can be arranged into nine possibilities. Upon closer examination two of these are eliminated, and the remaining seven lead to additional possibilities each with a number of solutions—sometimes many. There's a good chance that in solving puzzles of this nature something can be missed. Thus it's desirable to give the solution of such a puzzle with reservations. This factor makes such puzzles less attractive than others, and it is only by setting limitations in the course of the puzzle's introduction that the objections can be overcome.

Still less attractive—and, for the true puzzle lover, completely unsatisfactory—is the type of puzzle that has no systematic solution, whose answer can only be found by chance. An example of this type appeared in the Dutch newspaper, *De Telegraaf,* on August 11, 1966. In this puzzle it was asked that the twenty-eight domino bones be arranged in a square with a length of seven and a height of eight ends so that the sum of the dots in each row would total 21 and the sum of the dots in each column 24. Moreover, the two upward and the two downward oblique lines were to be arranged so that the dots on each would add up to the same sum, either 21 or 24. (An upward oblique line runs from bottom left to top right, a downward oblique line from top left to bottom right) (example 3.6).

Three answers from readers were printed in the newspaper of September 9. In two of them, all the bones were arranged vertically so that in both the two top and the two bottom rows the sum of the dots on the bones in each column was twelve. In one solution, the dots on the four oblique lines added up to 21, in the other to 24.

This arrangement of the bones is not an essential part of a reasoned solution to this problem, but only makes it easier to test a theory. The third solution is free of this limitation. Whether or not there are additional solutions to this problem and if so, how many, is not known.

Although they can serve as a pastime, such problems can never offer the satisfaction of a well-considered and possibly illuminating examination of the problem, rewarded by an integral solution. Therefore, no further attention shall be paid to this type of puzzle in this book; otherwise the overwhelming number of solutions to these puzzles would become puzzling in itself.

3. Equivalent Figures and Permutations

Two ideas that can be expressed by domino puzzles are discussed here: equivalent solutions and permutations.

In our discussion of magic squares of three by three spaces, it has already emerged that these can be turned and reversed. From that comes into being the examples of squares shown (example 3.7) that are called *equivalent squares* because they should be regarded not as separate solutions but as different versions of the same solution. If the perimeter of a diagram has two perpendicular axes of symmetry which are not the same length, as in a square, then by reversing and turning it can form four equivalent figures. For a diagram with only one axis of symmetry, there are only two equivalent solutions: the diagram and its mirror image. These equivalent solutions count as one and the same.

Now for a word about *permutations*. With many domino figures it happens that, after the placing of the seven doublets, the number of spots must be assigned to these doubles in a somewhat arbitrary manner. For the first double there is a choice from the numbers 0, 1, 2, 3, 4, 5, and 6, thus seven possibilities. Once the choice is made, there are six possibilities for the following double, five for the next, and so forth.

This determination of the number of spots on all seven doubles can be done in $7 \times 6 \times 5 \times 4 \times 3 \times 2 \times 1$ possible ways. This may be written as 7!, called "seven factorial."

The question of how many ways the spots of the domino game can be placed in boxes might be reduced to the question of how many ways seven different objects following each other in a row can be placed. Each of the possible arrangements of this one row is a permutation. Two arrangements that are the same if one is read from left to right and the other from right to left are considered two different permutations. The number of permutations of seven objects is 7!, which can be deduced in a similar way as is given above for the number of spots. For n objects the number of permutations is n!.

If a number among the objects is the same as another, the number of permutations is smaller. If we consider, for example, the letters *a b c d e e f*, we see that in each possible permutation of these seven letters there are two letters e. If these belong to the same type of letter and are therefore identical to each other, they can be exchanged in each permutation without affecting the arrangement. Since the two letters e can be exchanged in two ways (the original placement is included), there are 2! permutations the same. The number of permutations of the letters *a b c d e e f*—or seven objects of which two are the same—therefore is $\frac{7!}{2!}$.

The number of permutations of the letters *a b c d e e f f f* is determined by the number of ways the two letters e and f can be transposed: e in 2! and f in 3! ways. The number of permutations is therefore $\frac{9!}{2! \times 3!}$.

Finally we will consider how many ways an even number of objects can be arranged in pairs.

8	1	6
3	5	7
4	9	2

6	1	8
7	5	3
2	9	4

2	7	6
9	5	1
4	3	8

6	7	2
1	5	9
8	3	4

2	9	4
7	5	3
6	1	8

4	9	2
3	5	7
8	1	6

4	3	8
9	5	1
2	7	6

8	3	4
1	5	9
6	7	2

3.7

Let us consider four objects, for example the numbers 1, 2, 3, and 4, that must be divided into two groups of two numbers. This can be done by assigning the same letter, for example A, to two of the numbers and the letter B to two others. The question of the number of possible divisions can then be reduced to the question of the number of permutations of AABB, which is $2! \times 2!$ if a distinction is made between the one pair and the other. If it is not given which pair is the first and which the second, then the number of ways in which the numbers can be divided is equal to $\frac{4!}{2! \times 2! \times 2!} = 3$. This can be understood easily. Imagine that four people go walking in pairs without it mattering who goes in front. One walker can form a pair with any of the three others. With each of these three possibilities the other pair is also established. If six objects must be divided into pairs it can occur in $\frac{6!}{2! \times 2! \times 2!}$ ways. If the order of the pairs does not matter, the result is divided by 3!, the number of ways in which the three pairs can be arranged (exchanged). The number of ways in which the six objects can be divided then amounts to $\frac{6!}{2! \times 2! \times 2! \times 3!} = 1 \times 3 \times 5 = 15$.

In general the number of ways in which 2n objects can be divided into groups of two without a distinction being made among the pairs is

$$\frac{(2n!)}{(2n!)^n \times n!} = 1 \times 3 \times 5 \times 7 \times \ . \ . \ . \ . \times (2n-1)$$

4. Closing Remarks

In the following chapters puzzles that use the normal set of dominoes or the smaller set in which the doublet four is the highest stone are discussed. In some cases there follows afterward a discussion of puzzles of greater breadth.

In solving a domino puzzle, do not go to the stones too quickly. As long as you are still seeking the most appropriate method of solving it, you will do best to use only paper and pencil. Many puzzles can often be brought to a satisfactory solution without further help. Nevertheless it can be valuable to have a domino set for setting out the separate stones. You can see at a glance which stones have been used and which are still usable.

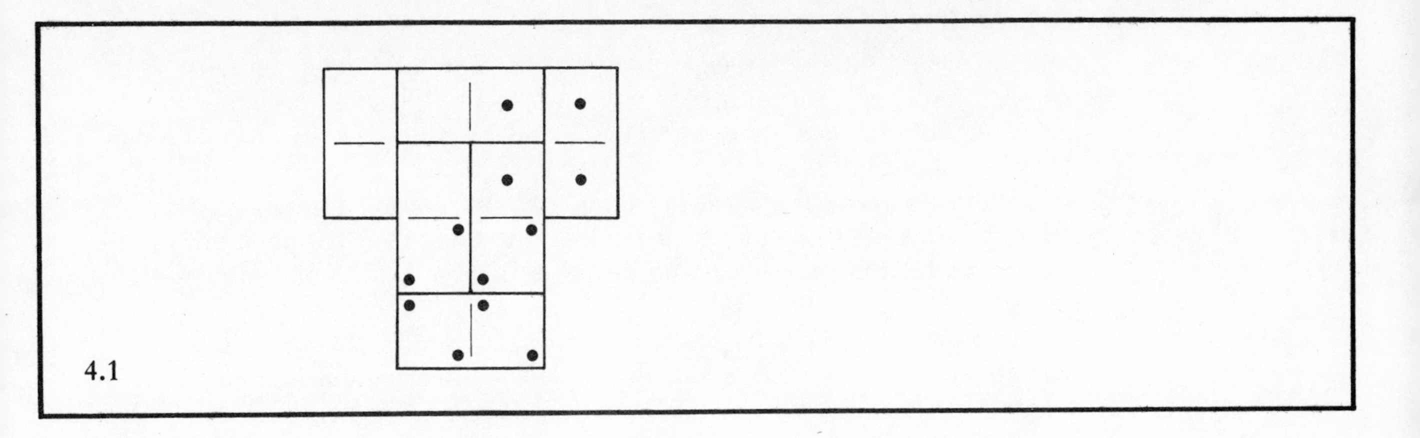
4.1

IV The Quadrilles of Lucas

The appearance of patterns appeals to the artistic side, which is strong in children. Good mathematicians are very sensitive to patterns.
——W.W. Sawyer, 'Mathematician's Delight'

1. Introduction

The French mathematician EDOUARD LUCAS gave the name *quadrilles* to figures made with domino bones so arranged that four of the same spots can be placed next to each other in squares. As an example (example 4.1) the simplest quadrille, made with a set in which double two is the highest stone, is shown. This quadrille has three squares and is the only one that can be made with this set. A quadrille made with the normal set having double six as the highest stone is built from fourteen squares.

The greater size of such a set makes many different figures possible. Three of these figures, outstanding because of their symmetrical or even double symmetrical form, were developed by Lucas, using a solution given to him by DELANNEY. One of these three quadrilles—the second in our discussion—was brought earlier to a solution by LAQUIÈRE. However, his notes were lost in the siege of Strasbourg in the Franco-Prussian War of 1870.

In his book 'Wonderlijke Problemen' (*Surprising Problems*), F. SCHUH goes into detail about the three "classic" quadrilles of LUCAS, which he supplements with other puzzles that follow from these. In the following discussion, grateful use is made of SCHUH's work.

2. Symmetrical Quadrilles

In example 4.2 the twenty-eight stones of the normal domino set must be placed so that four with the same number of eyes can be arranged next to each other in squares. This figure and the following are assumed to have no empty spaces.

It is simple to divide the figure in example 4.3 into fourteen squares. After that, the stones must be so indicated in the diagram that no stones are used which are the same and no more than seven doubles are required.

On the perimeter of a figure such as the one shown, the doubles can be joined in three ways, A,B, and C (example 4.4). Bearing this in mind, it becomes clear that squares a and h on the left half of the figure are doubles and that d and k on the right half of the figure are also doubles. Square 1 must also be a double. From this the placement of double h and of h–1, to which the double in 1 must join, can be no other or this must occupy the bottom half of the square 1. For a corresponding reason, the bottom half of the square is also a double. From this it follows further that the bottom half of square m must also be a double. In this way the arrangement of the seven doubles is found.

The remaining stones must be so placed that no new doubles arise. This is possible only in the manner shown in the diagram in example 4.5. The doubles have a darker tint. What number of spots they have is arbitrarily decided as they are filled in in the figure. The arrangement of stones 1–2 and 4–5 is discovered in the same way.

It appears that the figure is symmetrical not only in outline but also in the arrangement of the individual stones. However, in view of the number of eyes on the doubles this is not the case. A different solution can arise by the exchanging of 0 with 6, 1 with 5, and 2 with 4 and the folding down of the diagram on the vertical axis of symmetry. These two solutions are therefore interdependent and are considered one and the same.

The number of spots in the squares b, c, e, f, g, i, and j must be discovered to solve the puzzle further. The number of spots that appear four times in these squares are indicated by the same letter as the square itself, so that, for example $b = 5$ means that in square b the 5 spots appear four times.

There are only two squares with the same number of spots. The numbers b, c, e, f, g, i, and j are therefore all different. "Is not equal to" is written as $\neq$; so $b \neq c$, $b \neq d$, and so forth.

Since there is no second double blank $b \neq 0$. Likewise $b \neq 1$ and $\neq 6$, as, for those values, there are the stones e–1 and c–6. By continuing this method of reasoning one can arrive at the following list of stones which are not equal:

$b \neq 0, \neq 1, \neq 6$; $c \neq 0, \neq 5, \neq 6$; $e \neq 0, \neq 1, \neq 2, \neq 3$;
$f \neq 0, \neq 2, \neq 3, \neq 4, \neq 6$; $g \neq 3, \neq 4, \neq 5, \neq 6$, $i \neq 0, \neq 1, \neq 2, \neq 3$;
$j = 3, \neq 4, \neq 5, \neq 6$.

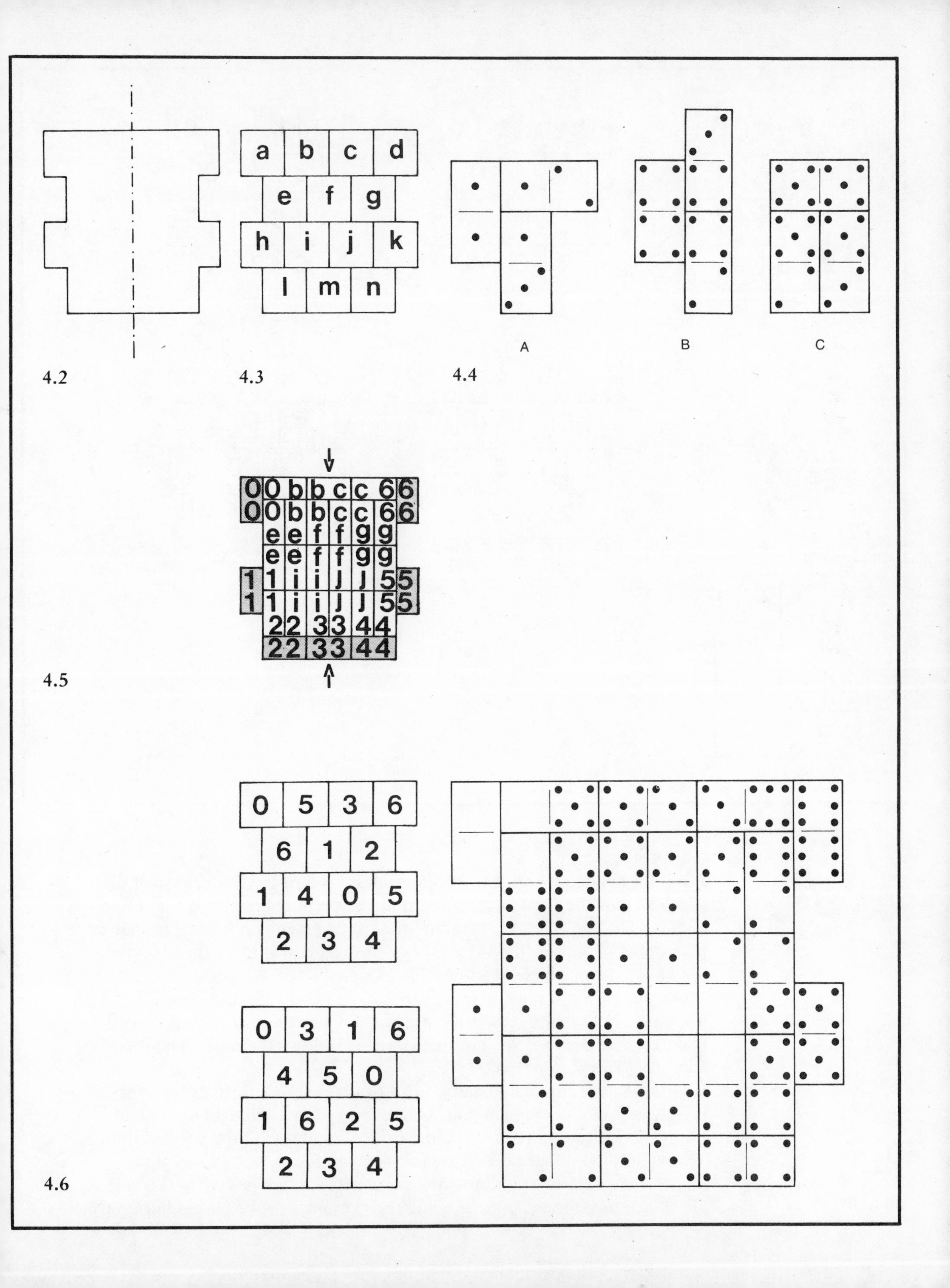
a b c d
e f g
h i j k
l m n
A
B
C
00bbcc66
00bbcc66
eeffgg
eeffgg
11iijj55
11iijj55
223344
223344
0 5 3 6
6 1 2
1 4 0 5
2 3 4
0 3 1 6
4 5 0
1 6 2 5
2 3 4

4.2

4.3

4.4

4.5

4.6

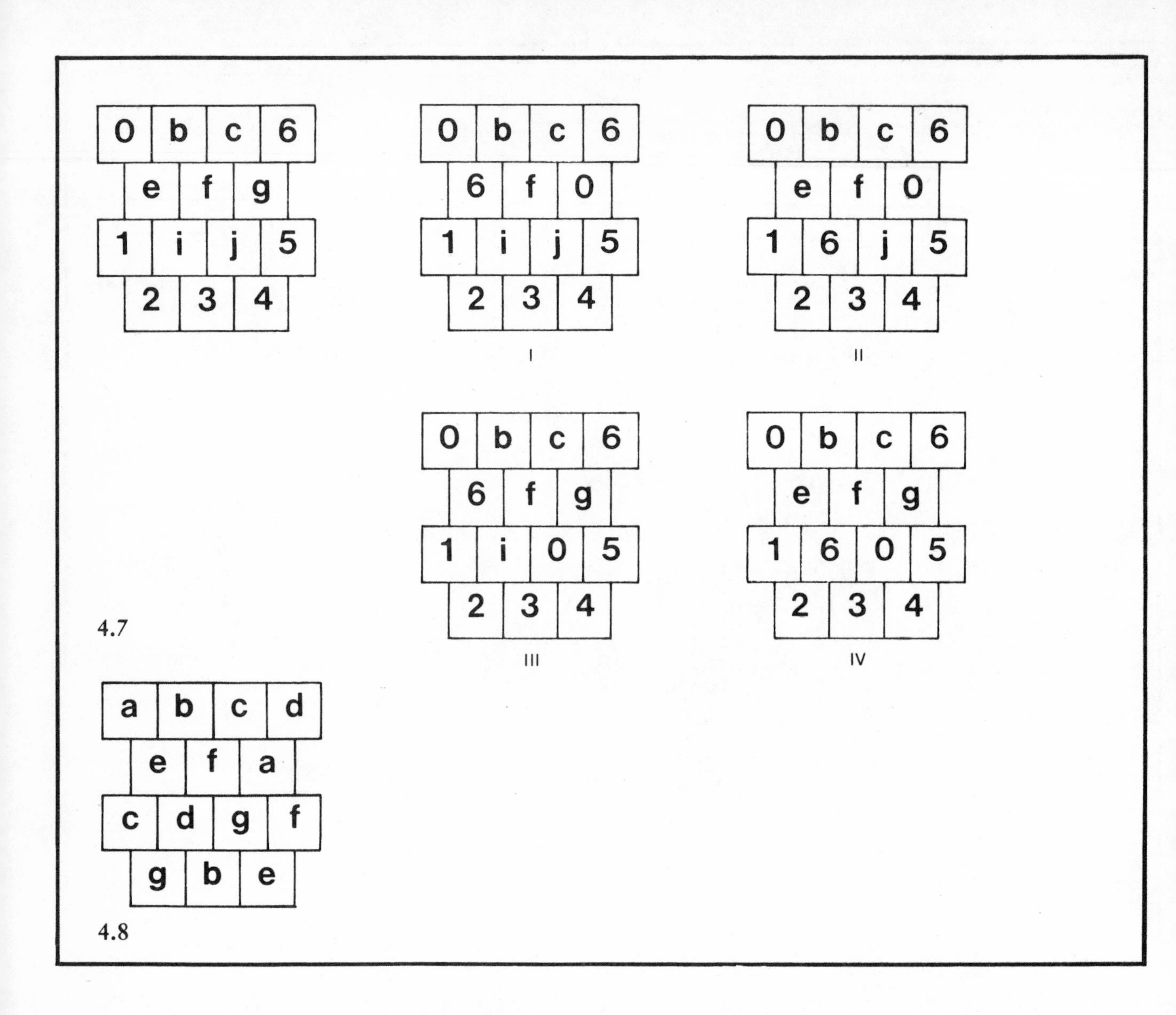

4.7

4.8

From these unequal objects it follows that f = 1 or f = 5. Because of the symmetry of the figure with respect to the vertical line, f = 1 and f = 5 resolves itself into f = 1. Since the stone 1–2 appears only once, it seems that stone f–j = 1–j, that is $j \neq 2$. For the value of j, there then remains only j = 0, from which it follows that g = 2.
The value of b can now no longer be b = 3 or b = 4 since stones 0–3 and 0–4 appear as j–3 and j–4. Therefore b = 5. Once the stone 5–4 is placed, b–e can no longer be equal to this stone; it follows that $e \neq 4$ and therefore e = 6, i = 4, and c = 3.
In this way the complete solution can be discovered. Besides this, there is only one interdependent pair, which emerge by exchanging 0 with 6, 1 with 5, 2 with 4 and folding the quadrille downward at the vertical line. This solution is illustrated in example 4.5.
Another method of solution can be applied in a simple way to this puzzle. Since the stones on the top and the bottom must be placed horizon-

tally but the other stones vertically it is easy to see which stones connect the squares.
In this way the square with the double blank (example 4.7) is joined with the adjacent squares b and 3 by means of stones b–0 and e–0. Since there is only one double blank, b and e cannot both = 0. Since these stones are b–c, b–f, and e–i, c, i, and f all ≠ 0. In addition to stone b–0, stone e–0. emerges. Only square g or square j can consist of four zeros.
In a similar way it is discovered that four sizes will fit only in square e or in square i. This leads to four combinations by which the second square 0 and the second square 6 can be filled in. Combination I is impossible because the figure includes two stones 0–6; combination IV is equally impossible since the 0–6 is missing. In Combination II e ≠ 0, ≠ 1, ≠ 2, ≠ 3, ≠ 6 and, due to the presence of the stone 0–5 on the right side of the figure, e = 5. Therefore e = 4.
Then c and f must be completed with 1 or 5. Since c ≠ 5 then c = 1 and f = 5. Now b and j must be completed with 2 or 3. Since b ≠ 2, b–c cannot be 1–2 — b = 3 and j = 2.
For Combination III it is found in the same way that g = 2, b = 5, and f = 1, i = 4, c = 3.
In this way both solutions can be obtained. Their interdependence is not as apparent as with the first method of solution.

Number of Solutions of the Quadrille
In general a solution of a quadrille laid out with a normal game in which the number of spots are filled in will lead to a total of 7! = 5,040 solutions. The above quadrilles thus have 2 × 5,040 solutions; folding down on the vertical line the one exchanges 5,040 times with the other. Solutions that are mirror images of each other are considered here as one and the same.

3. Completely Symmetrical Quadrilles

The quadrille discussed above demands that the total number of spots on the four squares on the top be the same as for the three squares on the bottom, for the four squares on the left hand side, the four squares on the right hand side, and for the three squares in the middle.
The general solution can be written as shown in example 4.8. The letters a, b, c, d, e, f, and g stand for the numbers 0, 1, 2, 3, 4, 5, and 6 in a still unknown order. The letters can also be reversed with respect to the vertical line. The required solution must satisfy:

$$a + b + c + d = a + e + c + g = d + a + f + e = g + b + e = f + d + g.$$

From this it follows: $d + f = c + g = b + e$ .... (1)
$b + c = e + f$ .... (2)
$a + e = g$ .... (3)
$a + c = b$ .... (4)

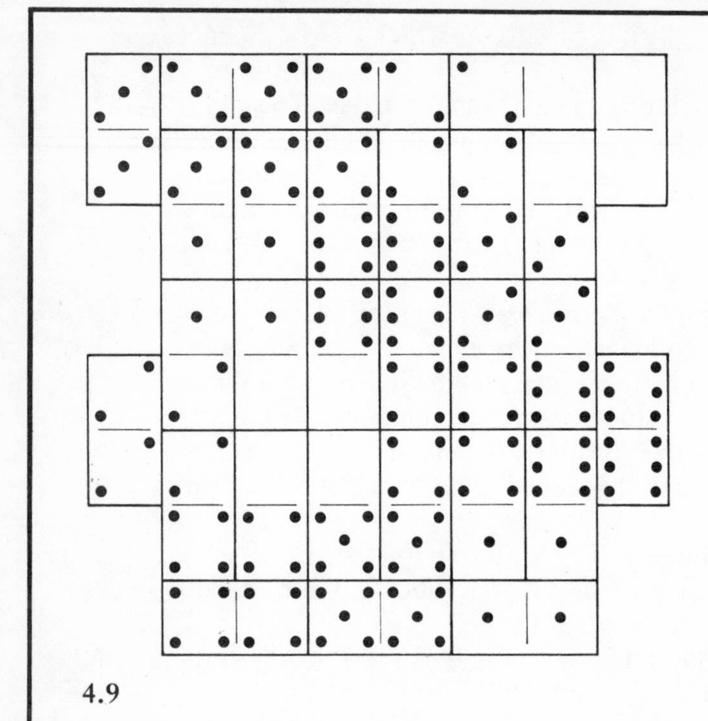

4.9

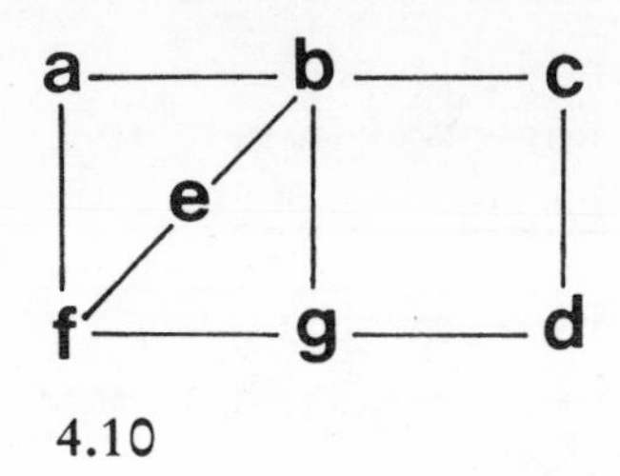

4.10

0	1	2	3	4	5	6
2	3	0	0	0	1	2
3	4	4	1	1	2	3
4	5	5	5	2	3	4
		6	6	6		

Table 4.1

Therefore $a = 6$ and a, b, c, e, and g are all $= 0$. It follows that $d = 0$ or $f = 0$. Furthermore:

$a + b + c + d + e + f + g = 0 + 1 + 2 + 3 + 4 + 5 + 6 = 21$, or

$3 (b + e) = 3 (c + g) = 3 (d + f) = 21 - a$ .... (5)

from which it follows that a is a multiple of three. Since a is not 0 or 6, $a = 3$.

From (5) it follows $b + e = 6$

From (4) it follows $\frac{b - c = 3}{c + e = 3}$

By the substitution of $e = 3 - c$ and $b = 3 + c$ in (2) it is discovered that $f = 3c$, so that $f = 0$. Therefore $d = 0$ and $f = 6$; further $c = 2$, $e = 1$, $b = 5$, and $g = 4$.
This brings us to the solution shown here (example 4.9). By flopping the quadrille with respect to a vertical line, there arises a second, interdependent solution that completes the problem.

4. Other Completely Symmetrical Quadrilles

Two squares of a quadrille are considered completely joined if they come against each other along an entire side (therefore with two domino stone ends). The demand is now made that each pair of completely joined squares belong to the number of spots that differ by 2, 3, or 4.
Two numbers are called complementary if they add up to 6. The numbers 0 and 6 are therefore complementary, 1 and 5, 2 and 4, while 3 is complementary with itself. The difference between two numbers is as large as that of their complements. If in a solution all numbers are replaced by their complementary numbers, a different solution results. We call this complementary shifting.
This is not the only possible shifting. If on two completely joined squares the number of spots in one is 0, the other can have 2, 3, or 4 spots. The same applies if the number of spots in one is 6. A solution therefore results by exchanging 0 and 6. We call this the 0 – 6 shifting. Still other solutions are obtainable by combining these shifts with the complementary; this gives the 1 – 5, 2 – 4 shifting in which all members from 1 through 5 are replaced and reversed and all numbers for 2 through 4 are reversed. From one solution a group of four solutions can be developed in this manner.

The diagram (example 4.10) tells which number of spots belong to completely joined squares and therefore must differ by 2, 3, or 4. These are the numbers that are joined directly by a line. Example 4.8 shows the squares in which these numbers, each indicated by a letter, belong.
In the diagram the numbers a and e are joined by a line with the same numbers b and f and with no others. In a solution therefore the numbers a and e can be exchanged; we call this the a – e shifting.
If a = 0 and e = 6 or the reverse this shifting is the same as the 0 – 6 shifting and offers no new solution. Every solution of this type that we discuss for the first time gives rise to a group of four solutions.
In the second type of solution the a – e shifting does not coincide with the 0 – 6 shifting. Each solution then belongs to a group of $2 \times 4 = 8$ solutions.

In table 4.1 the numbers standing below the line are those differing from the number above the line by 2, 3, or 4. There are four numbers under 2, 3, and 4 only. Since b is joined with four other numbers by a line, b = 2 or = 3 (because of shifting b = 4 is the same as b = 2). The numbers b and f are joined by a line with the same three numbers (that is a, e, and g) so that b = 2 and f = 3 or b = 3, f = 2 (which is the same as b = 3, f = 4). If b = 2 and f = 3 then none of the numbers joined by a line to b can be 1, so that d = 1. The three numbers that are joined by a line with f cannot = 4 because f = 3. The value 4 can only be awarded to c. Therefore it follows further that a = 0, e = 6. The hypothesis b = 2, f = 3 therefore leads to a group of four solutions of the first type (example 4.11).
If b = 3, f = 2, then the four numbers joined with b by a line are all = 4 so that d = 4. The numbers joined with a line to f cannot = 1 so c = 1.

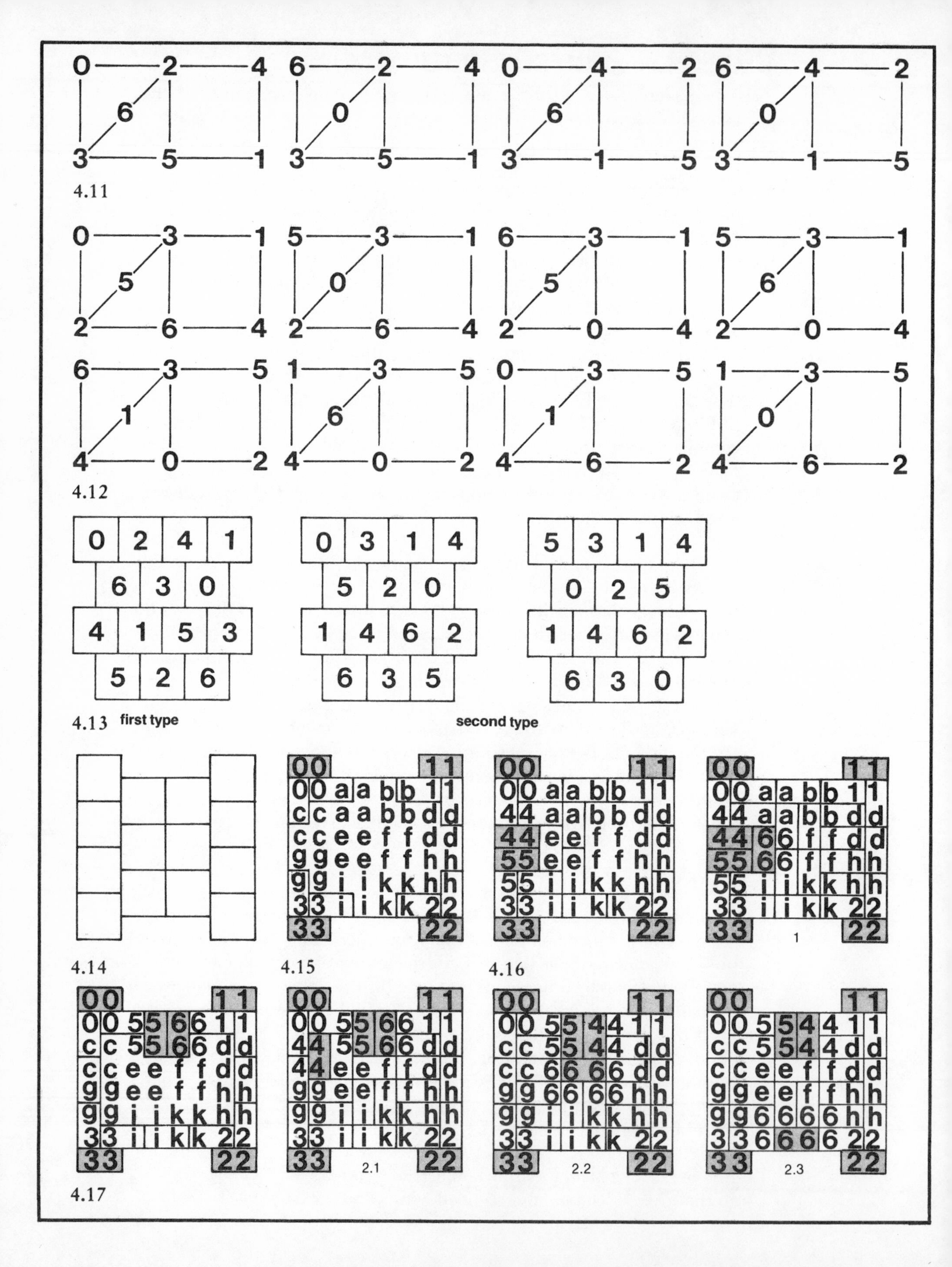

4.11

4.12

4.13

4.14

4.15

4.16

4.17

'Since d = 4, g = 5, so that, for example, g = 6, a = 0, e = 5. From this hypothesis comes a group of eight solutions of which two belong to the second type. Two schema placed one under the other develop from each other by shifting (example 4.12).
For the fourteen squares of the quadrille example 4.13 shows the first solutions of the first and second type in addition to the solution that develops from the latter by the a − e shifting. From each of these solutions three others arise by the 0–6 shifting, the 1–5, 2–4 shifting, or both combined.

5. First Double Symmetrical Quadrille

The problem is to place a quadrille within the indicated double symmetrical boundaries (example 4.14).
It is not difficult to see how the figure must be divided into fourteen squares and even less that a horizontally placed double must lie in each of the four corners. The choice of the number of spots on these doubles may be made at will, for example as in the second figure (example 4.15).
The number of spots in the squares without doubles is indicated by letters.
As there are no two stones the same the placing of two stones in each corner is fixed.
First of all, it must be determined how the three suitable doubles can be placed in the figure. Both on the vertical and on the horizontal sides there is space for two doubles placed crosswise. As these are placed on a side there is only one double left over; the other sides are then closed by a single stone. Because of symmetry, the satisfactory arrangement of one vertical and one horizontal is explored.

1. On the left side two doubles are placed, for example doublet four and doublet five. After that further arrangement of the stones can be done in no other way than by the horizontal placing of the stones 4−a and 5−i and, to avoid the same stones, by the vertical placing of stones a−e and e−i. In this way the position of the seventh double is determined. The filling in of the remaining stones offers no additional difficulties. This is type 1 (example 4.16).
2. Two doubles lie on the top edge. The seventh double can be neither e−e nor g−g (nor f−f or h−h) since this would give duplicate stones as a result. The seventh double can fill spot c−c. Further filling in leads to type 2.1 (example 4.17).
   The seventh double can also be formed by stone e−f or by stone i−k. From that comes types 2.2 and 2.3.
3. There is a double on none of the sides. There is then but one placing possible of the remaining three doubles that avoids duplicate stones, namely according to type 3 (example 4.18).

There are no other arrangements of the stones by which all seven doubles can find a place.

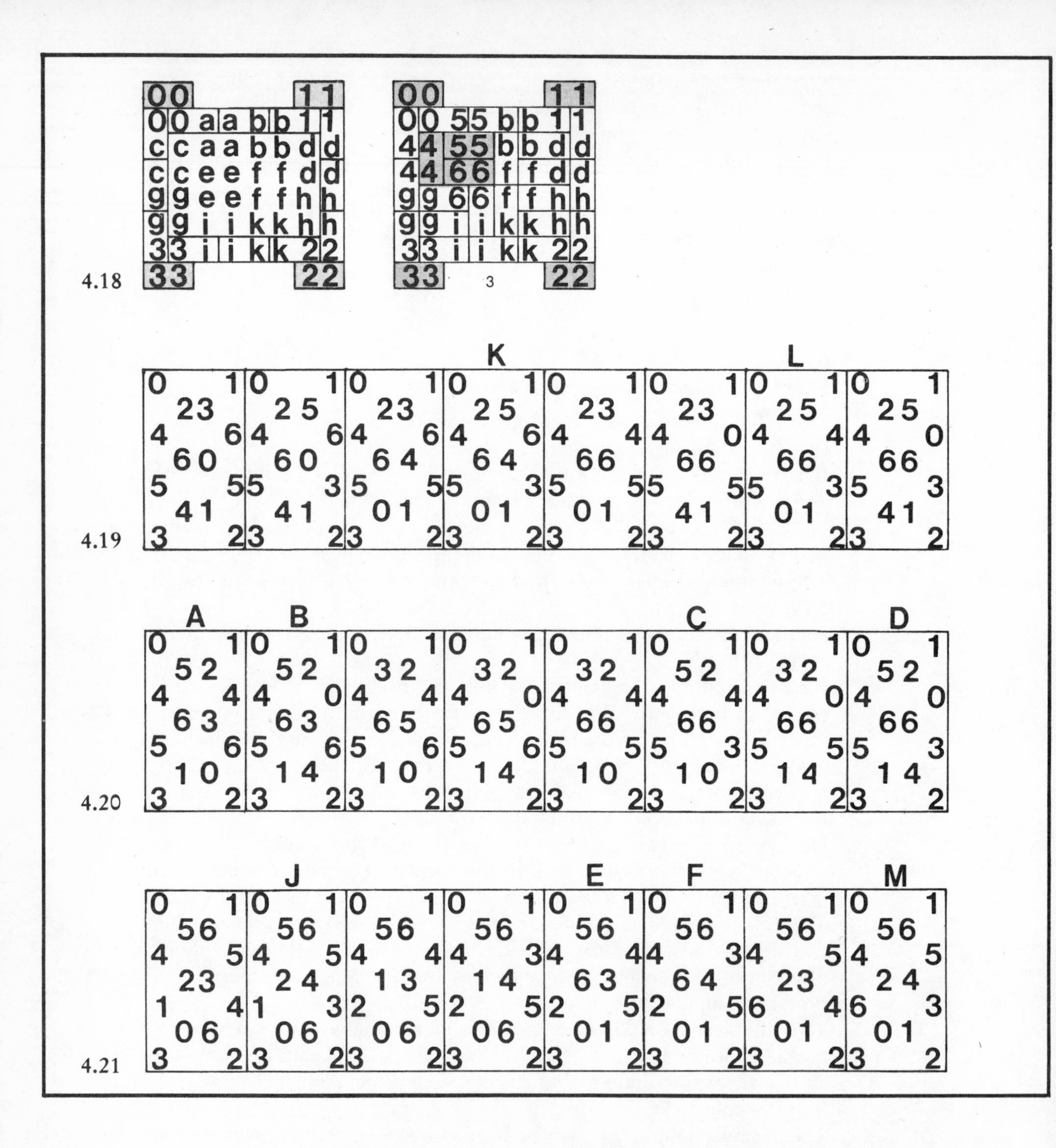

Further working out of the various types is easiest by means of discovering locations for the unlike numbers.

Type 1

This type is symmetrical with respect to a horizontal line. From one solution, therefore, a second solution can be developed by exchanging the number of spots that appear on the symmetrically placed doubles and by folding downward along the axis of symmetry.

The letters a, b, d, f, h, i and k stand for the numbers 0, 1, 2, 3, 4, 5, and 6 in one order or another. From the placing of the stones it appears:

$a \neq 0, \neq 1, \neq 4, \neq 6;$
$b \neq 0, \neq 1, \neq 4, \neq 6;$
$d \neq 1, \neq 2;$
$f \neq 1, \neq 2;$
$h \neq 1, \neq 2;$
$i \neq 2, \neq 3, \neq 5, \neq 6;$
$k \neq 2, \neq 3, \neq 5, \neq 6.$

From these dissimilarities it follows that either a or b = 2. If a = 2, stones 2–0 and 2–4 have found their place and there remains for k but one possibility, namely k = 1. Because of the symmetry, k = 1 comes to the same thing as b = 2. This last hypothesis therefore requires no further examination. The only symmetrically arranged square still to be filled in carries the number f. With this arrangement there is no observable difference between f = 0 and f = 3 nor between f = 4 and f = 5. The f = 0, f = 4, and f = 6 must be examined. These give rise to three possibilities:

a = 2, k = 1, f = 0, in which case i can be no other than = 4;
a = 2, k = 1, f = 4, in which case i = 0;
a = 2, k = 1, f = 6.
Further working out will lead to eight solutions (example 4.19).

From here we can develop eight other solutions by exchanging 0 with 3, 1 with 2, and 4 with 5 and folding down on the horizontal axis of symmetry (example 4.20).

Type 2.1

In type 2.1 the stones are not placed symmetrically. The following dissimilarities can be listed:

$d \neq 1, \neq 2, \neq 6;$
$e \neq 0, \neq 3, \neq 4, \neq 5;$
$f \neq 1, \neq 2, \neq 5, \neq 6;$
$g \neq 0, \neq 3, \neq 4, \neq 5;$
$h \neq 1, \neq 2, \neq 6;$
$i \neq 2, \neq 3, \neq 4, \neq 5;$
$k \neq 2, \neq 3;$

from which it appears that e = 2 or g = 2.
If i = 1, there is no square that can take 6; i = 6 excludes the placing of a square 1. From this it follows that i can only be = 0 and from that it follows that $k \neq 4, \neq 5$, thus d or h must be = 5. Further examination will lead to eight solutions of type 2.1 (example 4.21).

Type 2.2

Type 2.2 is symmetrical with regard to a vertical line. Once the sixes are all placed, c, d, g, h, i, and k all = 6. Furthermore:

$c \neq 0, \neq 3, \neq 5;$
$g \neq 0, \neq 3, \neq 5;$
$d \neq 1, \neq 2, \neq 4;$
$h \neq 1, \neq 2, \neq 4;$
$i \neq 2, \neq 3;$
$k \neq 2, \neq 3.$

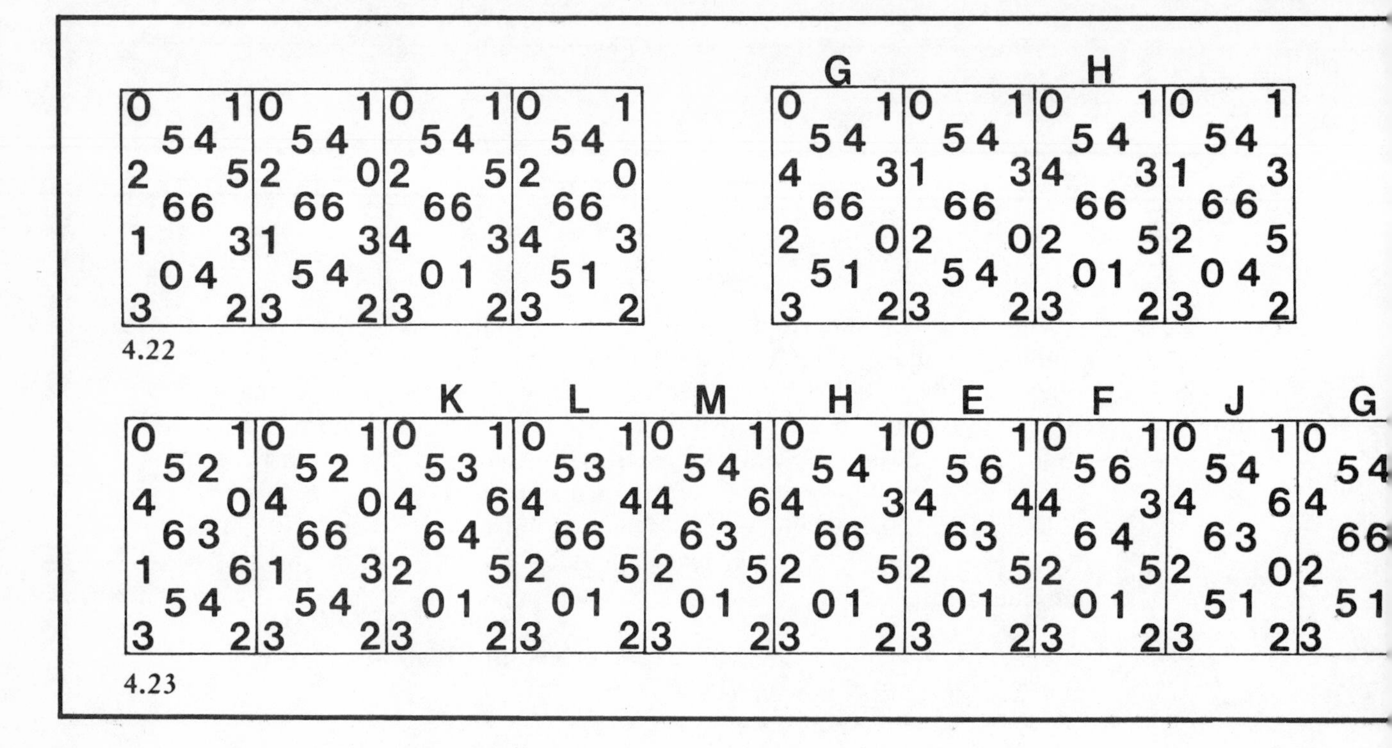

4.22

4.23

It follows from these dissimilarities that c = 2 or g = 2 and that d = 3 or h = 3. If g = 2 h cannot = 3; therefore either c = 2 or d = 3. Because of the symmetry it can be assumed that c = 2. From that we see that the values for h of 0 and 5 are eliminated and h = 3. This leads to four solutions from which four others come by the exchanging of 0 with 1, 3 with 2, and 5 with 4 and the folding of the axis on a vertical line. These solutions are shown in example 4.22.

Type 2.3

This symmetrical type has no solutions. Both e and g are $\neq 0$, $\neq 2$, $= 3$, $= 5$, and $= 6$. Therefore one of the two = 1 and the other = 4, which is impossible since the stone 1–4 is already placed.

Type 3

In this final asymmetrical type, it appears that:

$b \neq 0, \neq 1, \neq 5;$ $\quad g \neq 0, \neq 3, \neq 4, \neq 6;$ $\quad i \neq 2, \neq 3, \neq 4, \neq 6;$

$d \neq 1, \neq 2, \neq 5;$ $\quad h \neq 1, \neq 2;$ $\quad k \neq 2, \neq 3, \neq 6.$

$f \neq 1, \neq 2, \neq 5;$

From this follow the fourteen solutions of type 3 given in example 4.23. In total this quadrille has 8 + 8 + 4 + 14 = 34 different solutions. By mutually shifting the number of spots 34 × 5,040 = 171,360 solutions develop. On closer examination it appears that of the fourteen solutions of type 3 there are eight that differ from solutions of another type by the placing of certain stones but which are identical as far as the number of

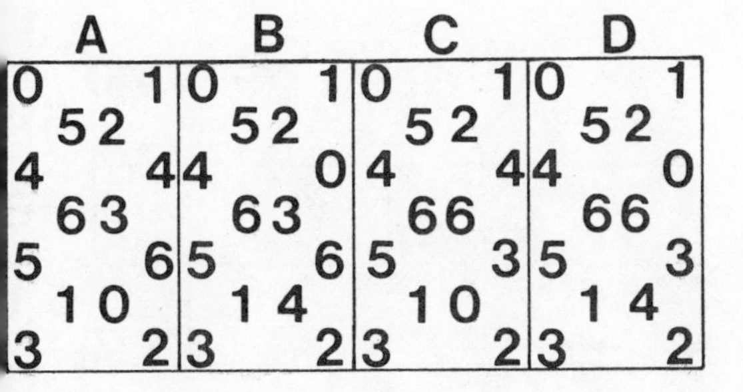

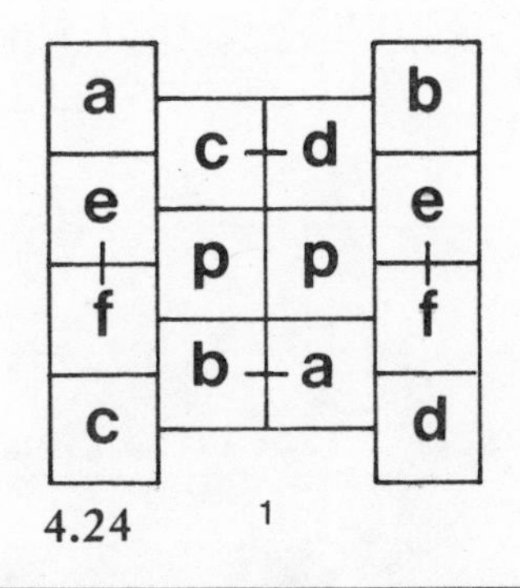

4.24

1

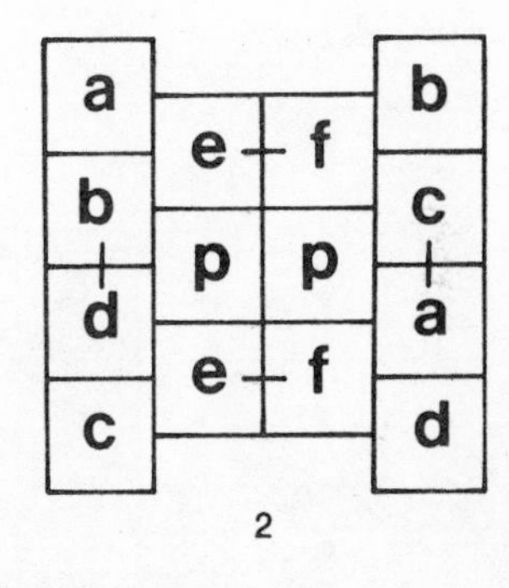

2

spots in the squares is concerned. In this way four solutions of type 3 come to the same thing as four of the "folded down" type 1; two as two solutions of type 2.1; and another two as two solutions of type 2.2, these last again folded down. They are given the letters A to H. Similar solutions develop by changing the placing of five stones.

6. Completely Double Symmetrical Quadrilles

The object is to arrange the quadrille so that, first, both squares in the middle have the same number of spots and, secondly, so that the total number of spots in the four squares on the top, the four squares on the bottom, the four squares on the side, and the four sqaures on the right side are the same.

Solutions take the shape of one of the two figures in example 4.24 in which the letters joined by a line can be exchanged. In every other arrangement of the letters, totals emerge that can be exchanged with only one other of the four sums; thus all four cannot be the same.
Let the sum of the spots in the four squares on the top = x and the sum of the spots in the four corner squares = y. Since the sum of the number of spots in the fourteen squares is $2 \times 21 = 42$, then $4x = 42 - 2p + y$.
From the figures it appears that $x = y$ and from this it follows that p must be a multiple of three. Therefore $p = 0$, $= 3$, or $= 6$, and $x = y$ is respectively $= 14$, $= 12$, or $= 10$. Because the same stone cannot be used twice, the four numbers totaling sums x and y must all be different.

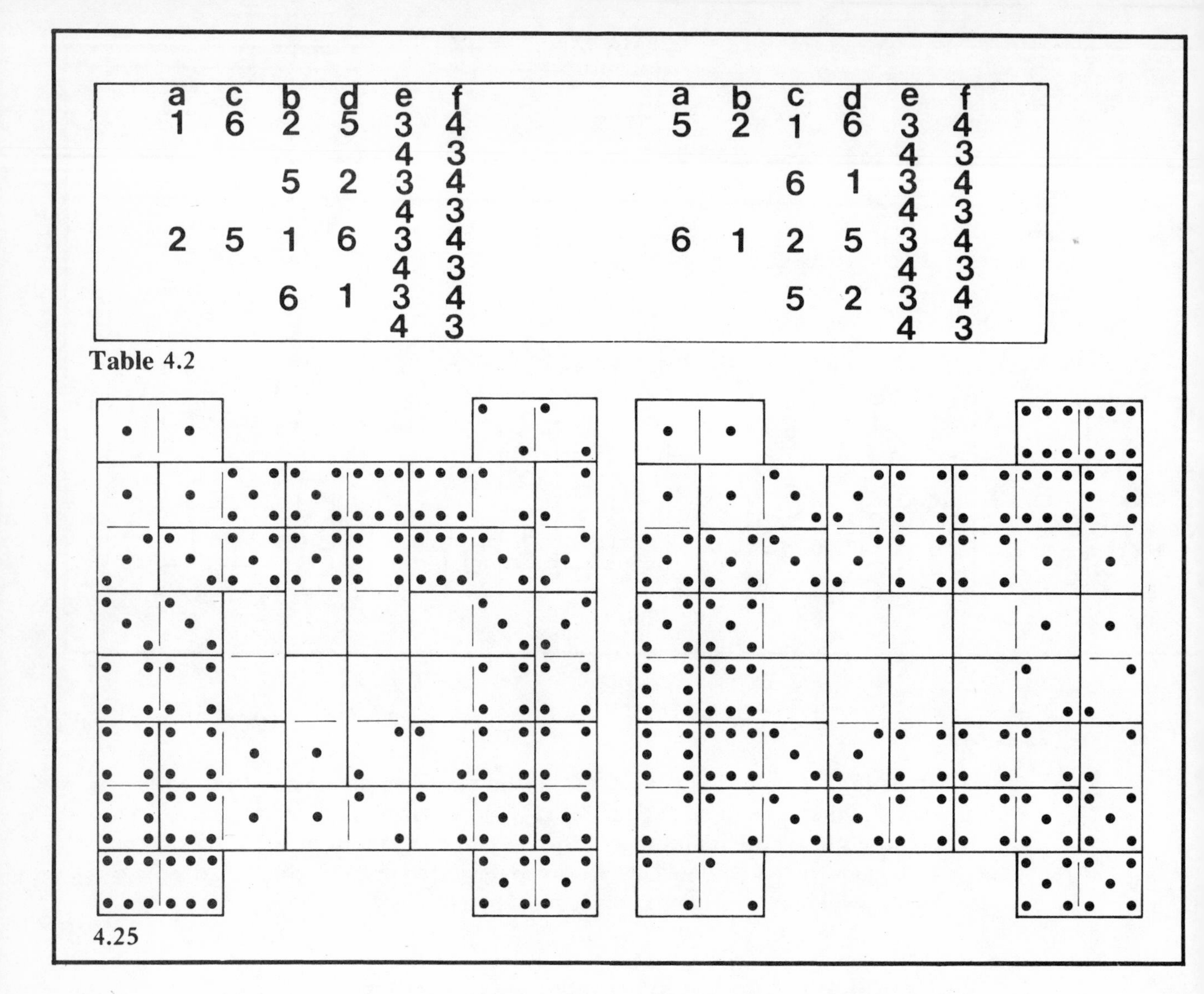

a	c	b	d	e	f
1	6	2	5	3	4
				4	3
		5	2	3	4
				4	3
2	5	1	6	3	4
				4	3
		6	1	3	4
				4	3

a	b	c	d	e	f
5	2	1	6	3	4
				4	3
		6	1	3	4
				4	3
6	1	2	5	3	4
				4	3
		5	2	3	4
				4	3

Table 4.2

4.25

For p = 0 the sum y = 14 can be built up from the four numbers 1 + 2 + 5 + 6 or the numbers 1 + 3 + 4 + 6 or the numbers 2 + 3 + 4 + 5.
If y = 1 + 2 + 5 + 6 corresponding solutions of the first figure are possible according to both type 1 and the "folded-down" type 1. The number of solutions appears from table 4.2, which is based on the problem as given: a + b + c + d = a + c + e + f = b + d + e + f = 14, from which it follows that a + c = b + d = e + f = 7.
This gives sixteen solutions according to type 1 and sixteen of the "folded-down" type. These solutions appear to be each others' mirror image. It follows that the doubles e, f, and p (3, 4 and 0) can be placed on one side as well as on the opposite. The examined case has thirty-two solutions.
By analogy, thirty-two solutions can also be discovered for the second figure belonging to type 2.2. A solution is illustrated for both figures (example 4.25).

For the cases y = 1 + 3 + 4 + 6 and y = 2 + 3 + 4 + 5, sixty-four solutions are found so that for p = 0 a total of 192 solutions exists.
An equally large number exists for p = 3 and p = 6.

7. Other Complete Double Symmetrical Quadrilles

The conditions are somewhat modified for these puzzles. The given problem states that the quadrilles must be so arranged that not only the sum of the spots in the four squares on each side of the diagram is the same, but also that the total of the spots on both squares in the middle have that value.
In a problem corresponding to the discussed symmetrical puzzle a solution of the quadrille can be found. Now we are concerned with a quadrille that in unlimited form has thirty-four solutions and leads to a method yielding a quicker result. For that matter, this method of working was followed in the previous question. We state again that the sum of the spots in the four squares on the top side and so forth = x and the sum of the spots in the four corners of the square = y. Then 5x = 42 + y. Because no two stones can be the same, every sum x and every sum y is built from four dissimilar numbers. This gives the following numbers:

1: x = 10	(0 + 1 + 3 + 6), or 0 + 1 + 4 + 5,	or 0 + 2 + 3 + 5, or
	1 + 2 + 3 + 4,	or 4 + 6, or 5 + 5)
y = 8	(0 + 1 + 2 + 5, or 0 + 1 + 3 + 4);	
2: x = 11	(0 + 1 + 4 + 6, or 0 + 2 + 3 + 6,	or 0 + 2 + 4 + 5, or
	1 + 2 + 3 + 5,	or 5 + 6)
y = 13	(0 + 2 + 5 + 6, or 0 + 3 + 4 + 6,	or 1 + 2 + 4 + 6, or
	1 + 3 + 4 + 5);	

3: x = 12, y = 18 (3 + 4 + 5 + 6).

The third case is impossible as, in addition to the two squares with six spots in the middle, at least two identical squares also are required.
Just as in the previous question we shall make a schematic figure and, because the number of possibilities is so much smaller, fill it in at once with numbers rather than letters.
There are six figures in which the numbers joined by a line can be exchanged with each other (example 4.26).
The first and the fourth figure can be omitted from further consideration because, in both, two numbers 6 stand to the right or obliquely above each other, a configuration requiring two identical stones. For the remainder, it must follow that three doubles can be placed in the corners according to one of the four types of solutions that we have found. For figures 2 and 3 these doubles are the double two, double five, and double

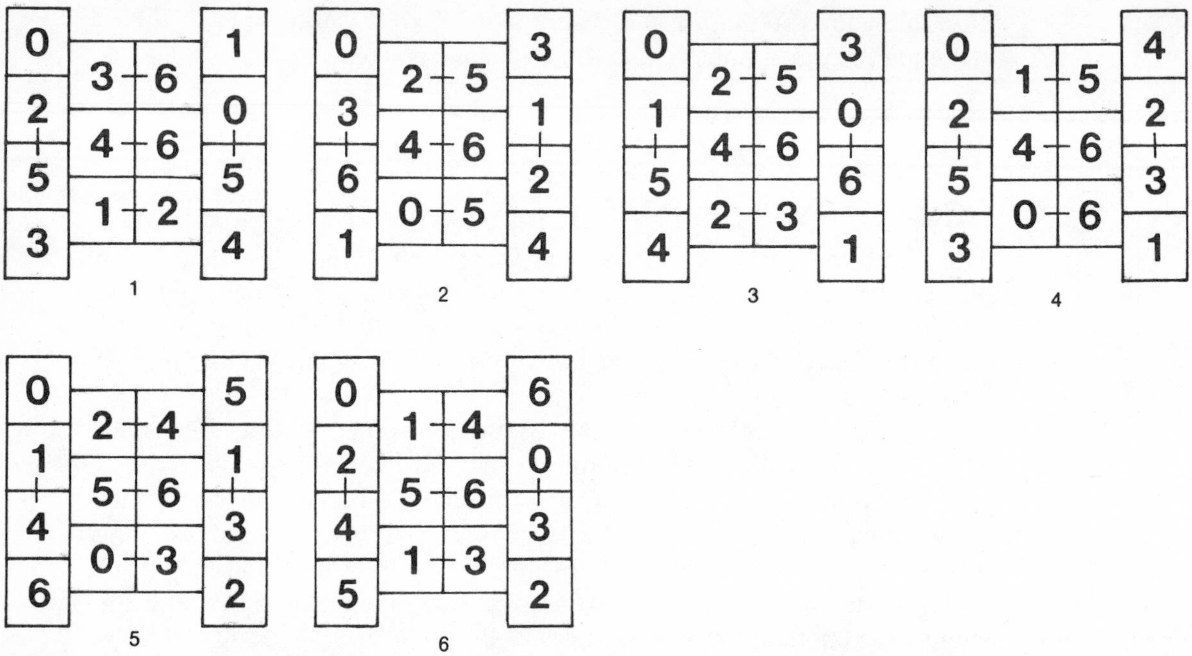

4.26

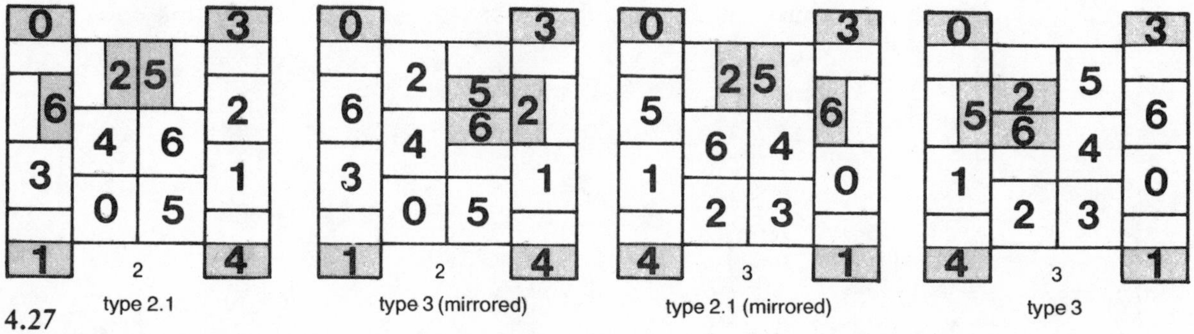

4.27

six and for the figures 5 and 6 double one, double three, and double four. Figure 5 does not lead to a solution due to the placement of the squares with 1, 2, and 3 spots. The second figure can be placed according to type 2.1 and also to type 3, reversed or turned with regard to the example on page 50.

Type 2.1 and the reversed type 3 each provide a solution. The turned type 3 runs into difficulties.

The third figure can belong to type 2.1 (reversed) and to type 3 (as shown and reversed). Two solutions follow from this, one for the mirror image type 2.1 and one for type 3. The mirror image type 3 fails to work.

Finally, the sixth figure can be worked according to type 2.1 in two ways, neither of which leads to a solution.

There are therefore four solutions, two of type 2.1 and two of type 3, which are presented schematically in the examples above (example

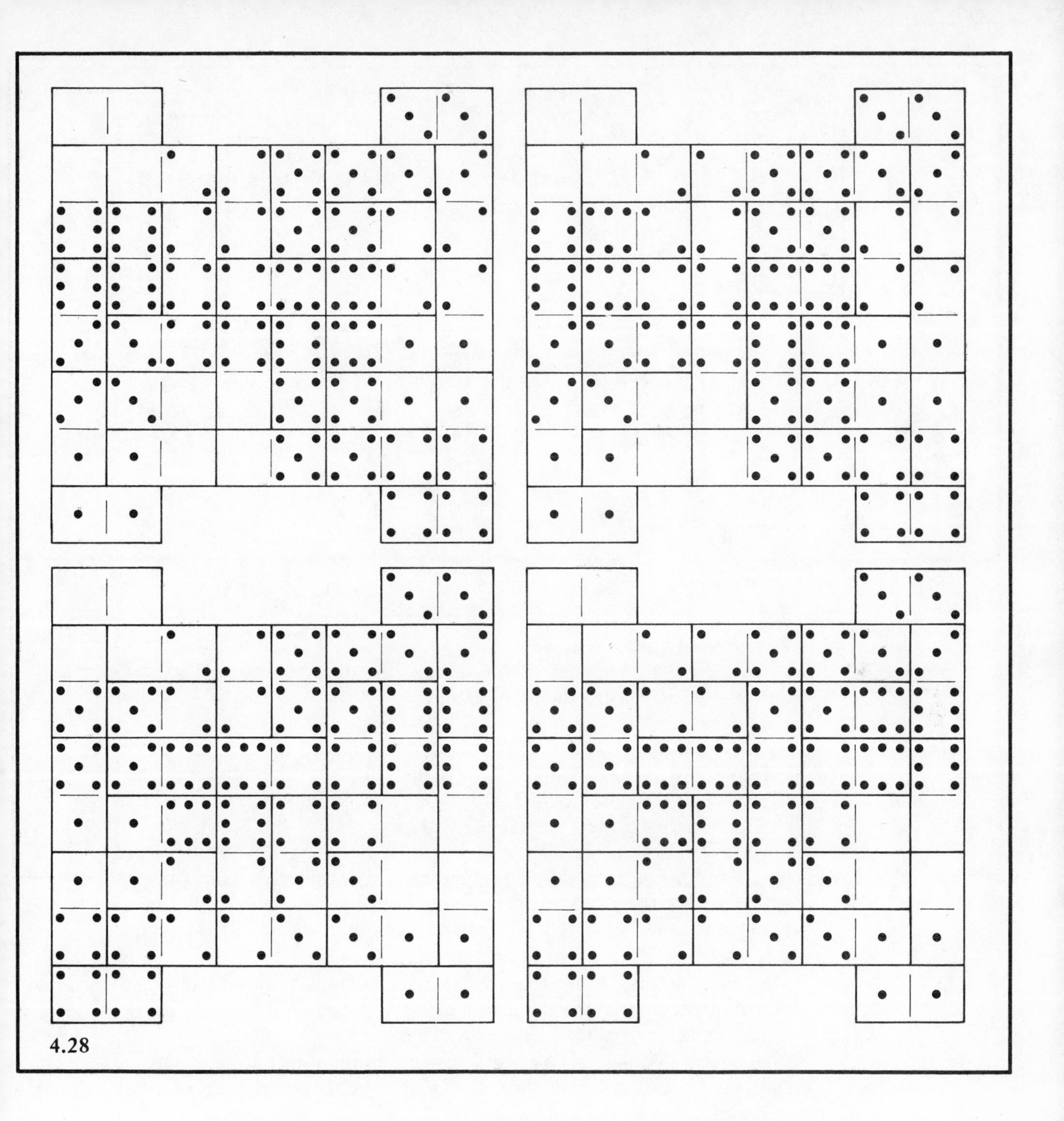
4.28

4.27). The doubles are indicated by a darker tint and the remaining stones only by the numbered squares.
The completely worked out solutions are shown below. They are all closely related. Solutions of the same type develop from each other by the exchanging of 0 with 3, 2 with 5, and the reverse. Solutions that stem from the same figures are identical with respect to the number of spots in the squares. By the shifting of seven stones, these are arranged as in example 4.28.

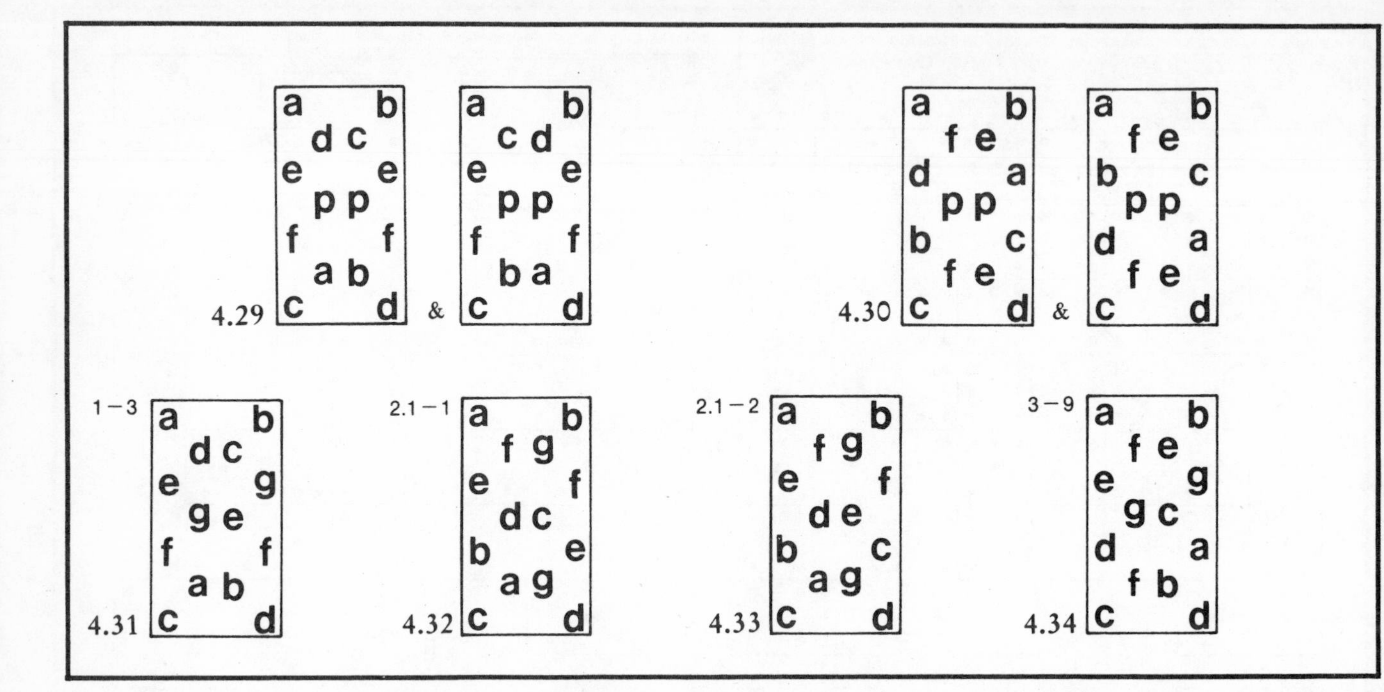

It is naturally possible to solve both problems of the quadrille with limited definitions by examining how suitable the thirty-four discovered solutions are for meeting the requirements.

By the conditions of the problem first stated in section 6, only those solutions come under consideration in which the two middle squares have the same number of dots. A great many are eliminated because two sums arise that can be exchanged with only one of the four groups of numbers and therefore do not have the same value. Five solutions of type 1 and their "folded-down" versions are considered, which, in general type, are the same as those in example 4.29. A second solution of type 2.2 and its "folded down" version are also considered in example 4.30.
These are nothing more than the starting point for the already mentioned method of solution that avoids the round about way involving the thirty-four known solutions of the quadrille.
The solution of the variant problem whose conditions are given at the opening of this section is more significant but also more difficult when accomplished by this last method.
Both quadrilles with their "folded-down" figures which brought the first problem to a solution are unusable for the second.
The fifth solution of type 1 yields:
$a + b + c + d = a + c + e + f = b + d + e + f = 2p$, or
$a + c = b + d = e + f = p$,
so that none of the letters a, b, c, d, e, f or p can represent the number 0.
The lack of value of the three other solutions can be shown in the same way.

There remain the twenty quadrilles in which the middle squares are filled by unequal numbers. Most of these are also unsuitable for the reasons mentioned. This leaves only five solutions to be examined, namely the third of type 1, the first, second, and seventh of type 2.1 and the ninth of type 3.

1 – 3 The third solution of type 1 (example 4.30) is generally formed with adjacent letters. From this it follows:
$a + b + c + d = a + c + e + f = b + d + g + f = g + e$, therefore:
$a + c + f = g$ and $a + c = g + f$, which means that $f = 0$.
At the same time $a + c + e = b + d + g$, from which it follows that the sum of these six numbers must be even. But this sum $= 21 - f = 21$, which is in conflict with the previous conclusion.

2.1 – 1 The first solution of type 2.1 (example 4.32) yields:
$a + b + c + e = b + d + e + f = a + b + f + g = a + c + d + g = c + d$.
From $a + c + d + g = c + d$ will follow:
$a + g = 0$, which is impossible.

In the same way the seventh solution of this type is unsatisfactory.

2.1 – 2 The second solution of type 2.1 (example 4.33) gives:
$a + b + c + e = a + b + f + g = b + c + d + f = a + c + d + g = d + e$.
From this it follows
$a + g = c + d$; $e = c + a + g$, therefore $e = 2c + d$.
The five equal sums amount to at least $1 + 2 + 3 + 4 = 10$.

To these sums belong $d + e$ so that—
since e cannot be larger than 6—
d is at least 4.
From $e = 2c + d$ it follows that: $d = 4$, $c = 1$, $e = 6$, and $a + b = 3$.
From this follow two solutions:
$a = 0, b = 3, f = 2, g = 5$, and $a = 3, b = 0, f = 5, g = 2$.

The ninth solution of type 3 (example 4.34) yields
$a + c + d + e = a + b + e + f = a + b + d + g = b + c + d + f = g + c$.
From this follows:
$a + e = c + d$; $g = a + d$, therefore $g = c + 2d$, analogous to the previous case.
This also leads to two solutions:
$c = 4, d = 1, g = 6, a = 0, b = 3, e = 5, f = 2$ and
$c = 4, d = 1, g = 6, a = 3, b = 0, e = 2, f = 5$.

Indeed, it appears that solving the puzzle with definite limitations from the thirty-four solutions of the unrestricted problem is more laborious than direct. There is another minor problem with this method. From the division of the number of spots on the fourteen squares, the ninth solution of type 3 and the second of type 2.1 appear to be each others' mirror image. They therefore do not stand on their own.

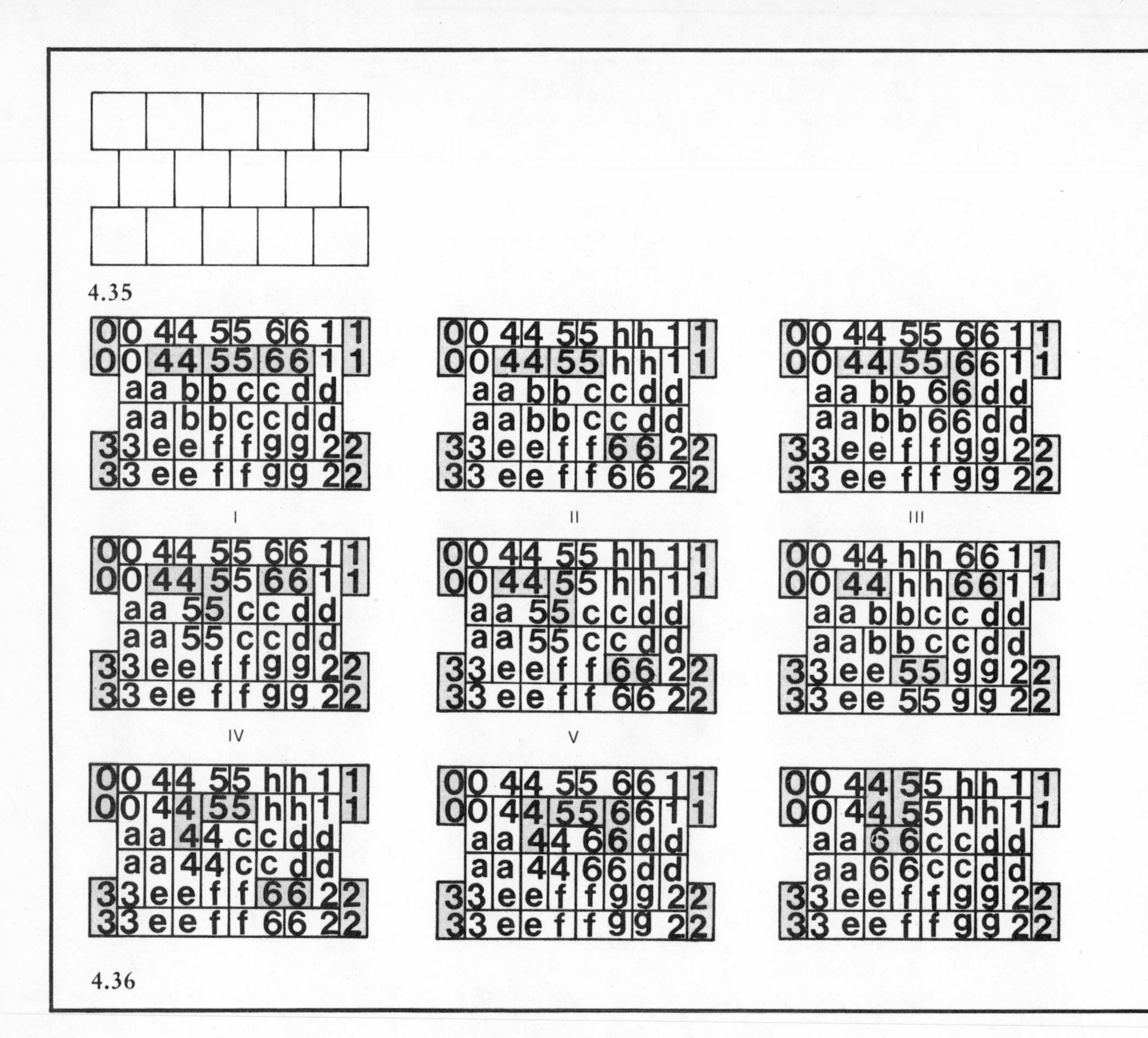

4.35

4.36

There is a similar relationship between the fifth solution of type 3 and the eighth of type 2.1, between the third and fourth solutions of type 3, and the fourth and seventh of the first type, not "folded down." These relationships are indicated in examples 4.21 and 4.23 by the letters from J to M.

8. Second Double Symmetrical Quadrille

The third quadrille examined by LUCAS is also a double symmetrical with the form illustrated (example 4.35). Neither LUCAS nor SCHUH give a complete solution to the puzzle. The stones can be shown in nine ways within the area so that seven and no more than seven doubles are placed and no stones are identical. Five of these ways yield a solution (example 4.36).

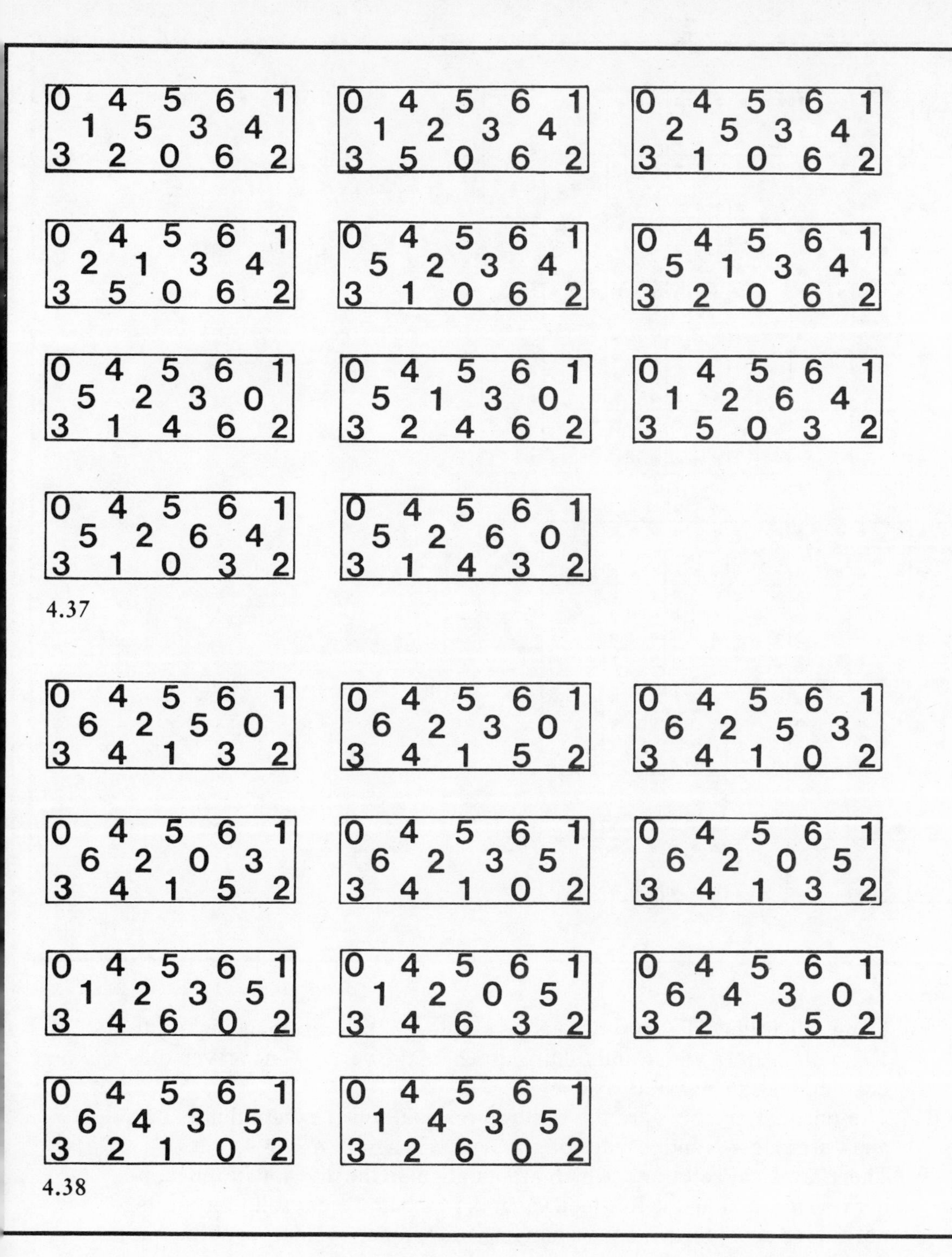

I. This figure is symmetrical in both outline and position of the stones. By the exchanging of the spots and the "folding down" of the vertical axis of symmetry, each solution goes with the other.
The unlike numbers are:
$a \neq 0, \neq 3, \neq 4$; $b \neq 0, \neq 3$; $c \neq 1, \neq 2$; $d \neq 1, \neq 2, \neq 6$; $e \neq 0, \neq 3$; $f \neq 2, \neq 3$; $g \neq 1, \neq 2$.

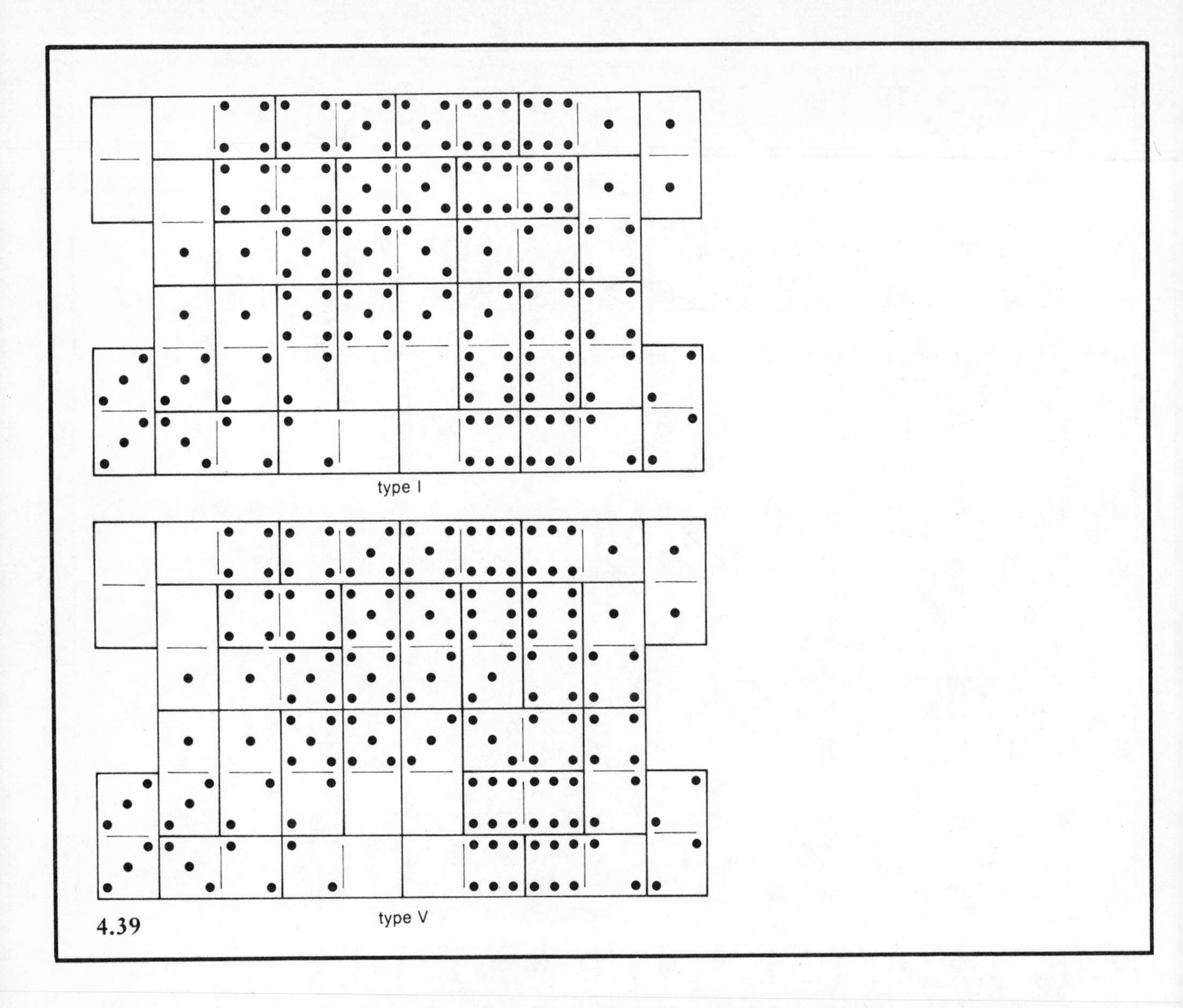

4.39

From this follow eleven solutions (example 4.37). By exchanging 0 with 1, 2 with 3, and 4 with 6 and folding down on the vertical line eleven other solutions can be made (example 4.38).

II. The unequal numbers are the same as for solution I, except that b, c, e and f are also $\neq 6$ and in place of $g \neq 1, \neq 2$, is $h \neq 1, \neq 2, \neq 4, \neq 5$. There are eight solutions, which are identical in the division of the number of spots among the fourteen squares to the first eight solutions of the not folded down type I. By exchanging four stones, a solution of the one type becomes a solution of the other.

III. For the third type the following dissimilar numbers are yielded:

$a \neq 0, \neq 3, \neq 4, \neq 6$; $d \neq 1, \neq 2, \neq 5, \neq 6$; $f \neq 2, \neq 3, \neq 6$;
$b \neq 0, \neq 3, \neq 6$; $e \neq 0, \neq 3, \neq 6$; $g \neq 1, \neq 2, \neq 6$.

From this arise three solutions that correspond with solutions 9, 10, and 11 of type I in the division of the number of spots among the fourteen squares.

IV. The dissimilar numbers are:

$a \neq 0, \neq 3, \neq 4, \neq 5, \neq 6$; $d \neq 1, \neq 2, \neq 5, \neq 6$; $f \neq 2, \neq 3, \neq 5$;
$c \neq 1, \neq 2, \neq 5$; $e \neq 0, \neq 3, \neq 5$; $g \neq 1, \neq 2, \neq 5$.

There are two solutions that correspond in the division of spots with solutions 1 and 3 of type 1.

V. The dissimilar numbers are the same as for type IV, with the understanding that $f = 6$ and, in place of g, $h \neq 1, \neq 2, \neq 4, \neq 5$.
This type has two solutions with the same result as for the solution of type IV.

In total, this second double symmetrical quadrille has $11 + 8 + 3 + 2 + 2 = 26$ different solutions. These twenty-six solutions fall into three groups, according to the division of the number of spots among the fourteen squares:

a. in two cases the division can be arranged according to type I, II, IV, and V;
b. six divisions can be made according to type I and II;
c. three divisions can be made according to type I and III.

As an example the complete solutions of two representatives of group a are written out, one according to type I, the other according to type V. They can change with each other by the exchanging of six stones (example 4.39).
The same type of similarity exists between type I and the remaining types after reversing and replacing 0 with 1, 2 with 3, and 4 with 6.

V. Other Quadrilles

1. The Quadrilles with the Lowest and the Highest Number of Corners

1. Introduction

The symmetrical quadrille discussed first has sixteen corners, both double symmetrical quadrilles twelve corners. SCHUH has raised the question of which quadrilles have the lowest and which the highest number of corners. For this question to be answered certain general characteristics of these corners must be more closely examined.

A figure that can be divided into fourteen identical squares and in which the twenty-eight domino stones can be laid out so that each of the fourteen squares contains a number of dots repeated four times has corners of no other than 90° (outward) and 270° (inward). It should be remembered that the figure is designed without empty space.
Let u be the number of outward and i the number of inward corners, then $u = i + 4$. This can easily be seen. If one imagines that one is going around the figure of a clock with the hands, then, as one returns to the starting point, one has moved an entire 360°. In passing an outward corner one turns 90° with the clock, and in passing an inward corner 90° against the clock. One therefore moves $u \times 90° - i \times 90°$. From this it follows that $u < 90° - i \times 90° = 4 \times 90°$ or $u - i = 4$.
The total number of corners is $= u + i = 2i + 4$, therefore even.

2. The Lowest Number of Corners

Shown are all imaginable figures (example 5.1) with a maximum of ten corners. The figures show how outward and inward corners can follow each other. No attention is paid to whether or not they can be divided into fourteen squares, and the form of the diagram has only schematic meaning. There is one figure with four corners and one with six corners. There are four figures with eight corners and eight with ten corners. Apart from the third figure with eight corners, which, as we said in the introduction to the previous chapter, can be made from a domino game in which double two is the highest stone, only one figure can be laid out as a quadrille to yield a similar diagram. This is the sixth, the one tinted a darker shade.
The quadrille with the lowest number of corners is therefore a figure with ten corners in the form of example 5.2. By careful placement of the seven doubles and by prohibiting duplicate stones, it appears that the arrangement of the stones can be drawn in only one way within this form (example 5.3).

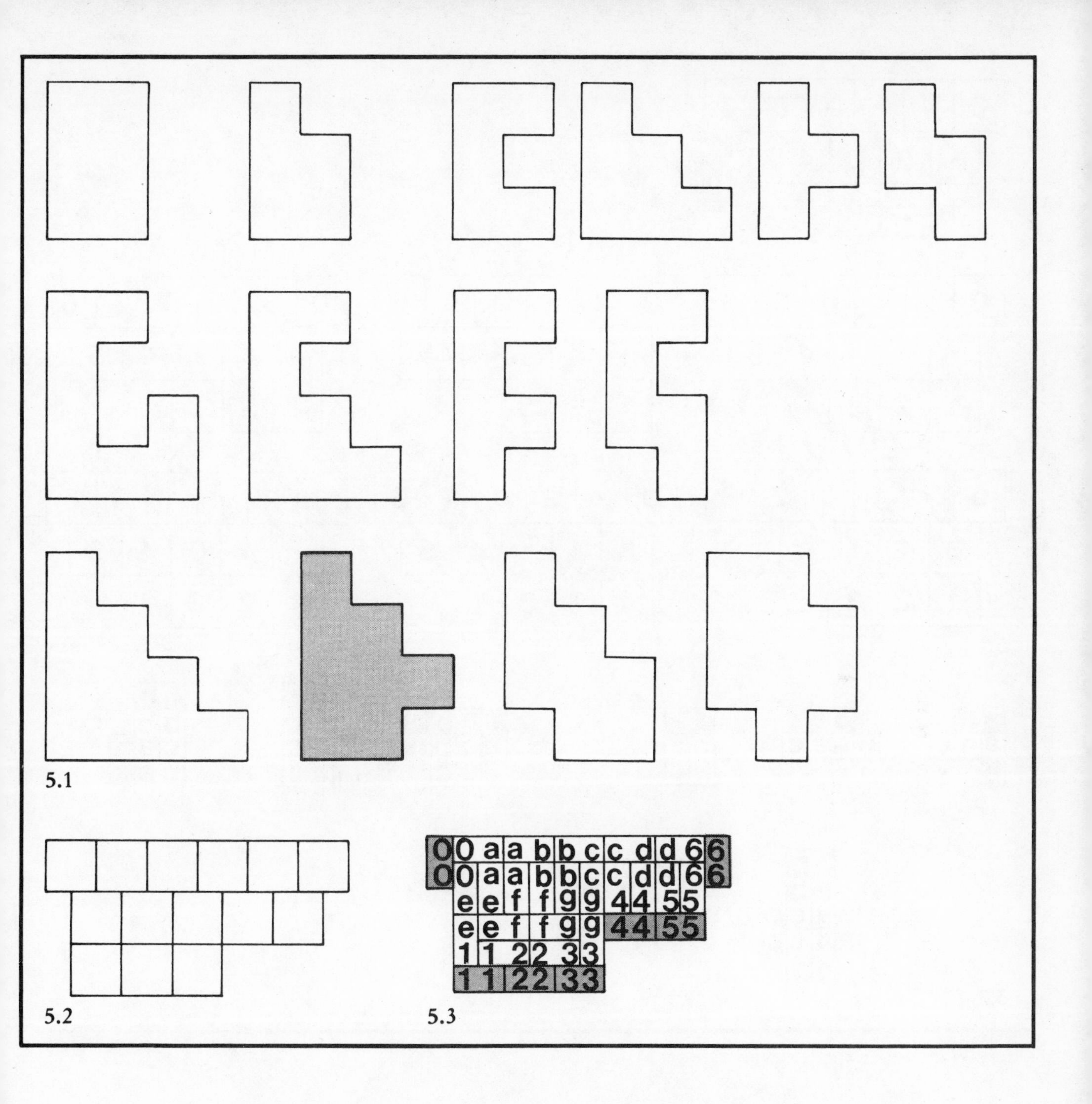

5.1

5.2

5.3

Once the number of spots on the seven doubles are arranged, the placement of the three other stones is clear. In the example they are the 1–2, 2–3, and the 5–6. Furthermore, the following unequal numbers appear:

a $\neq 0, \neq 1$;	c $\neq 3, \neq 4, \neq 5, \neq 6$;	f $\neq 0, \neq 1, \neq 3$;
b $\neq 0, \neq 3, \neq 4$;	d $\neq 4, \neq 5, \neq 6$;	g $\neq 2, \neq 3, \neq 4$.
	e $\neq 0, \neq 1, \neq 2$;	

Moreover f $\neq 5, \neq 6$, so one must place the 5 and 6 elsewhere as 5–6 is not suitable. Consequently f $= 2$ or $= 4$.

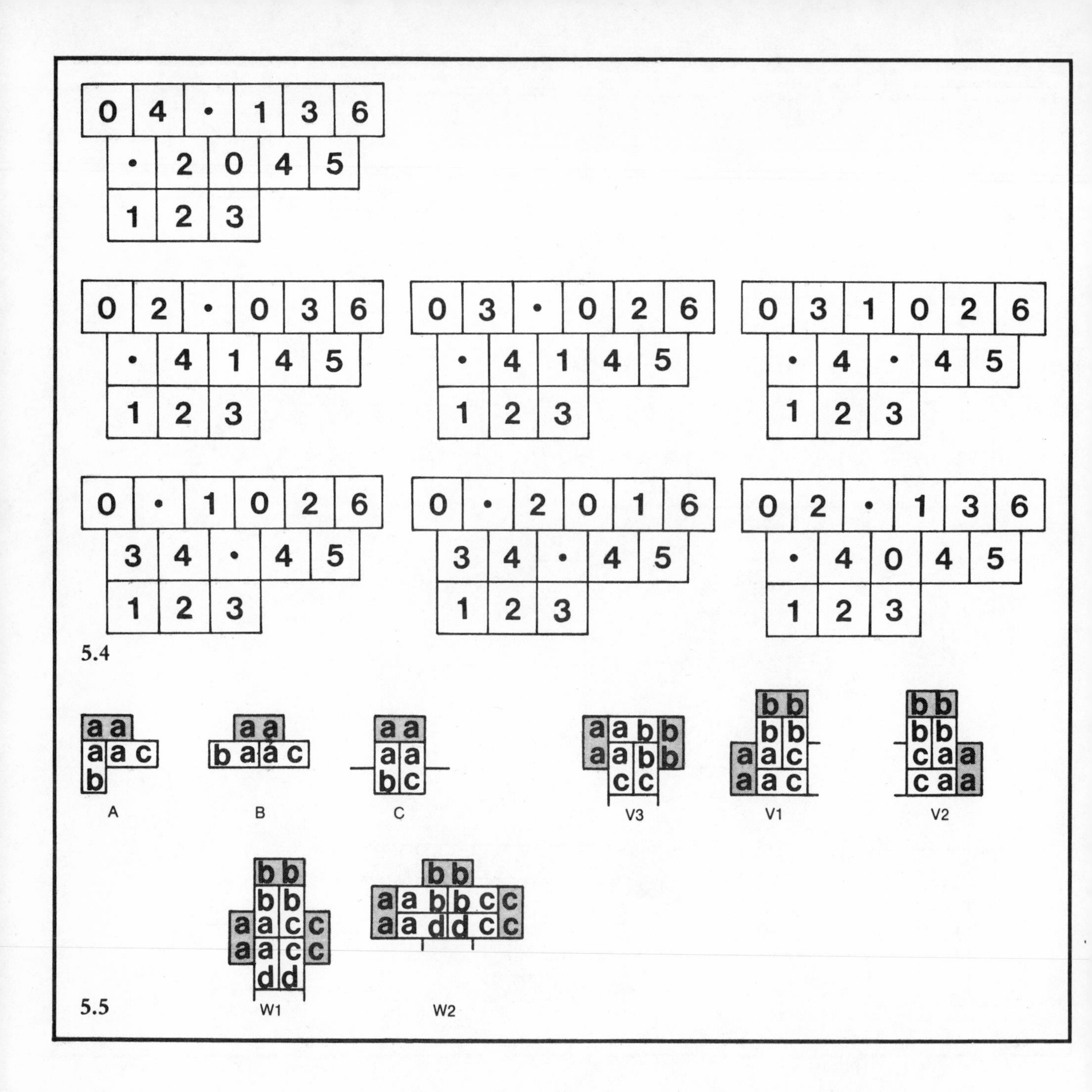

The numbers 5 and 6 are in the squares in which there is a double, are combined with each other as the stone 5–6, and further joined with d. Beyond these squares, both the 5 and the 6 shall be combined with four other numbers, indeed the same four. From one solution therefore there arises a second solution by exchanging the 5 and 6, which both stand in squares with doubles. For further filling in of the figure the choice between 5 and 6 is made at will.

If f = 2, then only 3 can be filled in in square d. After that 1 can go only in square c. Therefore only 0 can be placed in square g. Since 5 and 6

must not lie against each other, a = 4 and the numbers 5 and 6 can be filled in anywhere.
If f = 4, then c = 2, and there is no place for the 1. From that it follows that c = 0 or = 1. The exchangeable numbers 5 and 6 must be placed in squares e and b or in squares e and g or in squares a and g. This leads to the solutions as given in example 5.4. In the squares marked with a dot the 5 or 6 can be placed at will. In total there are fourteen solutions. In two of these solutions there are two squares with the same number of spots next to each other (see the top diagram).

3. The Highest Number of Corners

For every outward corner there is, of necessity, a duplicate, which can belong to a second outward corner. In view of the fact that there are seven doubles in the game the maximum number of outward corners is $2 \times 7 = 14$.
With fourteen outward corners the number of inward corners is $14 - 4 = 10$ so that a quadrille can have, at the most, twenty-four corners. The fourteen outward corners follow each other in pairs while four (but not six or more) outward corners can follow each other.
In a figure with twenty-four corners that meets all the requirements mentioned, the ten inward and the fourteen outward corners can follow each other in 250 ways.
SCHUH justly remarks that it is not worthwhile examining all of these; he therefore offers a single example.
It is, however, possible to determine the number of squares with twenty-four corners in another way, namely by considering the ways in which doubles with two outward corners can be arranged. All seven must be on the outside of the figure. A double can stand by itself or in a group of limited size (example 5.5).
An independent double can be joined to the figure in three ways: A, B, and C. Two arrangements A can form a symmetrical group of five stones among which there are two doubles. This symmetrical group is shown in V3.
The five stones can also be grouped in another way, namely according to V1 and V2, which two can also be worked out as a combination of A and C. In other words a figure belonging to group V has in general three variations, namely V3, V1, and V2. It is not to be inferred that these three variations all have the same number of corners.
A double from group V can be replaced by a second group V. For the forms of the resulting figures, see the discussion of quadrilles.
There are also figures imaginable with three groups of the V type combined as a total of 2 + 1. These figures have no solution, as shall be shown below.
A connecting C forms with two connecting B's a group of seven stones including three doubles. This grouping is shown as W1; there is a variation, W2, which consists of two connecting C's and one connecting B.
A figure of the type W has, therefore, in general two variations, the number of whose corners can again be different.

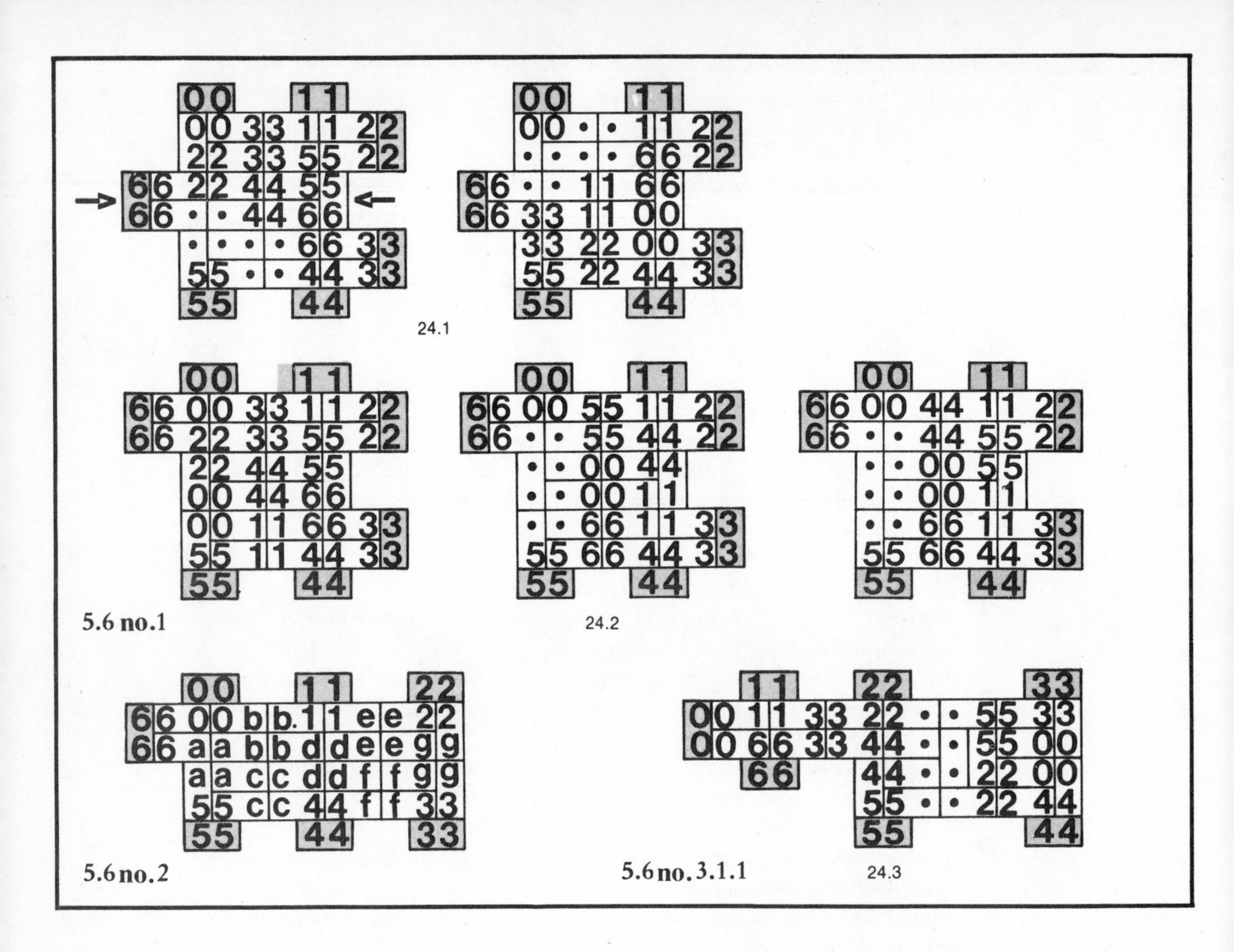

The groups V3 and W1 form, as it were, an independent unit whereby one of the doubles can change places at the twenty-four corners.

A quadrille with the highest number of corners—that is, twenty-four—is always in the general form of a rectangular core with protruding junctions A, B, C, V or W. The sides of the rectangle have an even number of half stones.
In the following discussion, the twenty-four corners are divided for the first time according to the form of the rectangular core and according to the junctions. Only diagrams in which the stones can be indicated without more than seven doubles or identical stones are discussed. In the examples solutions are presented that offer no further difficulties for completion. Only a few examples are given of the possible changing of a double with a group V3 or W1. The omitted examples are all variations of figures with a smaller number of corners, and can be checked in the general discussion of quadrilles if the mention in the text makes that seem desirable. As far as the solutions are concerned it should be mentioned that in the group V3 (or a variant of it) there are, in addition to the

doubles a–a and b–b, the stones a–b, a–c, and b–c. From this it follows that, in a figure which consists of such a group, the number of spots a and b, outside of the arranged group, combines with the same four other numbers of spots as the stones in the group. In other words, the numbers a and b outside the square can be exchanged with a double.
The same applies for the numbers a and c in figures that contain a group W.
Below follow the classifications of a figure with twenty-four corners (example 5.6). The numbers in smaller type below the diagrams refer to the general discussion of quadrilles in the afterword.

		Number of Figures	*Number of Figures with Solutions*	*Number of Solutions*
1.	A square of 6 x 6 half stones with four doubles in the corners of two opposite sides and on both other sides respectively one and two junctions C. There are two figures possible. One of these is symmetrical and has two solutions. Since the figure is also symmetrical with respect to placing of the stones, it follows that two other solutions can be made by exchanging 0 with 5, 1 with 4, and 2 with 3 in the chosen example and folding down on the horizontal line (24.1). The other figure (24.2) has five solutions. One of them is derived from the previous diagram by the shifting of four stones.	2	2	7
2.	A rectangle of 4 × 10 half stones with four doubles in the corners and one each in the middle of the long sides, and a junction C on one of the other short sides. There is one figure possible, which has no solution.	1	—	—
3.	A rectangle of 4 x 8 half stones with four doubles in the corners of the long sides and a junction C.			
3.1	The junction C lies on one of the short sides so			
3.1.1	The double of junction C is replaced by a group W. There is one figure possible with a total of two variations, each with two solutions (24.3);	2	2	4
	Carried Forward	5	4	11

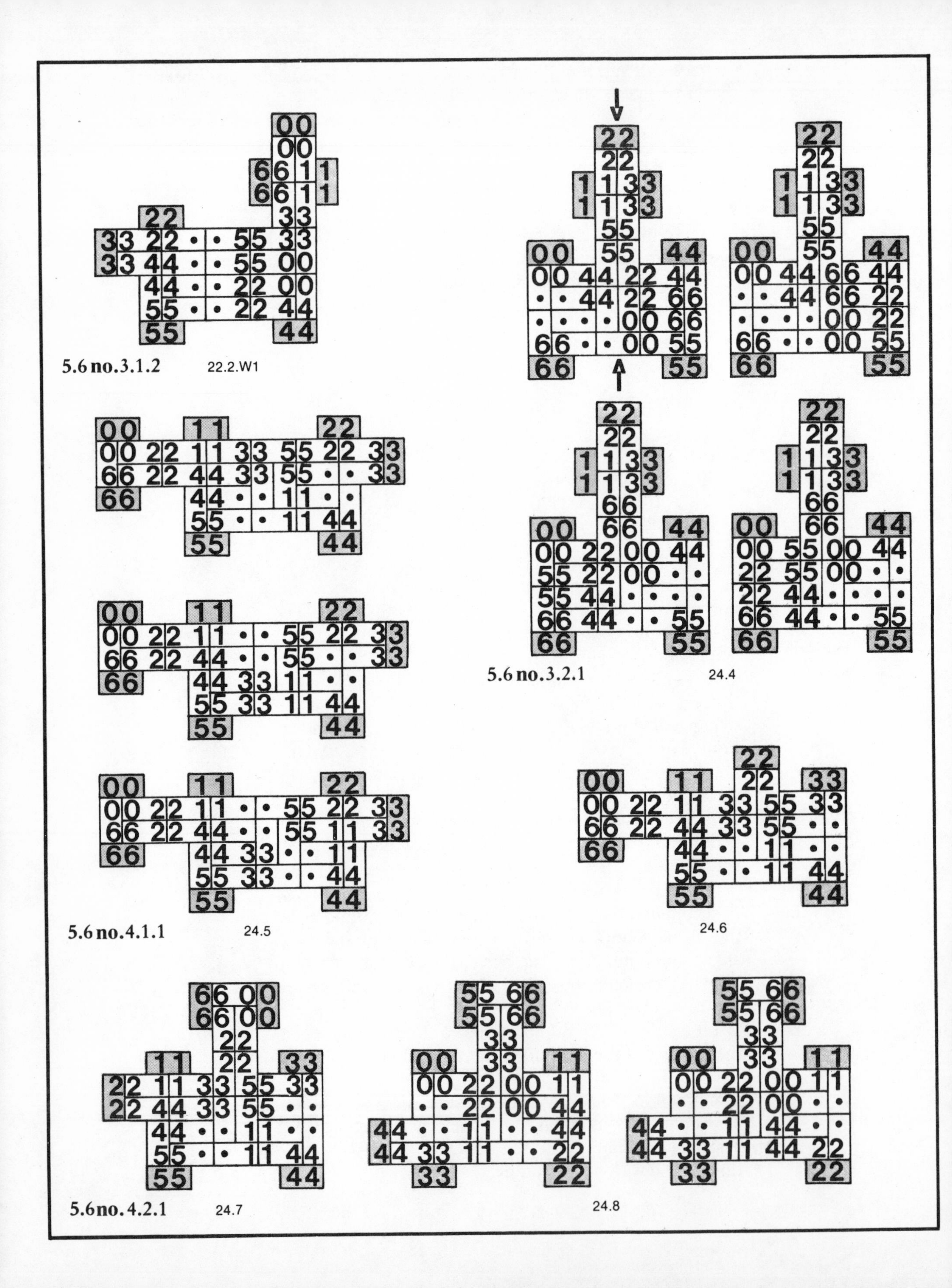

5.6 no.3.1.2 22.2.W1

5.6 no.3.2.1 24.4

5.6 no.4.1.1 24.5

24.6

5.6 no.4.2.1 24.7

24.8

		Number of Figures	Number of Figures with Solutions	Number of Solutions
	Brought Forward	5	4	11
3.1.2	a double in one of the corners is replaced by group W. There are four figures possible. Two of them (18.5W1 and 22.1W1) have ten solutions each; the third (22.2W1) has six. (Two solutions 22.2W1 are shown, see further discussion).	4	3	26
3.2	The junction C lies in the middle of a long side, by which:			
3.2.1	the double of junction C is replaced by group W1. There is one figure that is symmetrical in outline and in placement of the stones. This figure has four solutions from which four others can be developed by the exchanging of spots and folding down on the axis of symmetry (24.4);	1	1	4
3.2.2	a double on one of the corners is replaced by a group W. There is one figure with four solutions (22.3W1).	1	1	4
4.	A rectangle of 4 x 8 half stones with four doubles on the corners of the long sides and two junctions C.			
4.1	On each short side lies one junction C, whereby:			
4.1.1	the double of a junction C is replaced by a group V. There are two figures, each with a total of three variations. Only one of these figures leads to a solution (24.5).	6	3	18
4.1.2	a double on one of the corners is replaced by a group V. There are four figures; two of them each have a total of two variants. One figure (20.5V3) has solutions.	6	1	10
4.2	One connecting C lies on a short side, one in the middle of the long side, by which:			
4.2.1	the double of a junction C is replaced by a group V. There are four figures possible; two of which have a total of three variations each. One of these two figures and both of the others lead to solutions (24.6* –24.7–24.8);	8	5	12
	Carried Forward	31	18	85

*This example is given by Schuh

		Number of Figures	Number of Figures with Solutions	Number of Solutions
	Brought Forward	31	18	85
4.2.2	a double on one of the corners is replaced by a group V. There are four figures possible, from which three have a total of two variations each. Only one figure leads to a solution (20.7.V3)	7	1	4
4.3	A junction C in the middle of each of the long sides, by which the double of a junction C is replaced by group V3. There is one symmetrical figure, which has two solutions. From these two others can be developed by changing spots and folding down of the axis of symmetry (24.9). The internal variant made by placing the two stones in the center of the rectangle horizontally has no solution.	2	1	2
5.	A rectangle of 4 x 6 half stones with four doubles in the corners of the long sides, by which:			
5.1	a double is replaced by three joined groups of V. This figure has in total fifteen variations;	15	—	—
5.2	a double is replaced by two joined groups of V and a second double by a single group V. These groups can take three positions (I, II, and III) with respect to each other and yield respectively 16, 28, and 28 variations;	72	—	—
5.3	three doubles are replaced by a group V. There are six variations in all.	—	—	9
	None of the figures 5 lead to a solution			
	Total	133	20	91

Of the 250 ways in which a figure with fourteen outward and ten inward corners can be drawn to further meet the above-named conditions, 133—a few more than half—possess a form in which, within the twenty-eight stones of the domino game, letters can be filled in without using more than seven doubles or similar stones. Only a small portion, namely twenty, can indeed be laid out with domino stones. These twenty figures, which together have 91 solutions, form the quadrilles with the greatest number of corners.

2. Additional Symmetrical Quadrilles

In the previous section we have become acquainted with the three symmetrical quadrilles of LUCAS. The examination of the possible twenty-four corners produces three symmetrical diagrams. There are in addition three others which are discussed below.

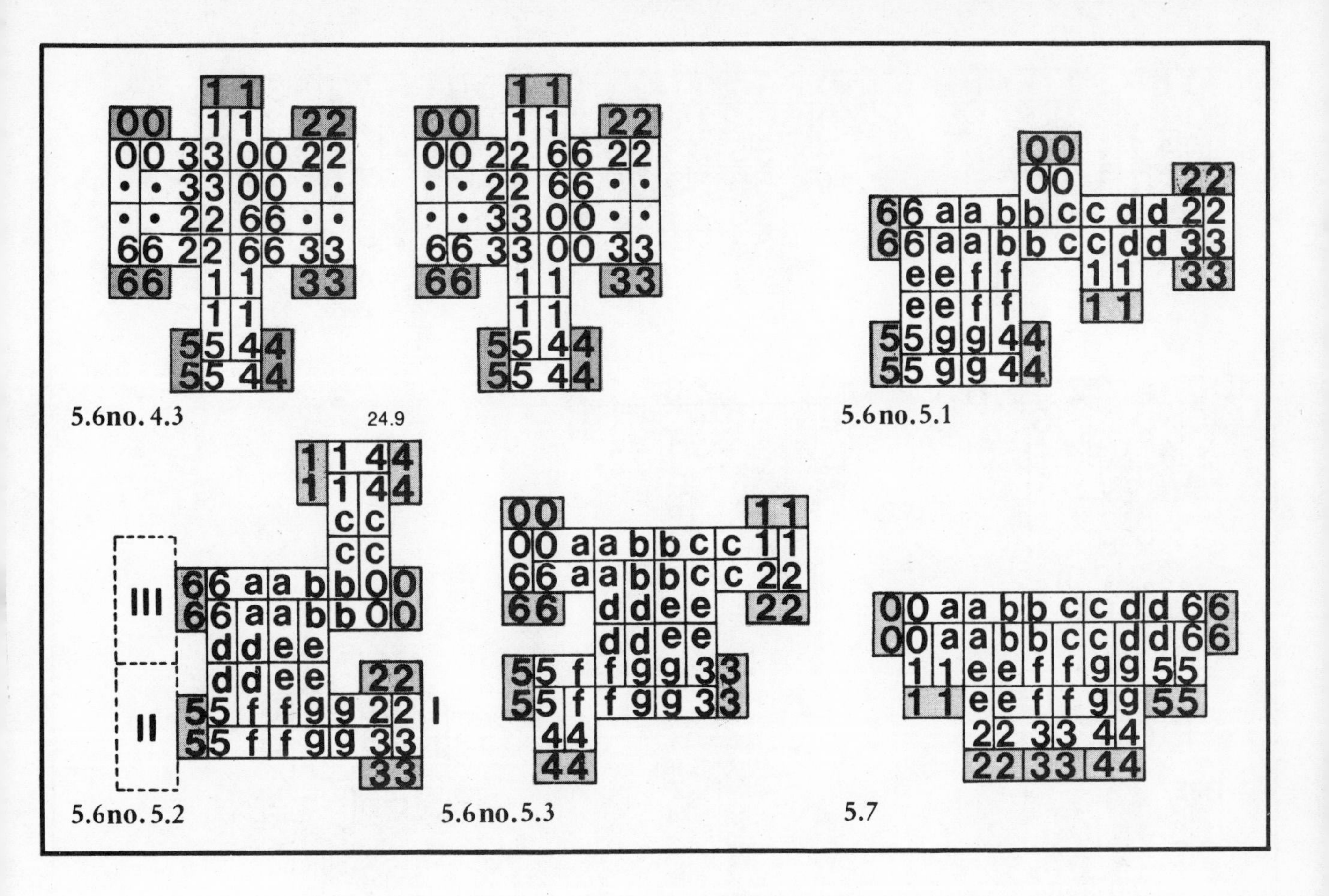
5.6no. 4.3 24.9 5.6no. 5.1
5.6no. 5.2 5.6no. 5.3 5.7

A symmetrical figure has on both sides of the axis of symmetry the same number of inward corners. The total number of inward corners i is therefore even.
The sum of all corners, inward and outward, is equal to 2i + 4, that is, the number of corners of a symmetrical figure is always divisible by four. Symmetrical diagrams are found in figures with twelve, sixteen, twenty, and twenty-four corners.

There is no symmetrical twelve-corner figure outside of the two of Lucas. The eight outward corners of such a figure are supplied by four doubles in the A position. This position can be on the corner of the long side or it can be on the corner of the short side of a rectangle of 6 × 8 half stones. It is true there is still a symmetrical figure (example 5.7) in which two doubles take two outward corners and the four other doubles one outward corner each and in which the numbers of the stones can be lettered. This figure, closely related to the figure with ten corners, has, however, no solutions because the stones e–2 and g–4 appear to be the same.

In addition to the sixteen-corner figure described by Lucas, there is still another in which the stones not only can be filled in but also can be placed.

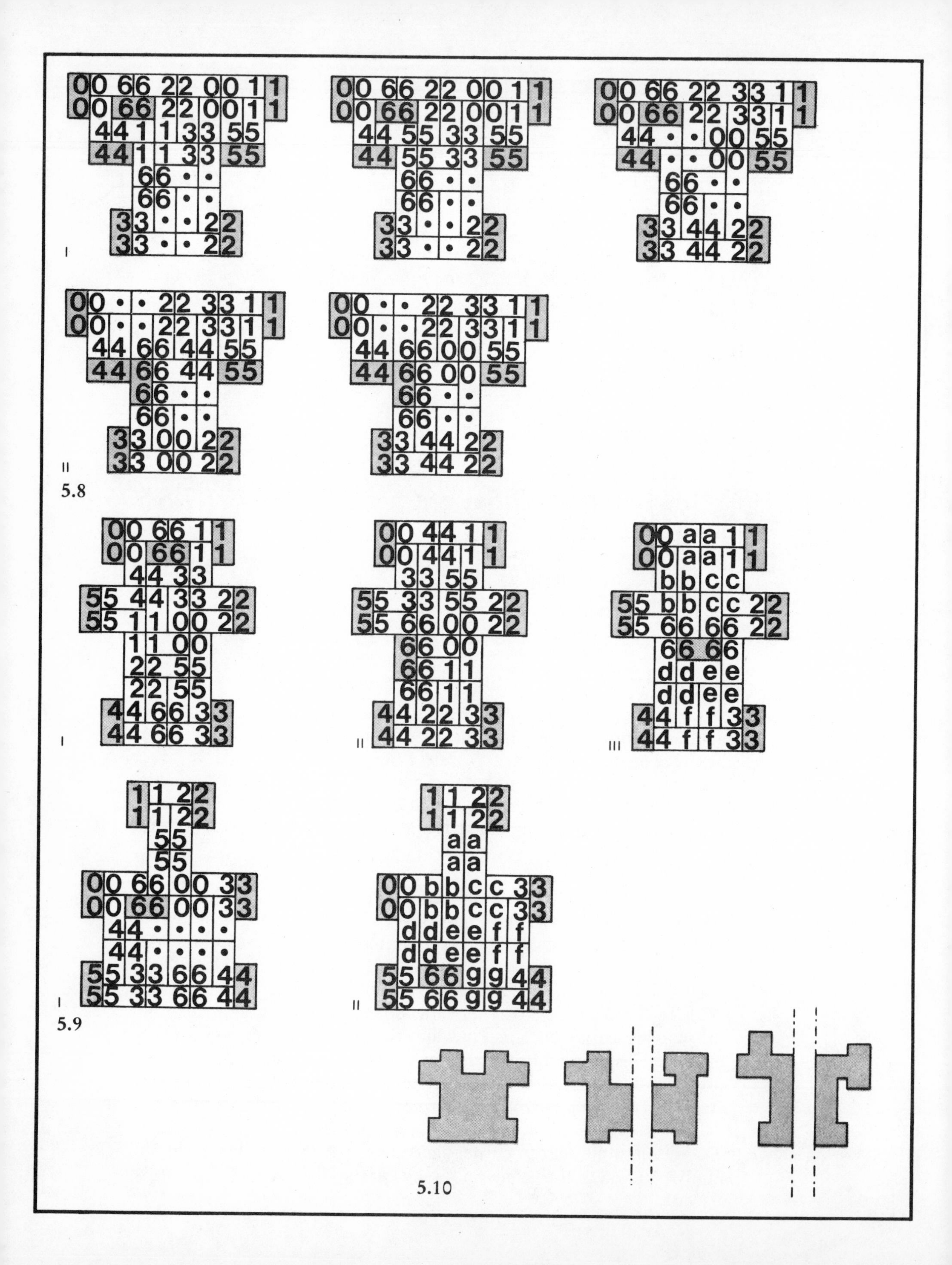

5.8

5.9

5.10

The stones can fill the figure in two ways (example 5.8). Type I has six solutions. In two of them group V (above right) and a double (below left) can be exchanged with each other. By the exchanging, a type 2.1 of the first-mentioned double symmetrical twelve-corner figure is developed. Type II with sixteen corners has four solutions. All four of these can be compared with the same twelve-corner type 2.2 in the way described above.

There are also two different symmetrical twenty-corner puzzles that have solutions (example 5.9). In the first the stones can be filled in in three ways, two of which have one solution each. The stones of the two twenty-corner figures can also be shown in a second way. From this only one type leads to a solution, in which the number of spots on the doubles in group V3 lying in the square can be exchanged. Finally there are five symmetrical twenty-corner figures that can be formed by moving and shifting of group V from the already known figures. These therefore offer nothing new. One of these is the first symmetrical twelve-corner type 1, two are of type 2.2, and the two remaining are both of the second type of the sixteen-corner figure discussed here (example 5.10).

3. Quadrilles with the Domino Set Up to Double Ten

In order to compose quadrilles with dominoes, the number of half stones on which the same number of spots appear must be divisible by four. This number is n + 2. After the normal set, the first with which quadrilles can be formed is the set with double ten as the highest stone. Quadrilles laid out with this set have thirty-three squares. The same number of spots appears on three squares.
The shape of the figure means that few possibilities remain once an arbitrary number of spots are given to the doubles. Because of this, the puzzles are too difficult to be solved with enjoyment.

4. A Variation on the Quadrille Theme

In the Dutch newspaper *De Telegraaf* for December 24, 1969 a variation on the quadrille was published that was developed by L. D. MINNIGH.*
The figure (example 5.11) is one in which the placement of the eight half stones is already given and which must be arranged from the stones of the normal domino game so that in each of the four sides A to N are placed four half stones with the same number of eyes. The reader was asked for all solutions.

The placing of six doubles, four at the corners and two on the bottom, is immediately evident. It also appears that neither square A nor square K nor square M can contain double one, so other identical stones must go

*This puzzle was submitted as the thousandth puzzle to appear in this newspaper after the Second World War. The jubilee number is therefore worked into it in a clever way.
Not every poem written for a special occasion reaches the heights of this puzzle for a special occasion!
The solution of the puzzle is the writer's.

there. For the same reason double zero cannot be placed in squares B, L, or N. The seventh double can be worked into the diagram in seven different ways; after the placement of the seventh double, the solutions can be divided into seven types.

The number of spots on the half stones in square A are indicated by a, in square B by b, and so forth.

For each type of solution it must be determined where double zero and double one should be placed. Following that, the number of spots that remain doubles can bė arranged at will. Except with type 4, the stones 1–g and 1–k can be placed either horizontally or vertically. From every solution there emerges a second by turning both these stones a half turn. Moreover, once the placing of the doubles is determined, the stones can in general be written in only one manner in the diagram; the few exceptions are mentioned below.

1. The seventh double is formed by the stone f−0; therefore f = 0. Double one can take three positions.

1.1 Double one is placed in the upper right-hand corner.
For the stones d−0 and h−0 the 2−0 and 3−0 are still suitable. Due to the already placed stone 1−3 neither d nor h = 3; thus there can be no solution.

1.2 Double one is placed in square L.
This leads to d−0 and h−0 which stand for 2−0 and 3−0. Therefore h cannot = 3, since h = 2 and d = 3. There are two solutions:

d = 5, d = 3, h = 2, e = 4, g = 6,
e = 6, g = 4.

1.3 Double one is placed in square N.
There are two solutions identical to 1.2 after the exchanging of the double one and the double five.
The first type has 2 × 4 = 8 solutions.

2. The seventh double is double zero formed by the two already placed zeros on either side of the center line. Double one can again take three positions.

2.1 Double one is placed in the upper righthand corner.
With respect to 1−6 and 1−k, the stones can be written in the figure in two ways; either the stones 1−h and 0–6 or 0−h and 1–6 can be used.

2.1.1 1−h and 0–6 are used. Because of stone 1–3, c can = 3 only. The stone 3–4 is already used; therefore d = 5 or d = 6. The hypothesis d = 5 falls by the wayside; d = 6 yields three solutions:

c = 3, d = 6, f = 2, h = 4, e = 5, g = 0
c = 3, d = 6, f = 4, h = 2, e = 5, g = 0
e = 0, g = 5.

2.1.2 0 − h and 1–6 are used.
There are two possibilities: c = 3 and h = 6 or c = 6 and h = 3. Neither of these leads to a solution.

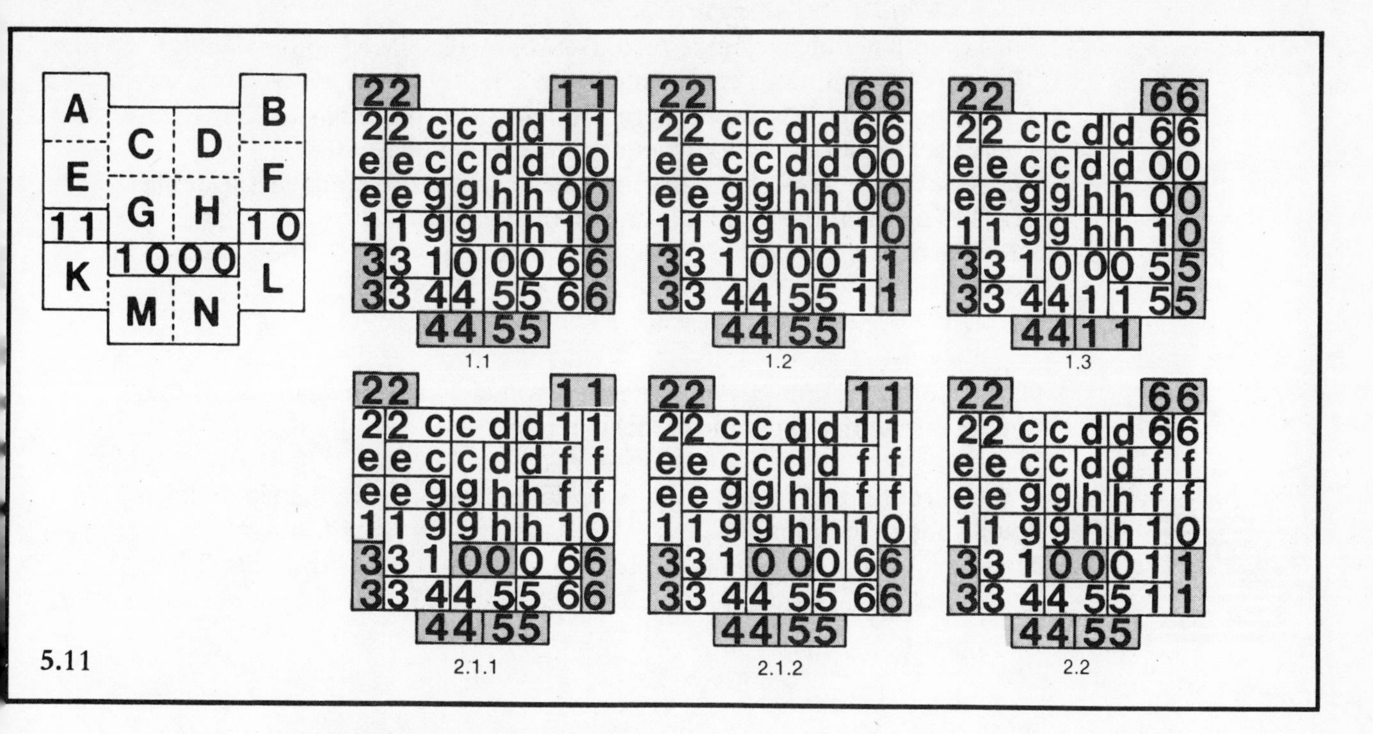

5.11

2.2 Double one is placed in square L.
Since none of the other letters for spots can be zero, c = 0. From this four solutions develop:
c = 0, d = 3, f = 5, h = 2, e = 4, g = 6
e = 6, g = 4
c = 0, d = 5, f = 3, h = 2, e = 4, g = 6
e = 6, g = 4.

2.3 Double one is placed in square N.
The number of spots for h can be decided as = 2. For e and g, 0 and 6 are usable. There are four solutions:
d = 5, e = 6, g = 0, h = 2, c = 3, f = 4
c = 4, f = 3
d = 5, e = 0, g = 6, h = 2, c = 3, f = 4
c = 4, f = 3.
There exist 2 × 11 = 22 solutions for type 2.

3. The seventh double is the stone 0−g, from which it follows that g=0.
In this way we discover that the stone 1 − g is identical to 1–0 and can exclude the double one from square L.

3.1 Double one is placed in the upper right.
There are two solutions developing from the solutions 2.1.1, by which g = 0.

3.2 Double one is placed in square N.
Two solutions develop as with the solutions 2.3, by which g = 0. The third type can form 2 × 4 = 8 solutions.

4. The seventh double lies in the under half of square G, away from the fixed half stones. It can be double zero or any other double with the exception of double one, which is placed by the stone e−1. There is no stone g−1, therefore only one possible placement for 1−k.

4.1 The seventh double is double zero. Double one is placed above right. There are two solutions conforming with 2.1.1 by which $g = 0$.

4.2 The seventh double is double zero. Double one is placed in square N. There are two solutions conforming to 2.3 by which $g = 0$.

4.3 The seventh double carries any number of spots; for example 2. Double zero lies on the top left, double one on the top right.
Because of stone 1–3, $c = 3$; because of stone 3–4, $e = 5$. There are two solutions:
$c = 3, d = 6, e = 5, f = 2, h = 4,$
$f = 4, h = 2.$
(These solutions can also be obtained from 4.1, by the changing of the double zero with the double in the upper left.)

4.4 If the seventh double is double two, double zero lies in the above left, double one in the square N.
There can be only one value given to h, namely $h = 2$. From that it follows that $e = 6$. There are two solutions.
$d = 5, e = 6, h = 2, c = 3, f = 4$
$c = 4, f = 3.$

(This develops from 4.2 by the changing of a double zero with the double in the top left corner.)

4.5 If the seventh double is double two, double zero lies in square M, double one in the top right. C can = 3 only. From this four solutions follow:
$c = 3, f = 4, h = 2, d = 5, e = 6$
$d = 6, e = 5$
$c = 3, f = 2, h = 4, d = 5, e = 6$
$d = 6, e = 5.$

The fourth type has twelve solutions. Following are five in which the squares G and H have the same number of spots.

5. The seventh double is stone g–h. This double cannot be double zero or double one because there are no remaining suitable half stones for these numbers. Let $g = h = 2$.
Double zero can only be placed in the top left, double one only in the top right.
There is no solution since no single value can be given to f.

6. The seventh double is placed in the right half of square H. This double can be double zero or any other double except double one.

6.1 The seventh double is double zero. Double one is placed in square L. There is only one solution:

$c = 5, d = 3, e = 4, f = 2, g = 6.$

6.2 The seventh double is double zero. Double one is placed in square N. The only solution follows from 6.1 by the exchanging of double one and double five.

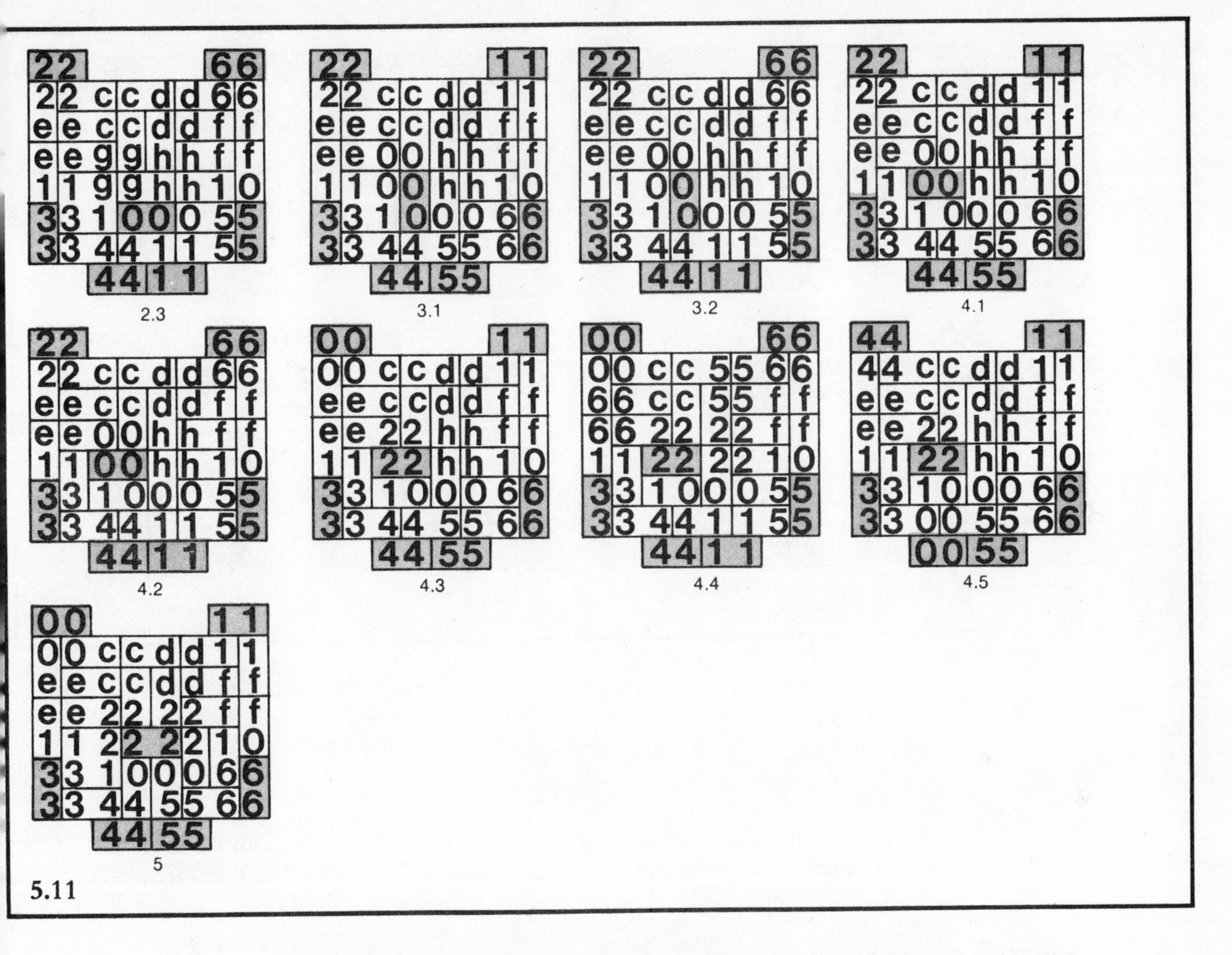

5.11

6.3 Double two is chosen as the seventh double. Double zero is placed in the square M, double one in the square L. The only possible value for f is 4. This leads to two solutions:

$e = 2, f = 4, g = 6, c = 3, d = 5$

$c = 5, d = 3.$

6.4 The seventh double is double two. Double zero is in square M, double one in square N.
The two solutions develop from 6.3 by the exchanging of the double one and double five.

6.5 The seventh double is double two. Double zero is placed on the top left, double one in the square L.
Because of 1–3 and $1-g$ the stones can be written in the diagram in two ways, namely by making use of either $2-g$, 0–4 and 0–5 or of $0-g$, 0–2 and 4–5.
Neither of these methods will lead to a solution.
Even less does:

6.6, in which double one and double five change places with regard to 6.5.
The sixth type has $2 \times 6 = 12$ solutions.

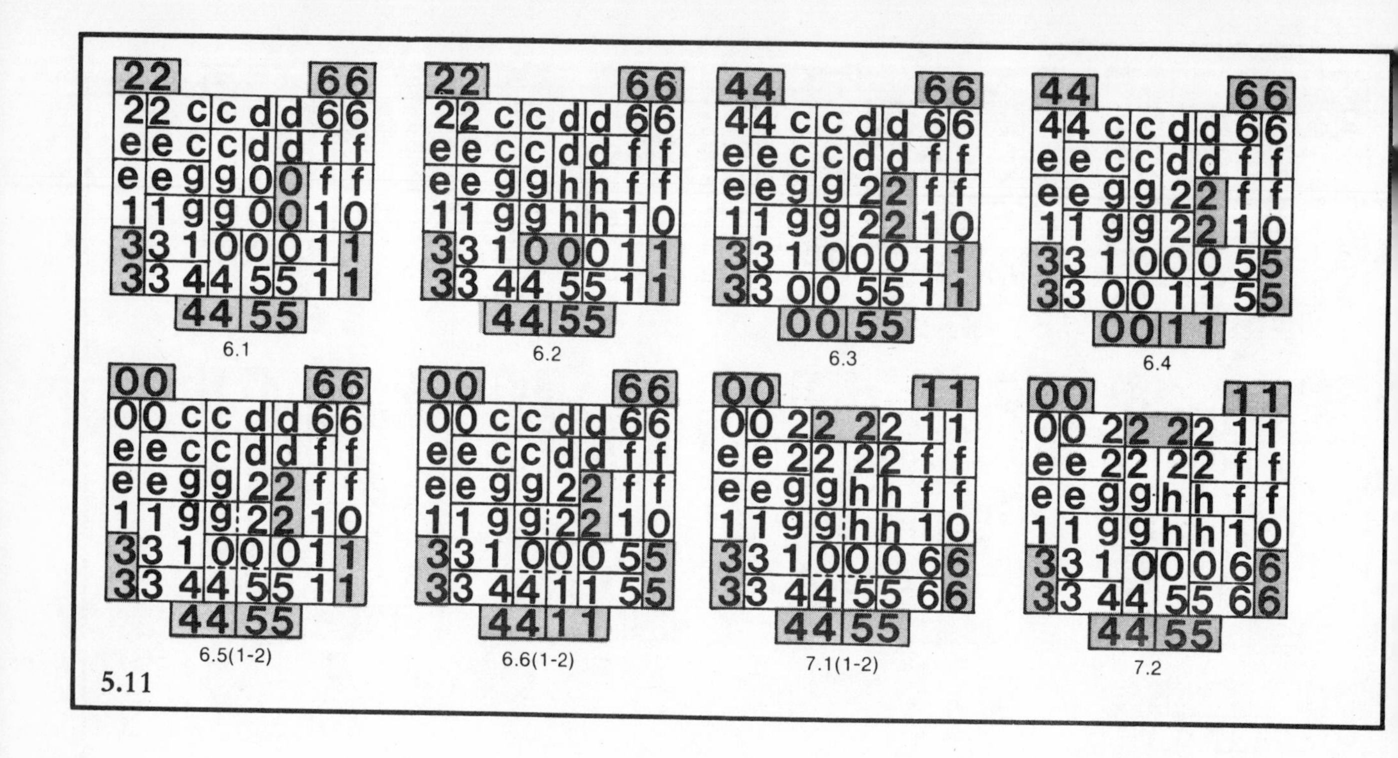

5.11

7. The seventh double lies on the top edge in the middle. This double cannot be double zero or double one (compare type 5). Let double two be selected for this seventh double. In order to be able to place the stones 0–2 and 1–2, double one and double zero must be placed in the top corners, double zero left and double one right.
0–h and 1–6 as well as 1–h and 0–6 can be placed.

7.1 1–h and 0–6 are used. Because of 1–3 and 1–g, the stones can be written in two ways in the figure. Neither of these leads to a solution as the second square with the four threes has no place.

7.2 0–h and 1–6 are used. There is no solution because h must both = 3 and = 6.

In total, the puzzle has sixty-two solutions. By mutual exchanging of numbers except 0 and 1, there are 62 x 5! = 7,440 solutions.
In 5 × 5!—600 solutions—the central square G and H have half stones with the same number of eyes. If the problem is so arranged at the beginning that the same number of eyes is required then a solution can quickly be found by reasoning that among the eight half stones in the squares G and H, two must be halves of a double. These doubles cannot be double zero or double one. The quadrille can be arranged in three ways; one of them leads to the answer.

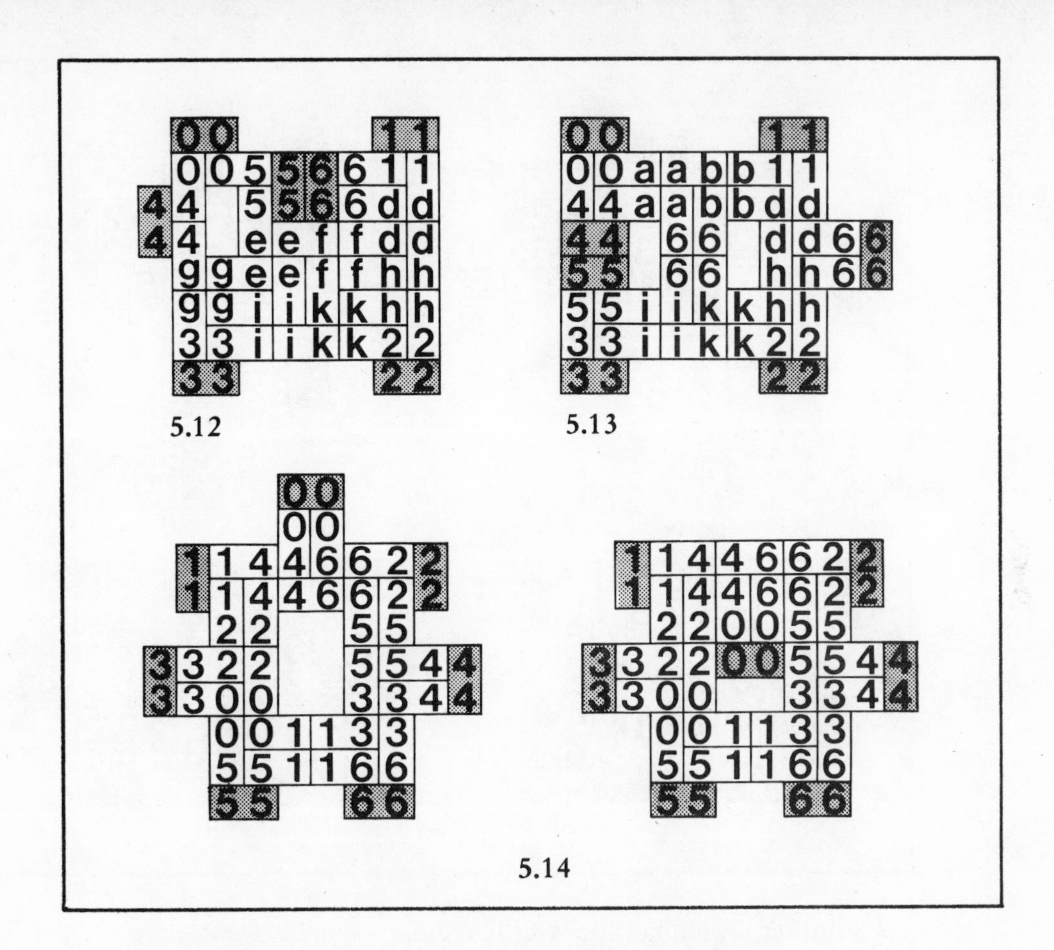

5.12

5.13

5.14

5. Quadrilles with One or More Empty Spaces

All the figures discussed to this point are presumed to be without empty spaces. There are, however, a number of quadrilles with one or more empty spaces.

Some of these are easy to find. In all cases in which a double lies parallel at a stone's width from the edge of a diagram, these doubles can be removed from the figure and placed on the outside, thus forming a quadrille with an empty space. If this is done to type 2.1 of the first double symmetrical quadrille of LUCAS (example 4.17), the figure of example 5.12 develops. By the moving of one or more of the three doubles in the center of type I of the two double symmetrical quadrilles (example 4.36), quadrilles with empty spaces of various sizes are formed. If the left and the right doubles are brought to the outsides, a symmetrical quadrille with two empty spaces is formed. These examples can be supplemented by many others.

In a somewhat more complicated way, by the shifting of four stones, some solutions of type 1 of the first double symmetrical quadrille (examples 4.16 and 4.19) can be developed into the symmetrical figure with two empty spaces shown in example 5.13.

There are numerous quadrilles with one or more empty spaces which can be connected in a similar manner with an entire independent figure. We will limit ourselves here to some splendid symmetrical examples.

Example 5.14 shows a quadrille with one empty space that can be enlarged or reduced by shifting the stones. There is only one independent

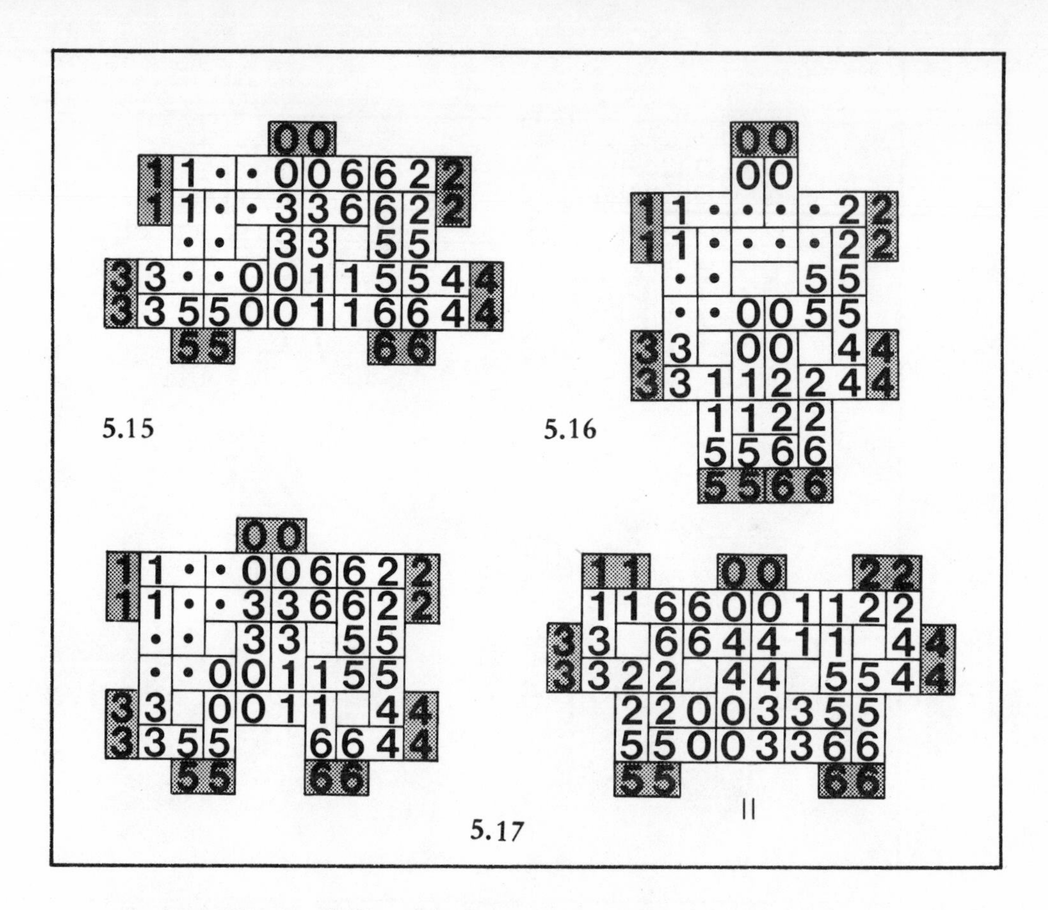
5.15

5.16

5.17

solution. The quadrille with two empty spaces of example 5.15 has two such solutions.

In symmetrical quadrilles with an uneven number of spaces, at least one of these must be the size of an entire stone (or entire stones) and be placed crosswise on the axis of symmetry. This is clear from example 5.16 showing a quadrille with three empty spaces. The figure has two independent solutions. Of the two quadrilles illustrated with four empty spaces—the largest possible number—the first are considered two independent solutions, the other only one (example 5.17).

For each solution of these diagrams that is symmetrical in outline and placement of the stones, the exchanging of the dots 1 with 2, 3 with 4, and 5 with 6 and the "folding down" on the vertical axis yields a second solution. One of the solutions of example 5.16, however, turns back into its original form after the "folding down."

VI Magic Squares

Je ne sais guere rien de plus beau en l'Arithmetique que ces nombres.
——Pierre de Fermat, 'Oeuvres,' Volume II

1. Introduction

A magic square is a square divided into n^2 sections in which numbers are arranged so that the sum of the numbers in the horizontal rows, the vertical columns, and the two diagonals is the same. This sum, S, is called the magic sum or constant. Usually the numbers placed in the square are the natural numbers of 1 to n^2; in that case $S = (n^2 + 1)$. Others numbers can, however, be used. The number of rows or columns is the same as n and is called the order of the square.

Magic squares of higher than the third order can be of either an even or an uneven order.
Various methods have been developed for making magic squares of even or uneven orders. Usually these methods are only for squares of an uneven order, unless the order is a prime. We shall turn our attention to these squares first. Squares that are systematically obtainable by such a method are called *regular* squares as opposed to irregular squares that can only be found with luck and persistence through trial and error and whose total number can never be determined. We begin with normal squares of uneven, indivisible order p, made up of the natural numbers from 1 to p^2.
In 1931 M. J. VAN DRIEL published rules for the formation of such squares. They rest on the framing of a basic table of p rows of p numbers from which the rows and columns of the required square are derived, starting from a certain section in the table and moving in a definite way. The same idea is the basis of the method developed by D. A. FLANDERS which was published by M. KRAITCHIC in his well-known book, *Mathematical Recreations.* KRAITCHIC's method, however, has a simple system of notations and is therefore much more conveniently arranged and easier to handle than VAN DRIEL's method, even though both lead to the same result.
KRAITCHIC begins with the framing of a basic table 6.1, in which the p^2 successive numbers are written from left to right and upwards. The rows and columns of the desired square are obtained from the table by means of a two-dimensional lattice.
The theory behind this lattice will not be discussed here.
A two-dimensional lattice has the form:
$(x, y) = (a, b) + r(t, u) + s(v, w)$,
and gives the method of discovering from the basic table the number which must be filled in in the magic square at coordinates x and y. Let us explain by reference to a magic square of the type $p = 5$.
We take our basic square (example 6.1) and repeat it, expanding it

21	22	23	24	25
16	17	18	19	20
11	12	13	14	15
6	7	8	9	10
1	2	3	4	5

Table 6.1

20	22	4	6	13
9	11	18	25	2
23	5	7	14	16
12	19	21	3	10
1	8	15	17	24

												13		
										6				
								4			2			
						22			25					
				20			18			16				
					11			14						
			9			7			10					
				5			3							
21	22	23	24	25	21			24						
16	17	18	19	20		17								
11	12	13	14	15										
6	7	8	9	10										
1	2	3	4	5										

6.1

across the plane of the example to the right and to the top. We then cover this expanded table with a two-dimensional lattice which yields the magic sum from the rows, columns, and both main diagonals. For this we use the lattice:

$(x, y) = (1, 1) + r\,(2, 1) + s\,(1, 2).$

The value (a, b) = (1, 1) gives the starting point, that is, the first square in both the upward and the right directions, in other words, the bottom left square. The first row of the magic square is obtained from this section by use of the lattice r (t, u) = r (2, 1), that is, from the starting point making two steps to the right and one toward the top.
The first column follows from the lattice s (v, w) = (1, 2), that is, from one step to the right and two toward the top. The further development of the magic rows and columns is clear from the illustration.
In practice, it is desirable to use the lattice in a simple basic table. We use the lattice of modulo p, which means that for p = 5 the lattice r (7, 6) is the same as r (2, 1). This is written: r (7, 6) = r (2, 1) (mod. 5). This means that when the arrangement passes the right edge it is continued in the left column of the next section and in the same way in the bottom row of the above section when the top edge is crossed.
In the illustrated example the lattice covers exactly p sections of the basic square; on any line of the lattice there is one section from each row or one from each column. In order that this shall be the case—and that, therefore, the lattice will be usable—the value of t, u, v, and w must satisfy certain conditions. If the rows and columns of the desired magic square shall be indeed magic series (that is, series with the sum = S) then must t, u, v, and w be not divisible by p? And if the lattice covers the entire basic square, then it must also satisfy the condition that tw – uv is not divisible by p.
If attention is paid to these conditions there emerges a magic square that is at least semi-magic in that the rows and columns but none, or, at best, one of the main diagonals, add up to the magic sum. By the shifting of rows and columns the entire square can then be made magic.
We can, however, also insure that the diagonal is a magic series. The upward slanting diagonal (from bottom left to top right) emerges by the movement (t + v, u + w), the downward slanting diagonal (from top left to bottom right) by (t – v, u – w). If none of the numbers t + v, t – v, u + w, u – w is divisible by p, the diagonals are also magic series, not only the main diagonals a – a and b – b, but also all the diagonals a' – a', a'' – a'', a' '' – a' '', a'' '' – a'''', b' – b', b'' – b'', b' '' – b' '', and b'' '' – b'' ''. A similar square (example 6.2) in which not only rows and columns but also all the diagonals add up to the magic sum is called a *complete* magic square. The square in example 6.1 is such a complete magic square because the lattice used fulfills all the conditions. There remains the connection of the lattices by which equivalent squares are formed. This is shown in example 6.3. From this it follows that the lattices:
(x, y) = (a, b) + r (t, u) + s (v, w) and
(x, y) = (a, b) + r (u, t) + s (w, v)
shall yield equivalent squares if t + w = u + v = p. Always in this case r (u, t) = r (–v, –w) (mod. p).

If the order m of a magic square is uneven but is combined (for example, m = 5 × 7 = 35) then the agreed conditions yield the formation of a lattice. The lattice (x, y) = (a, b) + r (t, u) + s (v, w) will cover each section of the basic table if tw – uv and m are incommensurable. The formed

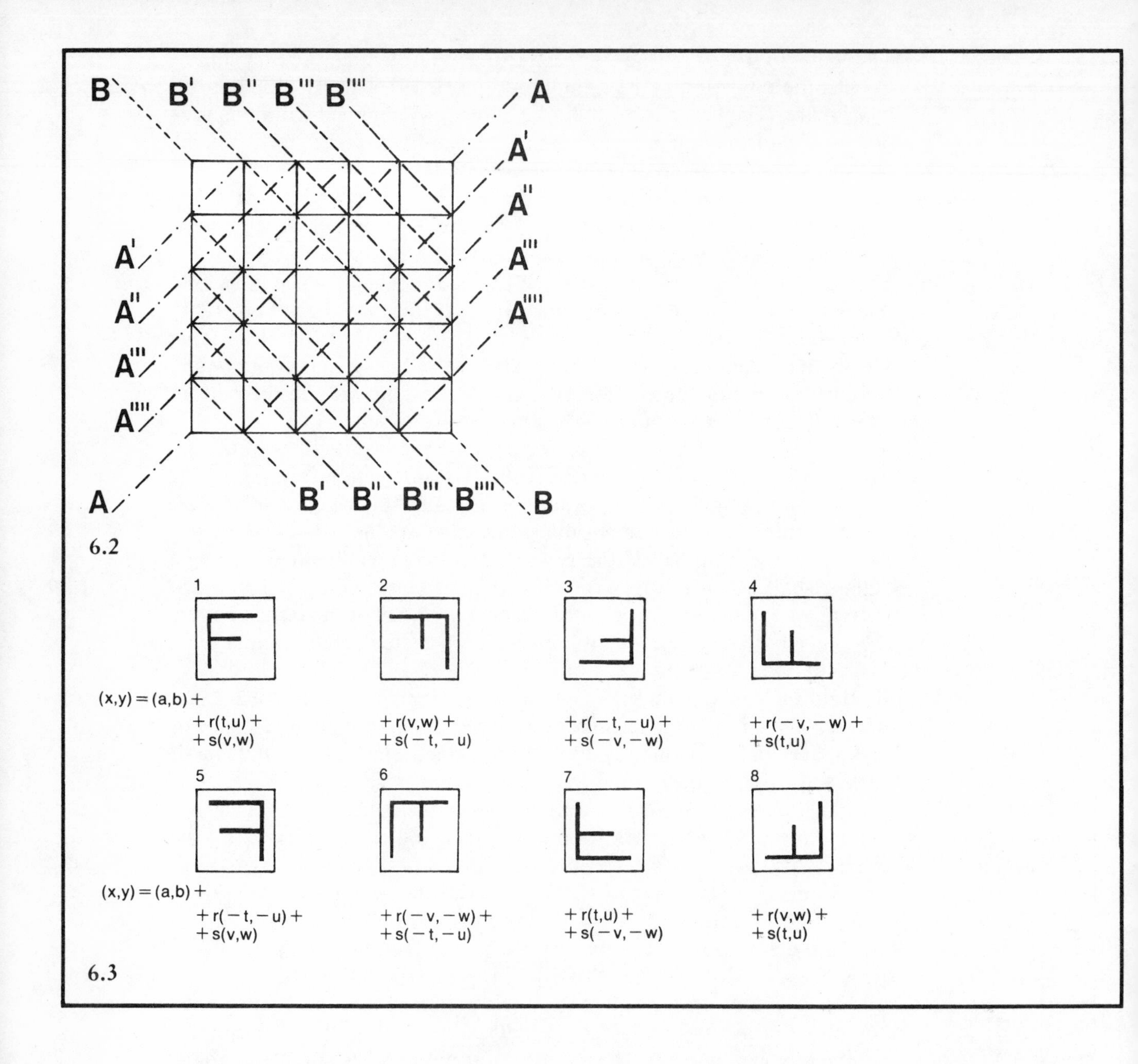

6.2

6.3

square shall be at least semi-magic as none of t, u, v, w have a common factor with m, and shall be complete magic squares if this is true for t + v, t − v, u + w, and u − w.
From this it follows that there are no regular complete magic squares of the order 3k. Since t, u, v, and w are not divisible by 3, one number from each of the arithmetical series (t − v, t, t + v) and u–w, u, u + w) must be a multiple of three. Therefore neither of the diagonals formed by (t + v, u + w) and (t − v, u − w) are magic.*

*VAN DRIEL has shown that there are exceptions to this rule. For p = 9 by which the basic table is formed by the numbers 1 to 49 it is possible to have complete magic squares if the basic table is reduced to a certain permutation before the lattice is used.
The permutations are done according to example 6.4.

9	73	74	75	76	77	78	79	80	81
8	64	65	66	67	68	69	70	71	72
7	55	56	57	58	59	60	61	62	63
6	46	47	48	49	50	51	52	53	54
5	37	38	39	40	41	42	43	44	45
4	28	29	30	31	32	33	34	35	36
3	19	20	21	22	23	24	25	26	27
2	10	11	12	13	14	15	16	17	18
1	1	2	3	4	5	6	7	8	9
	1	**2**	**3**	**4**	**5**	**6**	**7**	**8**	**9**

5	37	38	39	44	45	41	42	40	43
4	28	29	30	35	36	32	33	31	34
8	64	65	66	71	72	68	69	67	70
7	55	56	57	62	63	59	60	58	61
9	73	74	75	80	81	77	78	76	79
6	46	47	48	53	54	50	51	49	52
3	19	20	21	26	27	23	24	22	25
2	10	11	12	17	18	14	15	13	16
1	1	2	3	8	9	5	6	4	7
	1	**2**	**3**	**8**	**9**	**5**	**6**	**4**	**7**

6.4

75	70	41	12	52	59	30	7	23
10	51	62	28	6	26	73	69	44
31	9	20	76	72	38	13	54	56
77	66	43	14	48	61	32	3	25
17	46	60	35	1	24	80	64	42
29	4	27	74	67	45	11	49	63
79	68	39	16	50	57	34	5	21
15	53	55	33	8	19	78	71	37
36	2	22	81	65	40	18	47	58

6.5

s = 369

The columns of the normal basic table are numbered from left to right, the rows from bottom to top. The sequence of the columns and rows becomes altered now so that in the permutated table the sum of the numbers of the first, fourth, and seventh columns and rows and also of the second, fifth, and eighth columns and rows and finally of the third, sixth, and ninth columns and rows are equal to 15. There are twenty-four such permutations possible with both the columns and the rows; the entire table can therefore be permutated in 24^2 ways.

From the permutated tables complete magic squares can be developed with a suitable lattice. To make this clear, an example is given in which use is made of the lattice $(x, y) = (5, 8) + r(6, 2) + s(2, 3)$ (example 6.5).

2. Completely Magic Squares in Which the Order Is a Prime

Regular complete magic squares of the order p (p is prime) are formed by the lattice $(x, y) = (a, b) + r(t, u) + s(v, w)$ if $t, u, v, w, tw - uv, t + v, t - v, u + w$, and $u - w$ are not divisible by p. If p is not too large, the number of suitable lattices can be calculated.

In table 6.2 are all combinations of (t, u) and (v, w) for $p = 5$ indicated that yield complete magic squares. The figure consists of sixteen blocks. For eight of these, there are no usable lattices. The eight others have each four lattices that meet all conditions. Upon closer examination, it appears that these 8×4 lattices yield the eight equivalent forms of the same group of four squares. It is therefore not necessary to fill in the entire table; one-eighth, or an octant, is sufficient.

Complete magic squares have the characteristic that they remain complete magic squares when the rows or the columns are rotated. The choice of the value for the starting point (a, b) is therefore unimportant; for that purpose (1, 1) can correctly be used.

The four complete magic basic squares of the fifth order are shown in example 6.6. By rotating the rows and the columns a total of $4p^2 = 100$ squares can be made. The magic sum of these squares is 65.

To find the number of complete magic squares of the seventh order, it is sufficient to use one-eighth of the corresponding table. From this come fifty-four basic squares which, by the rotation of rows and columns, become $p^2 = 49$ times as large (table 6.3).

These tables can serve to develop a general formula from which the number of basic squares of an arbitrary order p (p is prime) can be discovered.

The table consists of $(p-1)^2$ blocks of which $2(p-1)$ yield no usable lattices. The blocks that do, have $(p-1)$ lines and on each line $(p-1)$ places of which three remain empty, namely in the octant three places where $u + w$, $u - w$ and $tw - uv$ are divisible by p.

The number of regular complete magic basic squares of the order p is therefore (equivalent squares being counted as one)

$$\frac{(p-1)^2 - 2(p-1)}{8}(p-1)(p-4) = \frac{(p-1)^2(p-3)(p-4)}{8} \quad \ldots\ldots\ldots\ldots\ (1)$$

By rotation of rows and columns

$$\frac{p^2(p-1)^2(p-3)(p-4)}{8} \quad \ldots\ldots\ldots\ldots\ (2)$$

complete magic squares can be developed from these.

This number of complete magic squares can be formed from the basic square in which the numbers 1 to p^2 are arranged in normal sequence, but the number of complete magic squares is thereby not exhausted.

The sequence of the rows and columns in the basic square can be permutated at will but the application of the right lattice will still yield complete magic squares. The number of possible permutations of rows and columns is $= p!$. In order to find the total number of complete magic squares one should, therefore, multiply by $(p!)^2$ the result found in (2). However:

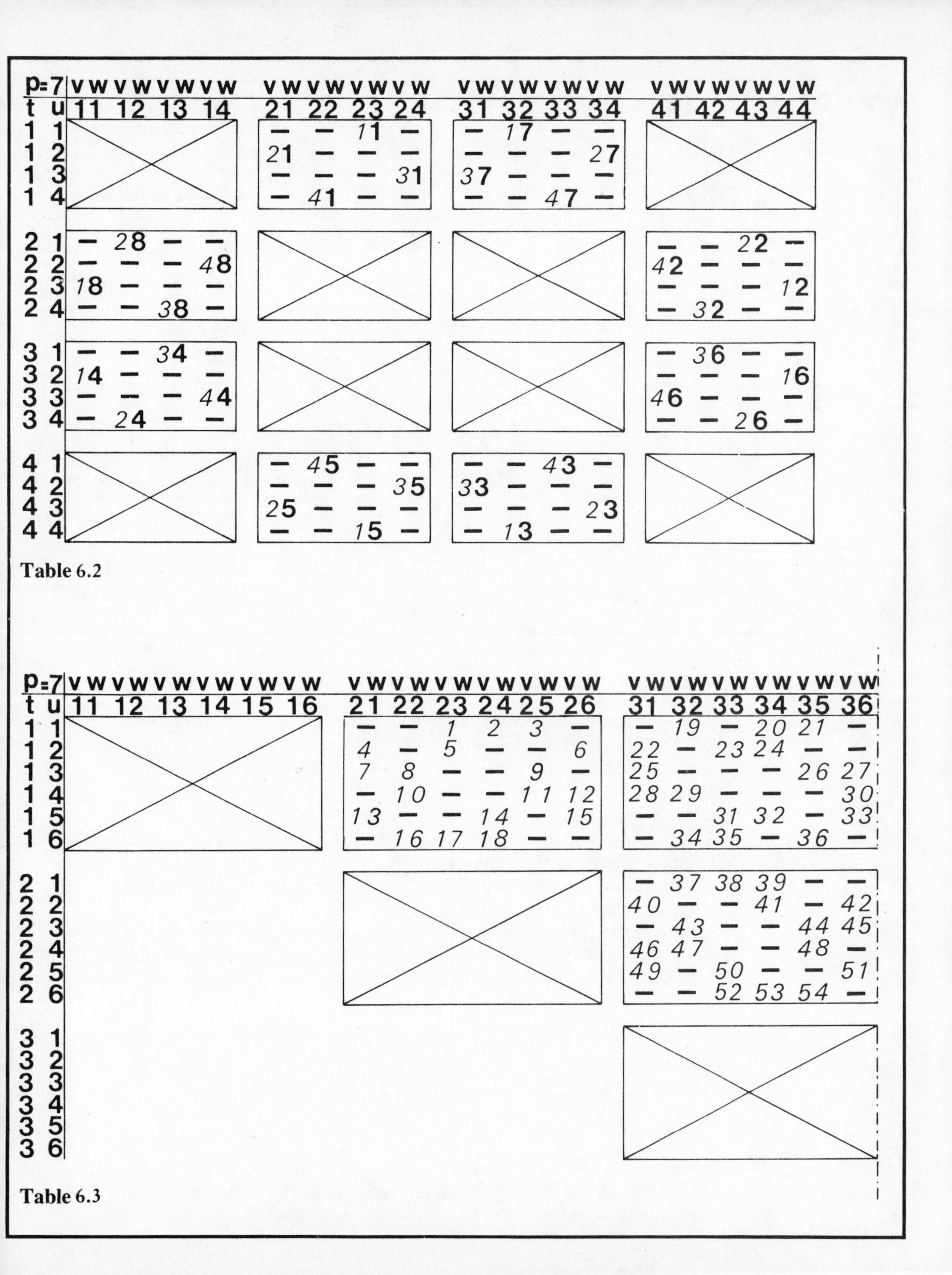

p=7	v	w	v	w	v	w	v	w	v	w	v	w	v	w	v	w
t u	11	12	13	14	21	22	23	24	31	32	33	34	41	42	43	44
1 1					–	–	11	–	–	17	–	–				
1 2					21	–	–	–	–	–	–	27				
1 3					–	–	–	31	37	–	–	–				
1 4					–	41	–	–	–	–	47	–				
2 1	–	28	–	–									–	–	22	–
2 2	–	–	–	48									42	–	–	–
2 3	18	–	–	–									–	–	–	12
2 4	–	–	38	–									–	32	–	–
3 1	–	–	34	–									–	36	–	–
3 2	14	–	–	–									–	–	–	16
3 3	–	–	–	44									46	–	–	–
3 4	–	24	–	–									–	–	26	–
4 1					–	45	–	–	–	–	43	–				
4 2					–	–	–	35	33	–	–	–				
4 3					25	–	–	–	–	–	–	23				
4 4					–	–	15	–	–	13	–	–				

Table 6.2

p=7	v	w	v	w	v	w	v	w	v	w	v	w	v	w	v	w	v	w
t u	11	12	13	14	15	16	21	22	23	24	25	26	31	32	33	34	35	36
1 1							–	–	1	2	3	–	–	19	–	20	21	–
1 2							4	–	5	–	–	6	22	–	23	24	–	–
1 3							7	8	–	–	9	–	25	–	–	–	26	27
1 4							–	10	–	–	11	12	28	29	–	–	–	30
1 5							13	–	–	14	–	15	–	–	31	32	–	33
1 6							–	16	17	18	–	–	–	34	35	–	36	–
2 1													–	37	38	39	–	–
2 2													40	–	–	41	–	42
2 3													–	43	–	–	44	45
2 4													46	47	–	–	48	–
2 5													49	–	50	–	–	51
2 6													–	–	52	53	54	–
3 1																		
3 2																		
3 3																		
3 4																		
3 5																		
3 6																		

Table 6.3

21	22	23	24	25
16	17	18	19	20
11	12	13	14	15
6	7	8	9	10
1	2	3	4	5

14	20	21	2	8
22	3	9	15	16
10	11	17	23	4
18	24	5	6	12
1	7	13	19	25

(x,y) = (1,1) + r(1,1) + s(2,3)

24	10	16	2	13
17	3	14	25	6
15	21	7	18	4
8	19	5	11	22
1	12	23	9	20

. . . r(1,3) + s(2,4)

9	25	11	2	18
12	3	19	10	21
20	6	22	13	4
23	14	5	16	7
1	17	8	24	15

. . . r(1,2) + s(2,1)

19	15	6	2	23
7	3	24	20	11
25	16	12	8	4
13	9	5	21	17
1	22	18	14	10

. . . r(1,4) + s(2,2)

6.6

1. with this multiplication the number of squares that result from rotation of the rows and columns of each of the complete basic magic squares are counted a second time;
2. keep in mind that, in the permutations of the rows and columns of the original basic square that are done in this way, the same number 1, 2, 3 . . . (p – 1) of rows and columns appears over and over and no new complete magic squares are produced. The lattice (1, 1) + r (t, u) + s (v, w) used in the permutation of the basic table by which n columns and m rows are produced again and again leads to the same complete magic square as the application of the lattice (x, y) = (1, 1) + r [(n + 1) t, (m + 1) u] + s [(n + 1) v, (m + 1) w] (mod. p) to the original nonpermutated beginning table. The number of permutations of this sort is $(p-1)^2$.

The total number of regular complete magic squares of the order p (p is prime) consists, therefore, of:

$$\frac{P^2 (p-1)^2 (p-3)(p-4)}{8} \times \frac{(p!)^2}{p^2 (p-1)^2} = \frac{(p-3)(p-4)(p!)^2}{8} \quad \ldots\ldots\ldots (3)$$

Table 6.4 contains some numbers calculated from (1) and (3).

It follows, therefore, both from this table and from the general form of this square, that there are no complete magic squares of the third order.

p	number of complete magic basic squares	total number of complete magic squares
3	0	0
5	4	3.600
7	54	38.102.400
11	700	11.153.456.455.680.000
13	1.620	–
17	5.824	–
19	9.720	–

Table 6.4

4-4	4-5	5-5	5-6	6-6
3-3	3-4	3-5	3-6	4-6
2-2	2-3	2-4	2-5	2-6
1-1	1-2	1-3	1-4	1-5
0-0	0-1	0-2	0-3	0-4

6.7

The number of complete magic squares of the fifth order that is shown in the table is the same as that reached by VAN DRIEL in a more roundabout way. This was also worked out by DUDENEY.

The number of complete magic squares of the seventh order can be determined by examining it according to the method which EULER developed for the construction of these squares.

3. Demonstration of the Formation of Completely Magic Squares from a Basic Square with the Assistance of Domino Stones

The ordinary domino set lends itself excellently to a demonstration of the formation of complete magic squares of the fifth order from a basic square.

First, the basic square is constructed (example 6.7) with each stone having the value of the dots on both halves.

The 0–0, 0–1, . . . 0–4 in the bottom row are placed from left to right. The 0–5 and 0–6 are left over and are set aside.
The second row is formed by 1–1, 1–2 . . . . . . 1–5. The 1–6 remains and is also set aside. The stones 2–2 to 2–6 fill the third row and 3–3 to 3–6 are used in the fourth row, completed by 4 – 6. The remaining stones 4–4, 4–5, 5–5, 5–6, and 6–6 form the top row. In this way a basic square is formed in which the rows from left to right increase by 1 and the columns from bottom to top by 2.
The twenty-five stones from which this square is formed have a total of 168–18 = 150 spots. The magic sum or constant of the magic square developed from this shall therefore be S = 30. The placing of the stones from the basic square according to one of the four known lattices in order to form the rows and columns of the magic square causes the one square to obviously stand out from the other. For the understanding of the application of lattices, this is extremely enlightening.
In example 6.8 are shown the four magic squares in each of whose central section the double zero can be placed, provided a suitable starting point is chosen. If the stones are placed as in the figure, a rectangle of ten by five half stones is formed. Each row in this rectangle adds up to thirty dots, each column to fifteen.

Basic table 6.5 does not consist of $p^2 = 25$ different numbers. The numbers 0, 1, 11 and 12 appear once, the numbers 2, 3, 5, 7, 9 and 16 twice and the numbers 4, 6, and 8 three times. Nevertheless, the lattices are suitable for the normal basic table because the different table is constructed in a completely regular fashion. In each row the numbers from left to right increase by one, in each column from bottom to top by two. Identical numbers lie in the table at a distance which can be bridged by moving them as the knight is moved in chess (one space to the side and one space diagonally).
In the four discovered completely magic squares, stones with the same number of dots can be exchanged. This results in $2^6 \times (3!)^3 = 2^9 \times 3^3 =$ 13,824 variations in addition to the variations which are possible by the rotation of the rows and columns of each complete magic square. Each square can therefore be laid out in 25 × 13,834 = 345,600 ways, using the selected domino stones.

4. Demonstration of the Formation of Completely Magic Squares of the Fourth Order

In contrast to squares of an uneven order, magic squares of an even order cannot be made with the help of a two-dimensional lattice. The even squares are difficult, lacking at present a general method for their construction, although there are rules for certain squares. Only the simplest square, the magic square of the fourth order, is completely worked out. It is discussed by Bergholt, Dudeney, and Kraitchic, among others.

Among the magic squares of the fourth order, there is a large group which have the peculiarity that the magic sum or constant is found not

5-5	3-0	1-5	2-2	3-4
1-1	2-3	5-3	6-5	0-4
3-6	6-6	0-0	1-2	4-2
0-1	1-3	5-2	6-4	4-4
6-2	3-3	4-5	0-2	4-1

$(x,y) = (5,3) + r(1,1) + s(2,3)$

3-5	3-0	6-2	4-4	1-2
2-2	5-4	1-3	6-3	4-0
4-1	4-6	0-0	2-3	5-5
0-1	2-4	5-6	1-5	3-3
6-6	1-1	3-4	2-0	2-5

$(x,y) = (5,5) + r(1,2) + s(2,1)$

2-4	3-0	4-6	1-1	4-5
3-3	1-2	5-5	5-2	0-4
5-6	2-6	0-0	3-4	3-1
0-1	5-3	4-1	6-6	2-2
5-1	4-4	2-3	0-2	6-3

$(x,y) = (5,2) + r(1,3) + s(2,4)$

1-3	0-3	6-6	3-3	2-3
4-4	3-4	2-4	4-1	4-0
5-2	5-1	0-0	4-5	3-5
1-0	5-5	6-3	2-6	1-1
4-6	2-2	1-2	2-0	5-6

$(x,y) = (5,4) + r(1,4) + s(2,2)$

6.8

8	9	10	11	12
6	7	8	9	10
4	5	6	7	8
2	3	4	5	6
0	1	2	3	4

Table 6.5

	a	b	c	d
A	A + a	A + b	A + c	A + d
B	B + a	B + b	B + c	B + d
C	C + a	C + b	C + c	C + d
D	D + a	D + b	D + c	D + d

Table 6.6

A + a	D + c	D + b	A + d
C + d	B + b	B + c	C + a
B + d	C + b	C + c	B + a
D + a	A + c	A + b	D + d

A + a	D + c	B + d	C + b
C + d	B + b	D + a	A + c
D + b	A + d	C + c	B + a
B + c	C + a	A + b	D + d

Table 6.7

only by adding up the numbers in all the rows, all the columns, and both diagonals, but also by totaling the numbers in each of the four quadrants into which the square can be divided. Such squares are called algebraic squares. Complete magic squares belong to this group.
Algebraic squares can be laid out with the help of an addition table. An addition table is made by writing four numbers, a, b, c, and d above the columns, and four numbers, A, B, C, and D at the ends of the rows of the table. In each cell we then write the sum of the numbers at the ends of the rows and columns to which the cell belongs. Table 6.6 gives the general form of such a table.
The addition table is transposed into another by exchanging each number with the number that lies diametrically across from it, except on the diagonals. If $a + d = b + c$ and $A + D = B + C$, this transposed table is already magic. If this is not the case, then exchanging the top right square with the bottom left square will produce a table which is magic for all values of the letters. All possible algebraic squares can be discovered by permutation of the rows and columns in the transposed tables. The magic constant of these squares is $a + b + c + d + A + B + C + D$.
This method can be illustrated with domino stones. We shall confine ourselves to the complete magic squares.
We take the stones 0–0 to 0–3, 1–1 to 1–4, 2–2 to 2–5, and 3–3 to 3–6 from the normal set. Each stone counts as the sum of the dots on both its halves. The selected sixteen stones can be arranged in an addition table in two ways with the understanding that a, b, c, and d as well as A, B, C, and D increase in these sequences.
Since $a + d = b + c$ and $A + D = B + C$ meets this condition, there is only one transposition of the addition table necessary.
From the transposed table a complete magic square can be obtained by placing the second row beneath the bottom row and the second column on the left behind the right. If the few required tricks are quickly executed the complete magic square does, indeed, appear, as if by a stroke of magic (example 6.9).
The complete magic character of the squares means that not only the four squares add up to the magic sum, but that each quarter of a square of arranged numbers has the same sum. This characteristic continues around the edge of the magic square.
Among the selected domino stones there are six pairs that have the same total number of dots. These stones in each pair can be exchanged in the magic square. Because each complete magic square can be changed into 4^2 nonequivalent forms by rotation of rows and columns, the total number of squares that can be made from the chosen domino stones is $2 \times 2^6 \times 4^2 = 2^{11} = 2{,}048$.
In the complete magic square shown on the left, we turn all the stones outside the diagonals a half turn. In the example on the right, we turn all stones in the bottom half a half turn. Doubles, naturally, do not need to be turned. Following this, in both squares we move the left column to the right side. The result is two rectangles of four by eight half stones in which all the rows total eighteen and all the columns nine dots (example 6.10). The diagrams, moreover, are made up of eight horizontally and eight vertically placed rectangles of two by four in which the sum of the

	0	1	2	3
0	0 − 0	0 − 1	0 − 2	0 − 3
2	1 − 1	1 − 2	1 − 3	1 − 4
4	2 − 2	2 − 3	2 − 4	2 − 5
6	3 − 3	3 − 4	3 − 5	3 − 6

	0	2	2	4
0	0 − 0	0 − 2	1 − 1	1 − 3
1	0 − 1	0 − 3	1 − 2	1 − 4
4	2 − 2	2 − 4	3 − 3	3 − 5
5	2 − 3	2 − 5	3 − 4	3 − 6

0 − 0	3 − 5	3 − 4	0 − 3
2 − 5	1 − 2	1 − 3	2 − 2
1 − 4	2 − 3	2 − 4	1 − 1
3 − 3	0 − 2	0 − 1	3 − 6

0 − 0	3 − 4	2 − 5	1 − 3
3 − 5	0 − 3	1 − 2	2 − 2
1 − 4	2 − 4	3 − 3	0 − 1
2 − 3	1 − 1	0 − 2	3 − 6

0-0	3-4	0-3	3-5
1-4	2-4	1-1	2-3
3-3	0-1	3-6	0-2
2-5	1-3	2-2	1-2

0-0	2-5	1-3	3-4
1-4	3-3	0-1	2-4
2-3	0-2	3-6	1-1
3-5	1-2	2-2	0-3

6.9

4	3	3	0	3	5	0	0
2	4	1	1	3	2	4	1
0	1	3	6	2	0	3	3
3	1	2	2	1	2	2	5

2	5	1	3	3	4	0	0
3	3	0	1	2	4	1	4
2	0	6	3	1	1	3	2
2	1	2	2	3	0	5	3

6.10

dots is also eighteen. Four series of numbers having the magic sum remain to be pointed out in the diagram; they lie on diagonal lines, one in an upward and one in a downward direction, that meet each other on the long side of the rectangle. In each half of the rectangle these lines form a diamond. The magic sum is yielded by the eight numbers on the sides of such a diamond; the half sum by the four numbers on the opposite corners, by the four numbers within and the four numbers outside the square.

The number of nonequivalent, *normal* magic squares of the fourth order—that is to say, squares formed from a sequence of natural numbers from 1 to 16—is 880. FRÉNICLE was the first to discuss these completely. Their magic sum or constant is 34. Among these 880 squares, 432 are algebraic, of which 48 are complete magic squares. In order to copy the formation of these last with domino stones, we use a set that goes to a double eight. From this group we choose sixteen stones which are linked according to the rules of ordinary dominoes: 0–1, 1–1, 1–2, 2–2, . . . 7–7, 7–8, 8–8. From these stones, which have from one to sixteen dots, we can form three addition tables (example 6.11) that can be transposed into three complete magic basic squares. By rotation of the rows and columns 3 × 16 = 48 nonequivalent complete magic squares can be made from the selected stones.
By turning one stone a half turn in each row and each column of the basic square (it may be possible in more than one way) and moving the subsequent stones together, three rectangles of four by eight half stones can be made (example 6.12) in which all the rows have thirty dots and all the columns seventeen dots. Furthermore, they have the characteristic described above that the third rectangle contains the double number of "magic" squares.

5. Demonstration of the Formation of Magic Cubes of the Third Order

In his discussion of magic cubes, ANDREWS talks about the twelve examples of the third order formed from the natural numbers from 1 to 27. One of these is shown, made from the basic table in example 6.13. The magic sum comes to:

$$\frac{3(n^3 + 1)}{2} = 42$$

In a magic cube, this sum appears thirty-seven times, namely in the rows and columns of all the outside planes and of the planes that run through the middle of parallel edges, in the diagonals of these planes and in the diagonals between the corners of the cube.
In the center of the cubes is the number:

$$\frac{n^3 + 1}{2} = 14.$$

This number forms the magic sum with all combined numbers that stand diametrically across from each other (example 6.14).
The cubes are formed from the three-dimensional basic table by means of a three-dimensional lattice. The twelve lattices are given in table 6.8.

This formation also lends itself to illustration by domino stones with each stone counting as the total of the dots on both halves.* The normal game of dominoes is suitable because the numbers from the basic table do not have to be consecutive. The lattices are also suitable where the

*This demonstration can be done by using small stones and the grid from a three-dimensional tic-tac-toe game.

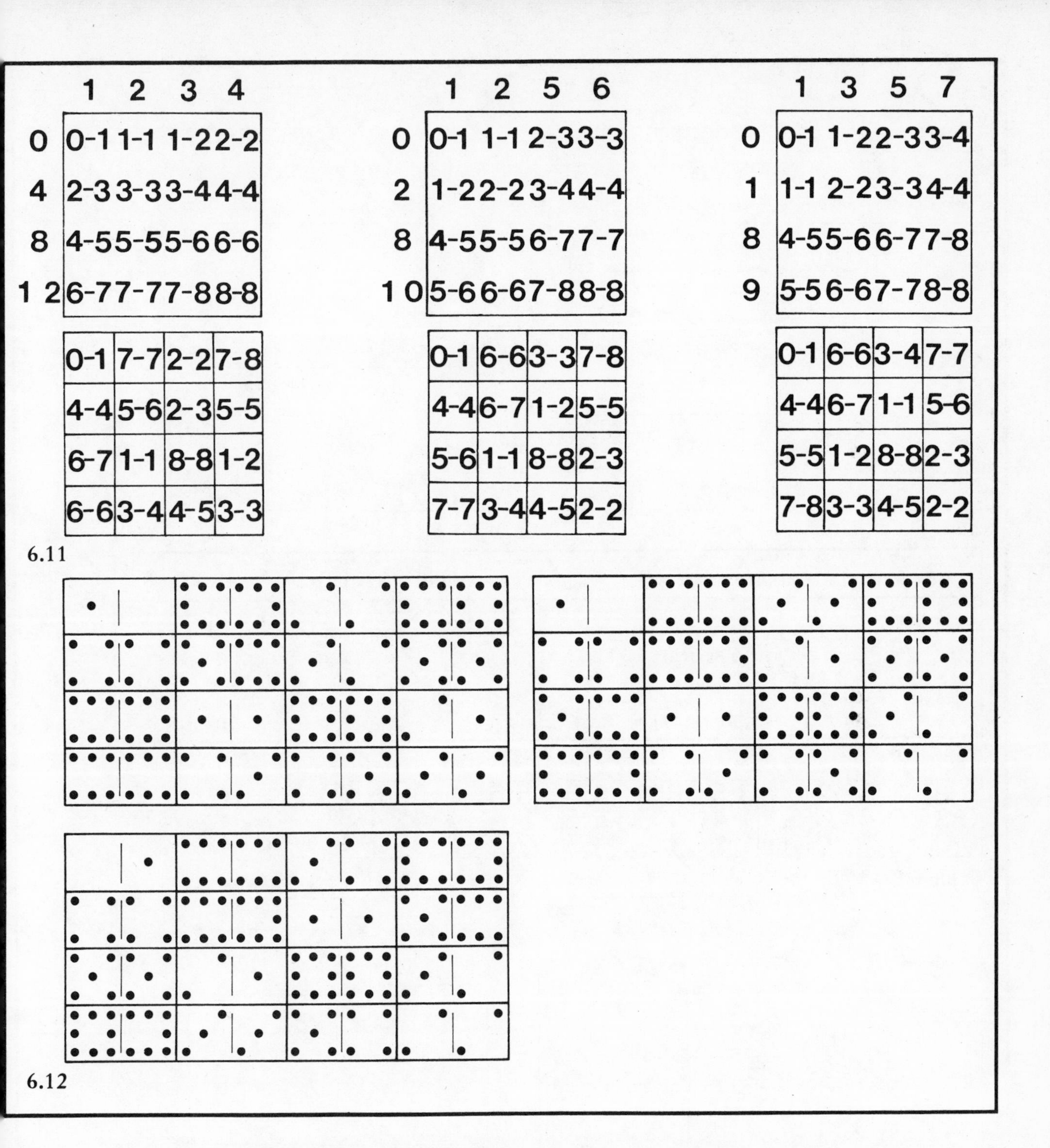

	1	2	3	4
0	0-1	1-1	1-2	2-2
4	2-3	3-3	3-4	4-4
8	4-5	5-5	5-6	6-6
1 2	6-7	7-7	7-8	8-8

0-1	7-7	2-2	7-8
4-4	5-6	2-3	5-5
6-7	1-1	8-8	1-2
6-6	3-4	4-5	3-3

	1	2	5	6
0	0-1	1-1	2-3	3-3
2	1-2	2-2	3-4	4-4
8	4-5	5-5	6-7	7-7
1 0	5-6	6-6	7-8	8-8

0-1	6-6	3-3	7-8
4-4	6-7	1-2	5-5
5-6	1-1	8-8	2-3
7-7	3-4	4-5	2-2

	1	3	5	7
0	0-1	1-2	2-3	3-4
1	1-1	2-2	3-3	4-4
8	4-5	5-6	6-7	7-8
9	5-5	6-6	7-7	8-8

0-1	6-6	3-4	7-7
4-4	6-7	1-1	5-6
5-5	1-2	8-8	2-3
7-8	3-3	4-5	2-2

6.11

6.12

table is built from three groups of consecutive numbers so that the numbers above each other on the vertical form an arithmetic series.

One stone of the set must be placed on its side. Consideration of the illustration of the stones in example 1.1 shows that there are four stones alone with six eyes, of which four one must be removed. We choose the double three and form table 6.9 from the remaining twenty-seven stones.

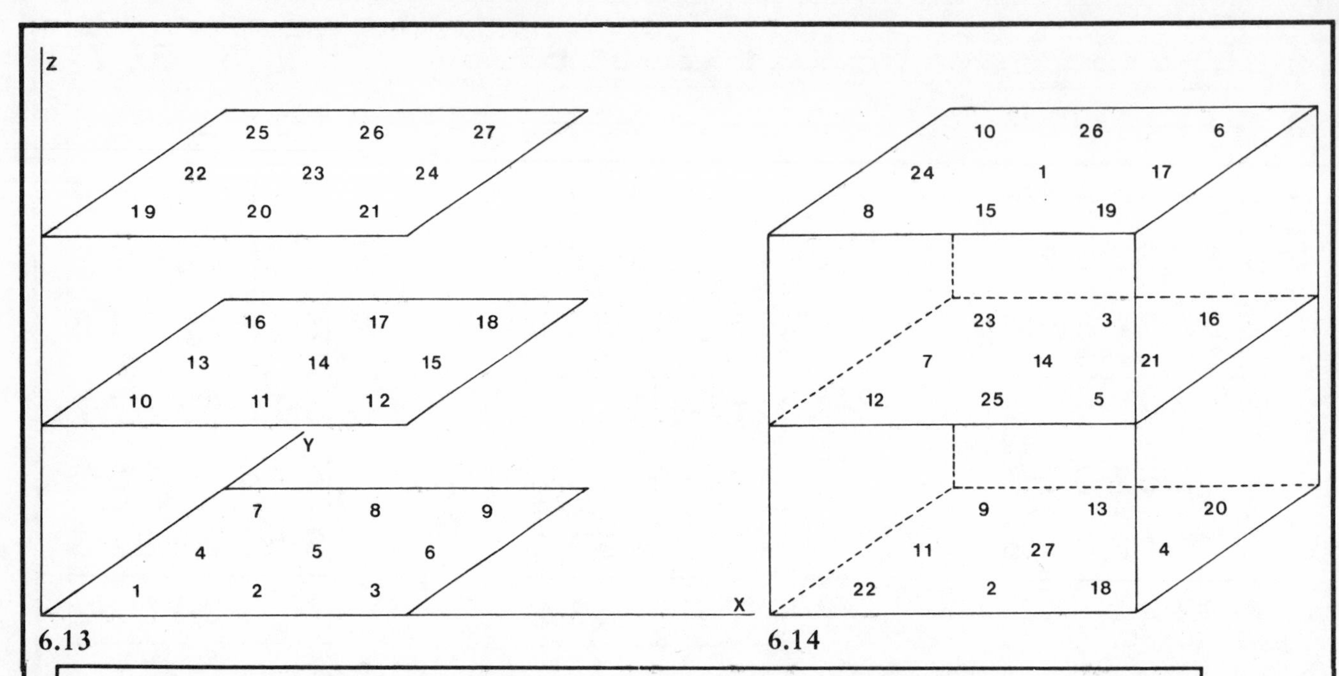

6.13

6.14

1. the number 1 in the center of the top level		2. the number 1 in the original	
1.1	$(x,y,z) = (1,2,3) + k(1,2,1) + l(1,2,2) + m(2,2,2)$	2.1	$(x,y,z) = (1,1,1) + k(1,2,1) + l(1,1,2) + m(2,1,1)$
1.2	$= (3,2,1) + k(1,2,1) + l(2,2,1) + m(2,2,2)$	2.2	$= (1,1,1) + k(1,1,2) + l(1,2,1) + m(2,1,1)$
1.3	$= (2,1,3) + k(2,1,1) + l(2,1,2) + m(2,2,2)$	2.3	$= (1,1,1) + k(2,1,1) + l(1,1,2) + m(1,2,1)$
1.4	$= (2,3,1) + k(2,1,1) + l(2,2,1) + m(2,2,2)$	2.4	$= (1,1,1) + k(1,1,2) + l(2,1,1) + m(1,2,1)$
1.5	$= (1,3,2) + k(1,1,2) + l(1,2,2) + m(2,2,2)$	2.5	$= (1,1,1) + k(1,2,1) + l(2,1,1) + m(1,1,2)$
1.6	$= (3,1,2) + k(1,1,2) + l(2,1,2) + m(2,2,2)$	2.6	$= (1,1,1) + k(2,1,1) + l(1,2,1) + m(1,1,2)$

Table 6.8

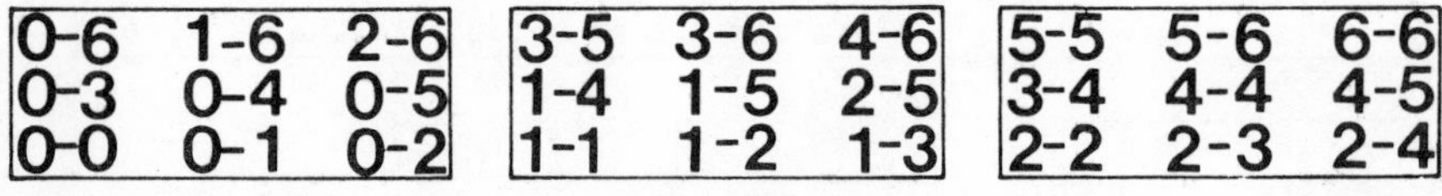

bottom level			middle level			top level		
0-6	1-6	2-6	3-5	3-6	4-6	5-5	5-6	6-6
0-3	0-4	0-5	1-4	1-5	2-5	3-4	4-4	4-5
0-0	0-1	0-2	1-1	1-2	1-3	2-2	2-3	2-4

Table 6.9

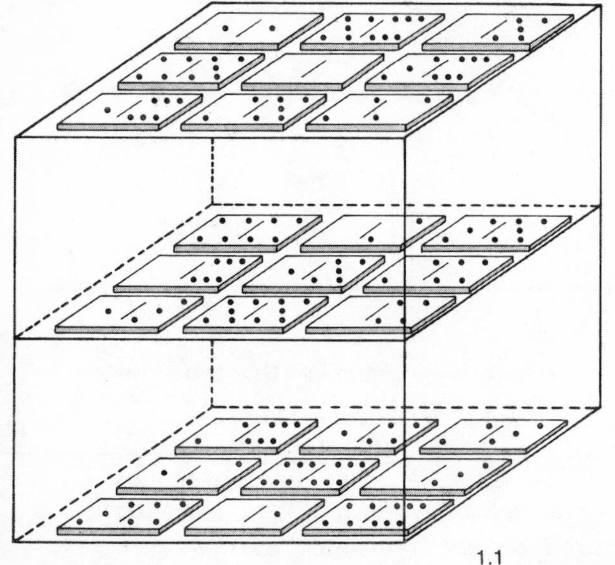

1.1

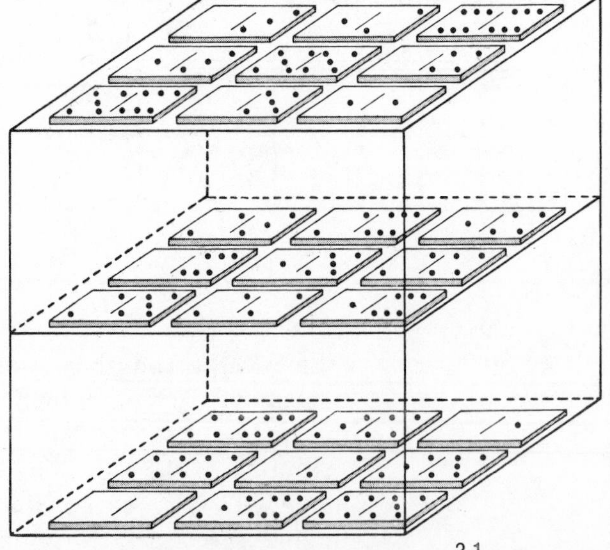

2.1

6.15

Application of the lattices 1.1 and 2.1 gives us the magic cubes of example 6.15.

6. Magic Squares to Be Arranged from a Complete Domino Set

The problem is to arrange from the stones of the ordinary domino game a magic square in which each section is represented by a half stone counting for the number of spots on it. It appears at first glance that this is impossible, since the number of half stones is always 56, and 56 is not a square number.

PAILLOT has a very elegant way of solving this apparently insurmountable difficulty. He arranged a rectangle of seven rows by eight columns, taking care that the eighth, superfluous column remains completely blank. This column assumes the character of a margin on a printed page, and the eye has no difficulty in separating the proper square from the white edge. Since the total number of the dots is not lessened by the separation of the seven empty halves, the magic sum of this square is of the

seventh order: $\frac{168}{7} = 24.$

PAILLOT discovered the square shown in example 6.16. This is more a curiosity than a puzzle. With a little effort, it is not difficult for us to find other examples. The same arrangement of the stones as used by PAILLOT is not necessary since the important unit is the half stone. In two other examples, the arrangement of the stones is both horizontal and vertical. The eighth zero is at the center of the magic square, and the selected doubles have their place. Even with such limitations, it is not difficult to find squares of this type by trial and error.

PAILLOT's idea can be the basis for a splendid puzzle if we now ask for the arrangement of domino stones into a square of the seventh order with a blank edge that is not only *magic* but *completely magic*. From that, the puzzle resolves itself into regular squares that can be methodically found.

The solution of the puzzle divides at once into discrete steps. The first is to find a basic table to which the lattices of the complete magic squares of the seventh order can be applied. The second is to consider how many of these lattices are also applicable in this exceptional case; the third is to construct squares with the suitable discovered lattices; and

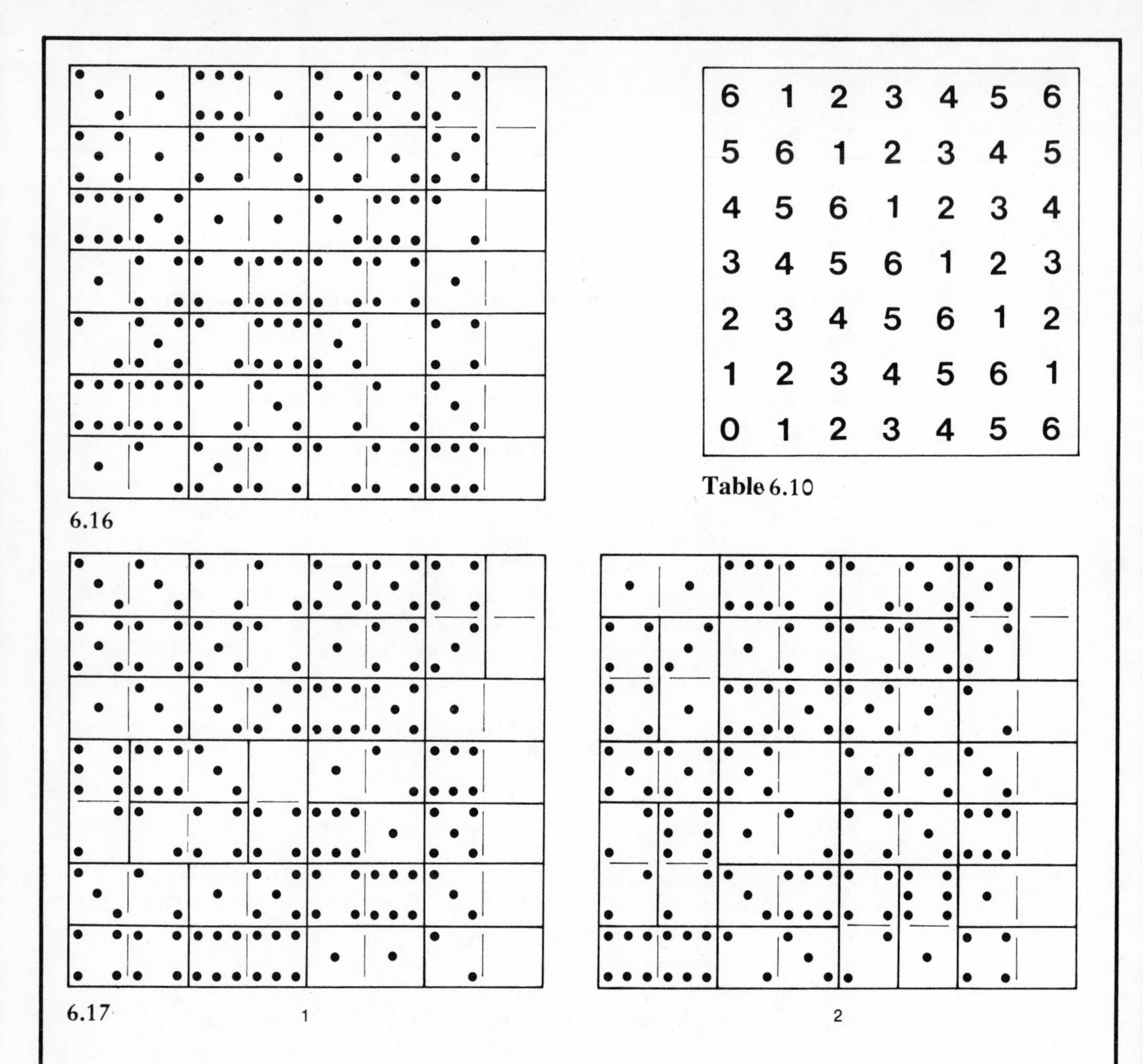

6	1	2	3	4	5	6
5	6	1	2	3	4	5
4	5	6	1	2	3	4
3	4	5	6	1	2	3
2	3	4	5	6	1	2
1	2	3	4	5	6	1
0	1	2	3	4	5	6

6.16

Table 6.10

6.17 1 2

2:	$(x,y) = (1,1) + r(1,1) + s(2,4)$	is equivalent to 21:	$(x,y) = (1,1) + r(1,1) + s(3,5)$
5:	$= (1,1) + r(1,2) + s(2,3)$	is identical to 37:	$= (1,1) + r(2,1) + s(3,2)$
6:	$= (1,1) + r(1,2) + s(2,6)$	is equivalent to 13:	$= (1,1) + r(1,5) + s(2,1)$
10:	$= (1,1) + r(1,4) + s(2,2)$	is equivalent to 42:	$= (1,1) + r(2,2) + s(3,6)$
12:	$= (1,1) + r(1,4) + s(2,6)$	is equivalent to 33:	$= (1,1) + r(1,5) + s(3,6)$
23:	$= (1,1) + r(1,2) + s(3,3)$	is identical to 38:	$= (1,1) + r(2,1) + s(3,3)$
26:	$= (1,1) + r(1,3) + s(3,5)$	is equivalent to 46:	$= (1,1) + r(2,4) + s(3,1)$
27:	$= (1,1) + r(1,3) + s(3,6)$	is equivalent to 38:	$= (1,1) + r(1,4) + s(3,1)$
44:	$= (1,1) + r(2,3) + s(3,5)$	is equivalent to 47:	$= (1,1) + r(2,4) + s(3,2)$

Table 6.11

the last is to determine if the discovered squares can be arranged with dominoes.

The basic table must be as regular as possible. It is not difficult to do this by writing from left to right and from bottom to top the number series given, namely 0 to 6 once and 1 to 6 seven times.

The noteworthy thing about table 6.10 is that on a diagonal line running from top left to bottom right, there is repetition of only one and the same number. This has its consequences for the applicable lattices, which must be so made that on a one-dimensional lattice, with which a row, column, or diagonal of the magic square is formed, each of these diagonal lines appears once and only once.

The diagonal lines running from bottom left to top right also give a repetition of numbers that must be considered. If a square is obtained from the basic table by means of the lattice $(x, y) = (a, b) + r(t, u) + s(v, w)$, which is completely magic, it must meet the following conditions:

$t + u$	is not divisible by seven
$v + w$	is not divisible by seven
$t + v + u + w$	is not divisible by seven
$t - v + u - w$	is not divisible by seven

As a result of these new conditions, eighteen squares of the seventh order remain from the original fifty-four complete magic squares.

Table 6.10 is, moreover, symmetrical with respect to the diagonal running from bottom left to top right. This is because the lattices:

$(x, y) = (1, 1) + r(t, u) + s(v, w)$ and $(x, y) = (1, 1) + r(u, t) + s(w, v)$ will produce identical squares. All squares that are equivalent to the square obtained from the first lattice are also equivalent to the squares obtained from the second lattice. The eighteen remaining lattices then also yield squares which are pairs of identical or equivalent squares (table 6.11).

Therefore, nine squares, shown later, remain (example 6.18). The following can *not* be illustrated by domino stones:

2	: because 1–4, 2–5, and 3–6 cannot be placed;
5, 10, 27	: because they have no doubles;
12, 44	: because neither 6–6, nor 6–3 can be placed.

The same is true of all rotation of rows and columns of the squares.

In the squares remaining it appears to be impossible to use number 6; the combinations 1–4, 2–5, and 3–6 appear too often.

Square 26 can be shown with domino stones in two ways. Both ways yield three solutions: each of the basic squares shown below can yield another two examples by rotation of the columns (example 6.19).

By rotation of rows and columns, square 23 yields $2 \times 2 = 4$ solutions (example 6.20).

The solutions to 26b and the equivalent of 23 are worked out by:

$(x, y) = (2, 4) + r(-1, -2) + s(-3, -3) \equiv (2, 4) + s(6, 5) + s(4, 4)$ (mod. 7) (example 6.21).

The three basic squares and the seven squares that result from these by rotation of rows and columns form the only solutions to this problem. The basic table permits no permutations in the sequence of rows and col-

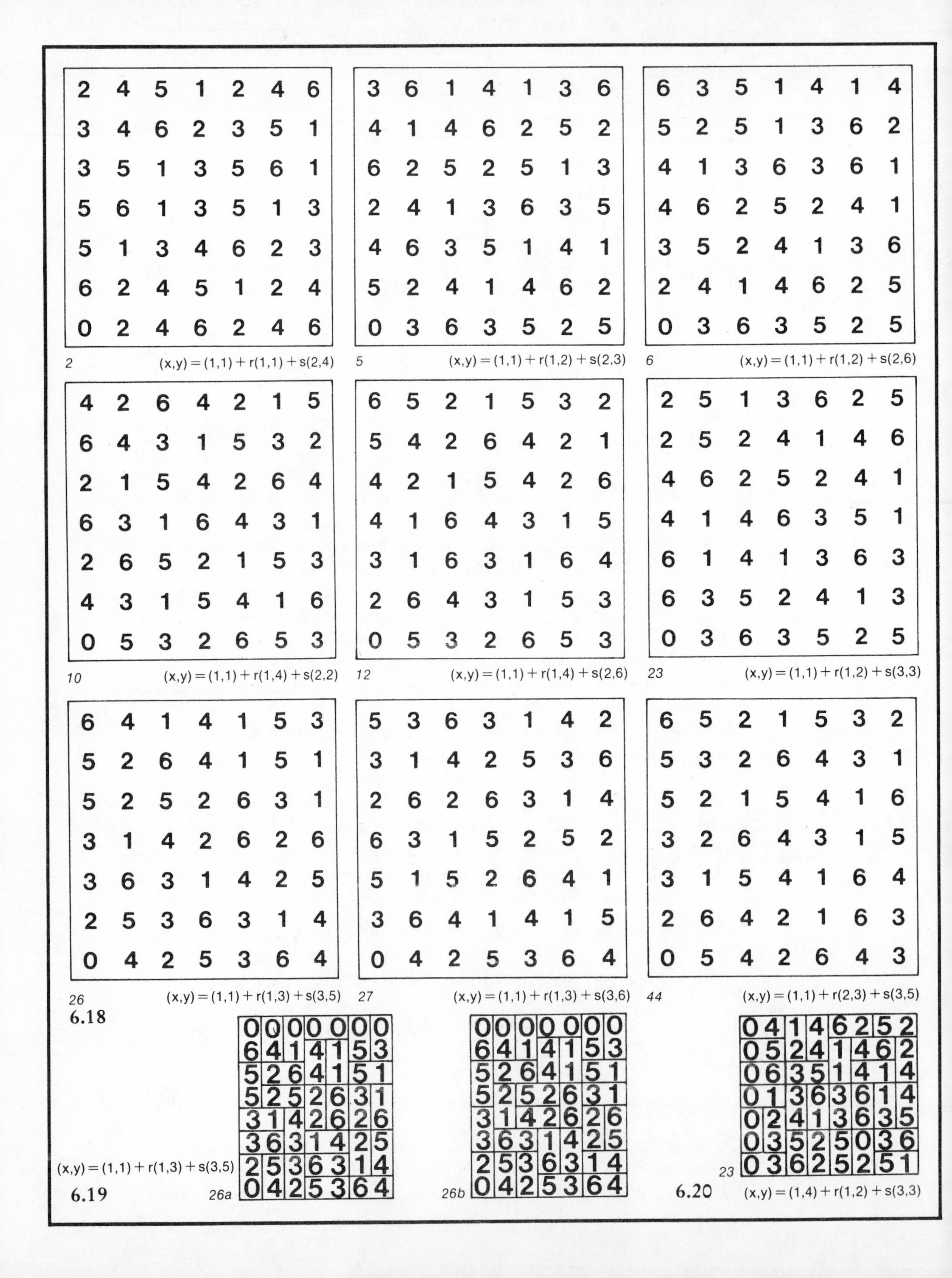

2 4 5 1 2 4 6
3 4 6 2 3 5 1
3 5 1 3 5 6 1
5 6 1 3 5 1 3
5 1 3 4 6 2 3
6 2 4 5 1 2 4
0 2 4 6 2 4 6
2
(x,y) = (1,1) + r(1,1) + s(2,4)
3 6 1 4 1 3 6
4 1 4 6 2 5 2
6 2 5 2 5 1 3
2 4 1 3 6 3 5
4 6 3 5 1 4 1
5 2 4 1 4 6 2
0 3 6 3 5 2 5
5
(x,y) = (1,1) + r(1,2) + s(2,3)
6 3 5 1 4 1 4
5 2 5 1 3 6 2
4 1 3 6 3 6 1
4 6 2 5 2 4 1
3 5 2 4 1 3 6
2 4 1 4 6 2 5
0 3 6 3 5 2 5
6
(x,y) = (1,1) + r(1,2) + s(2,6)
4 2 6 4 2 1 5
6 4 3 1 5 3 2
2 1 5 4 2 6 4
6 3 1 6 4 3 1
2 6 5 2 1 5 3
4 3 1 5 4 1 6
0 5 3 2 6 5 3
10
(x,y) = (1,1) + r(1,4) + s(2,2)
6 5 2 1 5 3 2
5 4 2 6 4 2 1
4 2 1 5 4 2 6
4 1 6 4 3 1 5
3 1 6 3 1 6 4
2 6 4 3 1 5 3
0 5 3 2 6 5 3
12
(x,y) = (1,1) + r(1,4) + s(2,6)
2 5 1 3 6 2 5
2 5 2 4 1 4 6
4 6 2 5 2 4 1
4 1 4 6 3 5 1
6 1 4 1 3 6 3
6 3 5 2 4 1 3
0 3 6 3 5 2 5
23
(x,y) = (1,1) + r(1,2) + s(3,3)
6 4 1 4 1 5 3
5 2 6 4 1 5 1
5 2 5 2 6 3 1
3 1 4 2 6 2 6
3 6 3 1 4 2 5
2 5 3 6 3 1 4
0 4 2 5 3 6 4
26
(x,y) = (1,1) + r(1,3) + s(3,5)
5 3 6 3 1 4 2
3 1 4 2 5 3 6
2 6 2 6 3 1 4
6 3 1 5 2 5 2
5 1 5 2 6 4 1
3 6 4 1 4 1 5
0 4 2 5 3 6 4
27
(x,y) = (1,1) + r(1,3) + s(3,6)
6 5 2 1 5 3 2
5 3 2 6 4 3 1
5 2 1 5 4 1 6
3 2 6 4 3 1 5
3 1 5 4 1 6 4
2 6 4 2 1 6 3
0 5 4 2 6 4 3
44
(x,y) = (1,1) + r(2,3) + s(3,5)
6.18
0 0 0 0 0 0 0
6 4 1 4 1 5 3
5 2 6 4 1 5 1
5 2 5 2 6 3 1
3 1 4 2 6 2 6
3 6 3 1 4 2 5
2 5 3 6 3 1 4
0 4 2 5 3 6 4
(x,y) = (1,1) + r(1,3) + s(3,5)
6.19
26a
0 0 0 0 0 0 0
6 4 1 4 1 5 3
5 2 6 4 1 5 1
5 2 5 2 6 3 1
3 1 4 2 6 2 6
3 6 3 1 4 2 5
2 5 3 6 3 1 4
0 4 2 5 3 6 4
26b
0 4 1 4 6 2 5 2
0 5 2 4 1 4 6 2
0 6 3 5 1 4 1 4
0 1 3 6 3 6 1 4
0 2 4 1 3 6 3 5
0 3 5 2 5 0 3 6
0 3 6 2 5 2 5 1
23
6.20
(x,y) = (1,4) + r(1,2) + s(3,3)

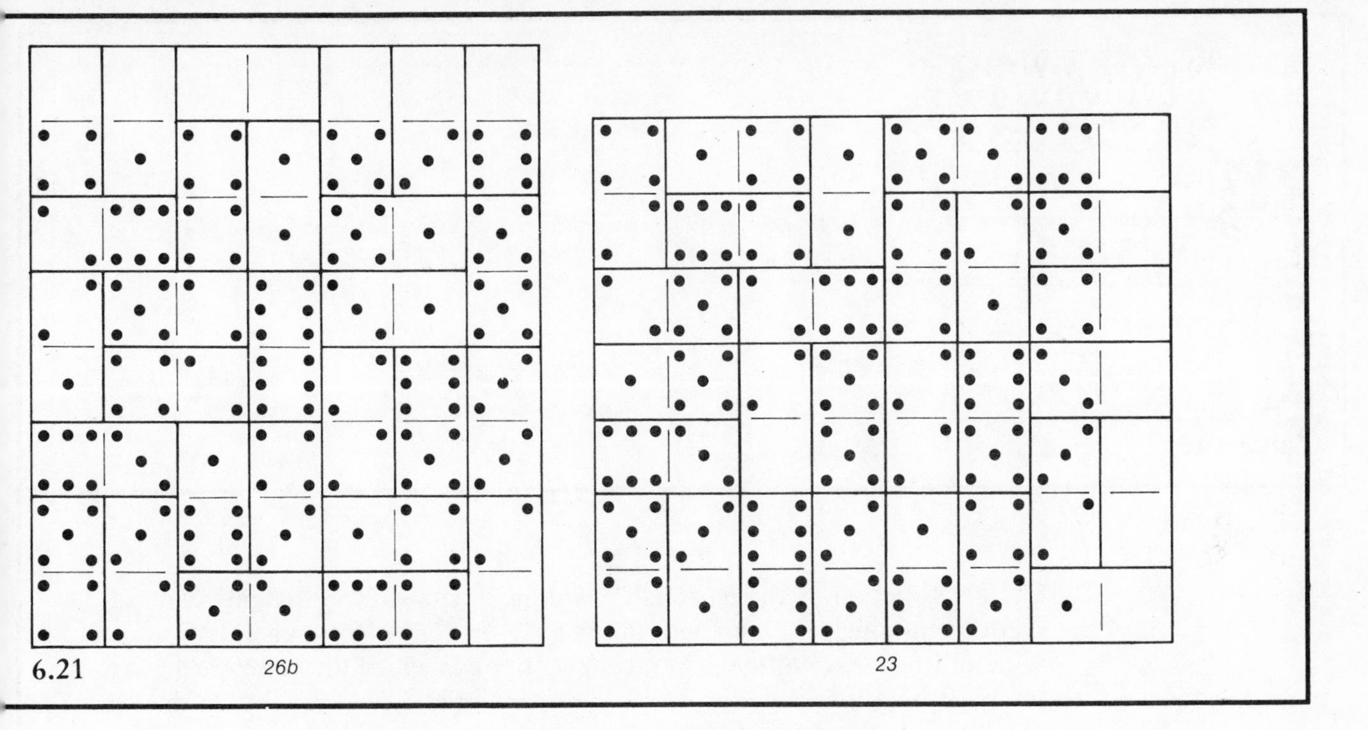

6.21

umns unless these are so executed that over and over one and the same number of rows or columns are skipped. But, as we have seen, such permutations do not lead to new solutions.
There exist, therefore, not more than ten true distinct completely magic squares of the seventh order with an empty margin that can be shown with the stones of an ordinary domino set. The question of whether there are corresponding squares of the fifth order that can be shown with the set in which double four is the highest stone must be answered in the negative. None of the four lattices that yield completely magic squares of the fifth order fulfill the additional conditions.

The written method of solution is the most obvious but not the most direct. After the framing of the basic square and of the additional conditions with respect to the lattices that follow, the solution can be found as follows.

1. The square must have doubles, that is, perhaps horizontally, perhaps vertically, there must be some adjacent cells with the same number of dots. The best way to realize this is with a one-dimensional lattice which moves from a diagonal line running from top left to bottom right on which a certain number appears, to the second similar line with the same number. The most critical is doublet six (in general n – n) that can appear only as one of the numbers of the top-left-to-bottom-right main diagonal line and the number in the top right corner. It is therefore necessary that (t + u) or (v + w) be the same as 6 if the movement goes from the diagonal to the corner or 8 if it goes from the corner to the diagonal. We put v + w = 6 or v + w = 8 (in general v + w = n or = n + 2).

		v+w=n		v+w=n+2	
		v 2 w 4	v 3 w 3	v 2 w 6	v 3 w 5
t+u=3	t 1 u 2	—	23	6	—
	t 2 u 1	X	38	X	—
t+u=4	t 1 u 3	—	—	—	26
	t 2 u 2	X	—	X	—

Table 6.12

2. The construction of the basic table is done in such a way that adjacent sections in which the numbers differ by 1 or 5 arise from each lattice without further conditions. Adjacent sections in which the numbers differ by 2 or 4 also emerge. It can be discovered from the table in the same way as the doubles that $t + u = 2, 3, 4,$ or 5 and that there are no lattices that do not fulfill one of these conditions.
It is different with the adjacent sections 1–4, 2–5, and 3–6 which have a difference of 3. It appears from table 6.10 that $t + u = 3$ or $t + u = 4$ in order to obtain these combinations. If $t + u = 5$, there is only one combination 1–4, one 2–5, and one 6–3. The six in this last is the six from the top right corner. Because this must serve as double six at the same time, the formula does not lead to a square which can be laid out.
Table 6.12 contains all possible constructions that are suitable for two-dimensional lattices for the values $t + u$ and $v + w$. Lattices which are outside the example considered on page 84 ($1 \leq t \leq \frac{n-2}{2}$; $2 \leq v \leq \frac{n}{2}$; $t < v$) are shown by a cross; lattices that do not meet the conditions are shown by a dash. Four lattices remain: the already known numbers 6, 23, and 26 together with lattice 38 which apparently is identical with 23 (see table 6.11).

7. Bordered Squares

A bordered magic square remains magic if the outside rows and columns are removed. A square can also have more borders that can be removed successively without destroying the magic character.
Is it possible to place domino stones in a pattern of bordered magic squares with a margin after PAILLOT's method? In order to answer this question it is necessary to consider the outstanding characteristics of the bordered square.

If a magic square of the order m (m can be even as well as uneven) with the magic sum of S is given a border, the order increases by 2 and S increases by s_1. Then the sum of the numbers in the central square + the sum of the numbers in the border = the sum of the numbers in the bordered square

$$mS + \frac{(m+2)^2 - m^2}{2} s_1 = (m+2)(S+s_1),$$

from which it follows that $s_1 = \frac{2S}{m}$.

A second border, which increases by the magic constant s_2, yields

$$s_2 = \frac{2}{m+2}(S+s_1) = \frac{2S}{m},$$

and so forth. Each additional border increases the magic sum by $\frac{2S}{m}$
A bordered magic square of the seventh order can consist of:

1. a double bordered square of the third order. If S_3 is the magic sum of the central square, then $\frac{7S_3}{3}$ is the constant of the bordered square;
2. a single bordered square of the fifth order. The magic sum of this square is $\frac{7S_5}{5}$, as S_5 is the magic sum of the central square.

To lay out with domino stones a square of the seventh order with an empty margin $S_7 = 24$. Since 24 is not divisible by 7, there is no existing value for S_3 or S_5; the problem is insoluble.
A double-bordered square of the seventh order is possible if the magic constant is reduced to 21. The margin then becomes covered by threes, by which much of the charm of PAILLOT's solution is lost.
The magic sums become $S_7 = 21$; $S_5 = \frac{5}{7} \times 21 = 15$; $S_3 = \frac{3}{7} \times 21 = 9$.
From the general form of the magic square of the third order (see example 3.3), it follows that the number in the central section $\neq \frac{1}{3} S_3 = 3$. As the last three is placed in that way, $a \neq 0$ and $b \neq 0$. For the same reason $(a - b) \neq 0$, therefore $a \neq b$.
Since the highest number of dots is six $(a + b) \leq 3$. From this it follows: $a = 2$ and $b = 1$.
There is, therefore, only one square of the third order possible with the eighth three in the center section. The number of ways, however, in which the borders can be filled in is extremely large, by estimate 10^7 or possibly 10^8. It is unfeasible to discuss how many of these squares can be shown with domino stones. Therefore we will give a single example (6.22).
In this example three of the four unbroken slanting lines that appear in the square have a magic sum. The diagram therefore almost meets the conditions discussed on page

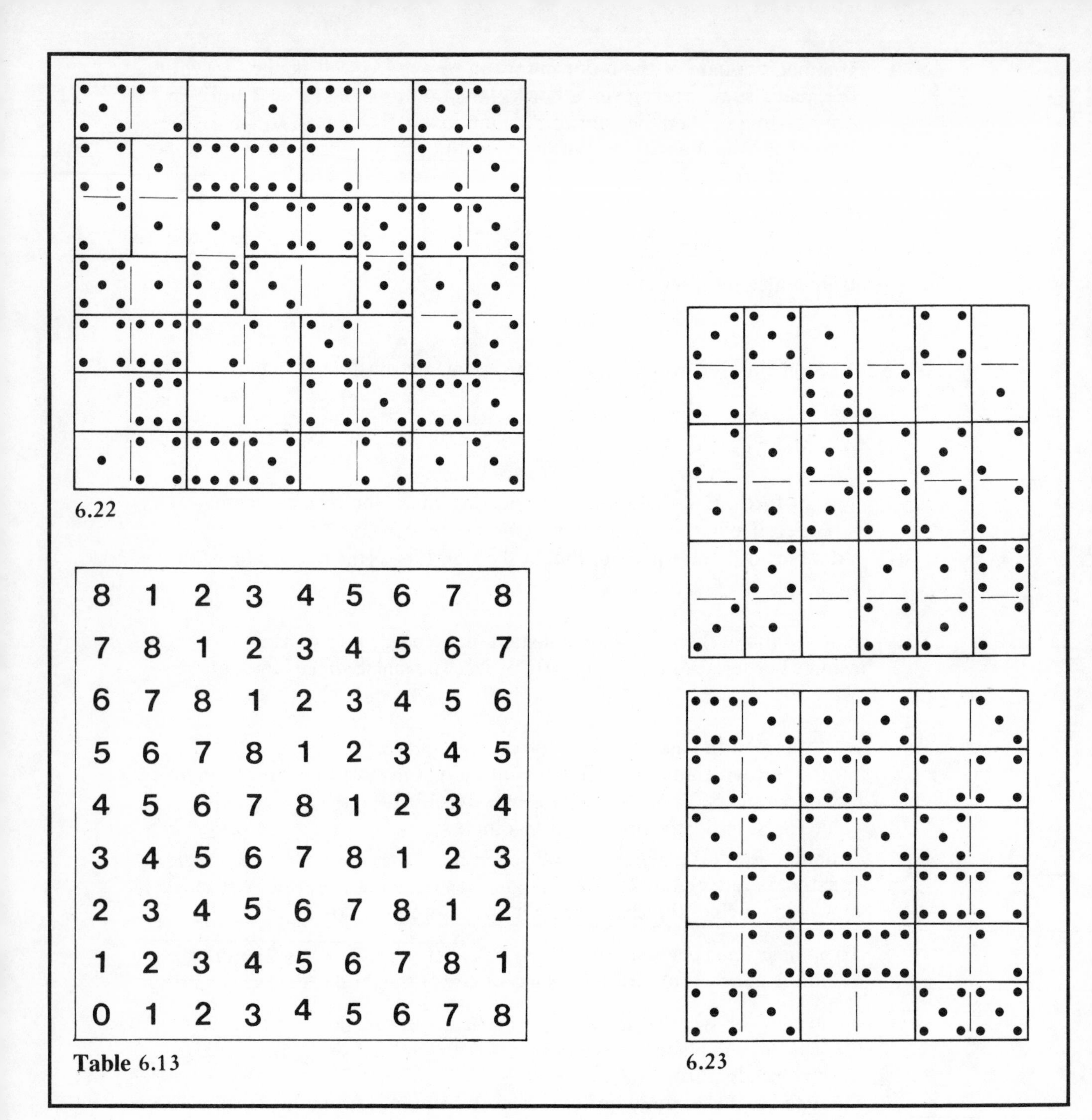

6.22

8	1	2	3	4	5	6	7	8
7	8	1	2	3	4	5	6	7
6	7	8	1	2	3	4	5	6
5	6	7	8	1	2	3	4	5
4	5	6	7	8	1	2	3	4
3	4	5	6	7	8	1	2	3
2	3	4	5	6	7	8	1	2
1	2	3	4	5	6	7	8	1
0	1	2	3	4	5	6	7	8

Table 6.13

6.23

8. Regular Completely Magic Squares with Empty Margins of a Higher Order

Completely magic squares with empty margins can be laid out only with a set in which the highest number of dots = n is even.

The order of such a square p = n + 1. If the magic sum of the square =

s, then the total number of dots from the set S = (n + 1)s. From this follows:

$$(n+1)s = \frac{n(n+1)(n+2)}{2} \text{ or } s = \frac{n(n+2)}{2}$$

only if n is even and yields a whole number as the value for s.
For the set in which double eight is the highest stone the basic table of the number of dots is illustrated here.
For the lattices, by which eventually completely magic squares from table 6.13 can be made, it holds that:

a. for the adjacent sections with the same number $v + w = n$ or $n + 2$;
b. adjacent sections with numbers which differ by 2 or 6 can be developed if $t + u = 2, = 3, = 6,$ or $= 7$.
c. adjacent sections with numbers which differ by 3 or 5 can be developed if $t + u = 3, = 4, = 5,$ or $= 6$;
d. adjacent sections with numbers which differ by 4 can be developed if $t + u = 4$ or 5.

There is no value of t + u that equally satisfies b, c, and d. With the set that goes to double eight, no complete magic squares can be laid out and it needs no discussion that for larger sets this is even less possible. The ten regular completely magic squares of the seventh order are the only ones that can be arranged with a domino set.

9. Three Magic Squares of Dudeney

DUDENEY discovered a trio of magic squares of the sixth order that can be arranged with eighteen of the stones from the ordinary domino game. The stones all lie in the same direction (Example 6.23).
The choice of the stones is not made at random, since for each square a certain selection must be made.
The top square has the smallest magic sum that can be made from the eighteen chosen pieces, namely 13. From that, the square with the largest sum can be laid out without difficulty by exchanging each number of dots with its complement to six. 6 is replaced by 0 and 0 by 6; 4 is replaced by 2, 2 by 4, 5 is replaced by 1 and 1 by 5. Only 3 remains 3. In this way a square that has 23 for the magic sum is created.
The bottom square with the magic sum = 18 lies precisely between these two.*
It is easy to see that the largest sum must be 23 and the smallest 13.
Ten stones must be removed from the game. The smallest number of spots that these can have is 28 (1 × 0, 1 × 1, 2 × 2, 2 × 3, 3 × 4, and 1 × 5 dots). The remaining 18 stones have a maximum of 140 eyes; the multiple of six that is closest to this is 138 = 6 × 23. (In order to obtain this multiple of six 0–6 is set aside in place of the 1–4. The stone with five dots is the 1–4.)

*By changing the stones in the square for their complements, a fourth square which also has 18 for the magic sum can be developed.

S=23		
12	15	19
19	12	15
15	19	12

S=13		
12	9	5
5	12	9
9	5	12

S=18		
12	11	13
12	10	14
12	15	9

6.24

The highest number of dots that the ten stones can have is 92 (1×12, 1×11, 2×10, 2×9, 3×8, and 1×7 dots). The smallest sum of the magic square therefore is $\frac{78}{6} = 13$. (In place of the 6–2 the 6–0 is set aside and the stone with seven dots is the 5–2.) The stones not used in the formation of the square with the magic sum = 18 have a total of sixty dots.
It should be noticed the regular way in which the solutions are developed. If by the contraction of four adjacent sections at a time the diagrams of squares of three-by-three sections are restored, three semimagic squares develop as shown above (example 6.24).

10. Magic Squares of the Eighth Order

There are undoubtedly countless magic squares of the eighth order that can be laid out by the method of the DUDENEY squares with a selection from the game having double eight as the highest stone: each section of the magic square is occupied by a half stone and all stones are placed in the same direction.
The smallest possible magic sum is 25, the largest 39. Between these there is a large number of selections imaginable. With thirty-two stones to be arranged in each selection it is an endless task to try to find a complete solution.
To give some examples is not difficult as half squares of the type sought are already contained in the complete magic squares of the fourth order (see page 94). It follows, therefore, to take from the set a second group of sixteen stones that can be formed into rectangles able to serve as the other half of the desired square. The magic sum of the square to be formed is then 34.

The second group of sixteen stones must, like the first, be chosen in as regular as possible a sequence. The highest suitable stone has fourteen dots. The chosen stones must have 136 dots. This leads to the following choices: 0–3 and 0–4 (or 1–3), 1–4 and 1–5 (or 0–6), 2–4 to 2–7, 3–5 to 3–8, 4–7 and 4–8 and finally 5–8 and 6–8. With these stones three addition tables can be formed:

a b c d	A B C D	a b c d	A B C D	a b c d	A B C D
1 2 3 4	2 5 7 10	1 2 4 5	2 4 7 9	1 3 4 6	2 3 7 8

The entire range of possibilities is shown in those two examples.
Once the rectangle has been found by using the addition table to obtain the completely magic square of the fourth order, the columns are closed up by turning some stones a half turn (example 6.25). In the example on the left the sum of the eyes of all columns is 17; in the right, 16 and 18 and 18 and 16 in turn.

Now care must still be taken that two pairs of diagonal lines in the rectangles can be joined to form the two diagonals of the square on which the number of dots equals the magic sum. This is done by rotating rows or columns. The rotations and movements are shown with a darker tint. Once they are carried out, the rectangles are ready to be placed against each other, the first group above the second.
In the example on the right, only a few moves are needed. There remains only one move if the stones 1–4 and 1–5; 2–5 and 2–7; 3–6 and 3–8; 4–7 and 4–8 are already turned, which can happen.
From the spectacular formation of both completely magic squares follows the equally spectacular square of the eighth order.

The illustrated examples form only some of the many ways and the simplest in which the given rectangles can be joined to form a magic square.
Another method of construction is applicable only to the example on the left. Both rectangles—1.1 and 2.1—can be divided into two halves on which the alternate rows have fifteen and nineteen dots and the diagonals have twenty-five and nine as a total. This means that half of a rectangle can be placed as opposite squares in the magic square. The diagram shown here (example 6.26) is an example of this. It can be arranged from the earlier givens by folding down on a horizontal line.
With their many rectangles of two by four half stones that contain the magic sum, these squares betray their origin as algebraic squares of the fourth order.

From each pair of suitable rectangles a large number of magic squares can be made. In this respect, two rectangles which can be formed from the selection, divided into two groups in table 6.14, are interesting.
The division comes in the usual way after the left and right halves of the two top rows in the table are exchanged. The resulting rectangle can be split into halves that are semi-magic. In all the rows and columns the sum of the eyes is 17 and the sum of both diagonals together is double that number, namely 25 + 9 and 22 + 12 (example 6.27).
By rotation of the two rows and columns each half rectangle, while keeping the characteristic mentioned above, can be formed into four different figures. Each of these can form four equivalent figures. (Not eight, because the stones must remain oriented in one direction.) From this it follows that the two halves of a rectangle can be placed in the two opposite squares of the magic square in $2 \times 2^3 \times 2^3 = 2^7$ ways. The other two squares can fill the halves of the second rectangle in two ways.

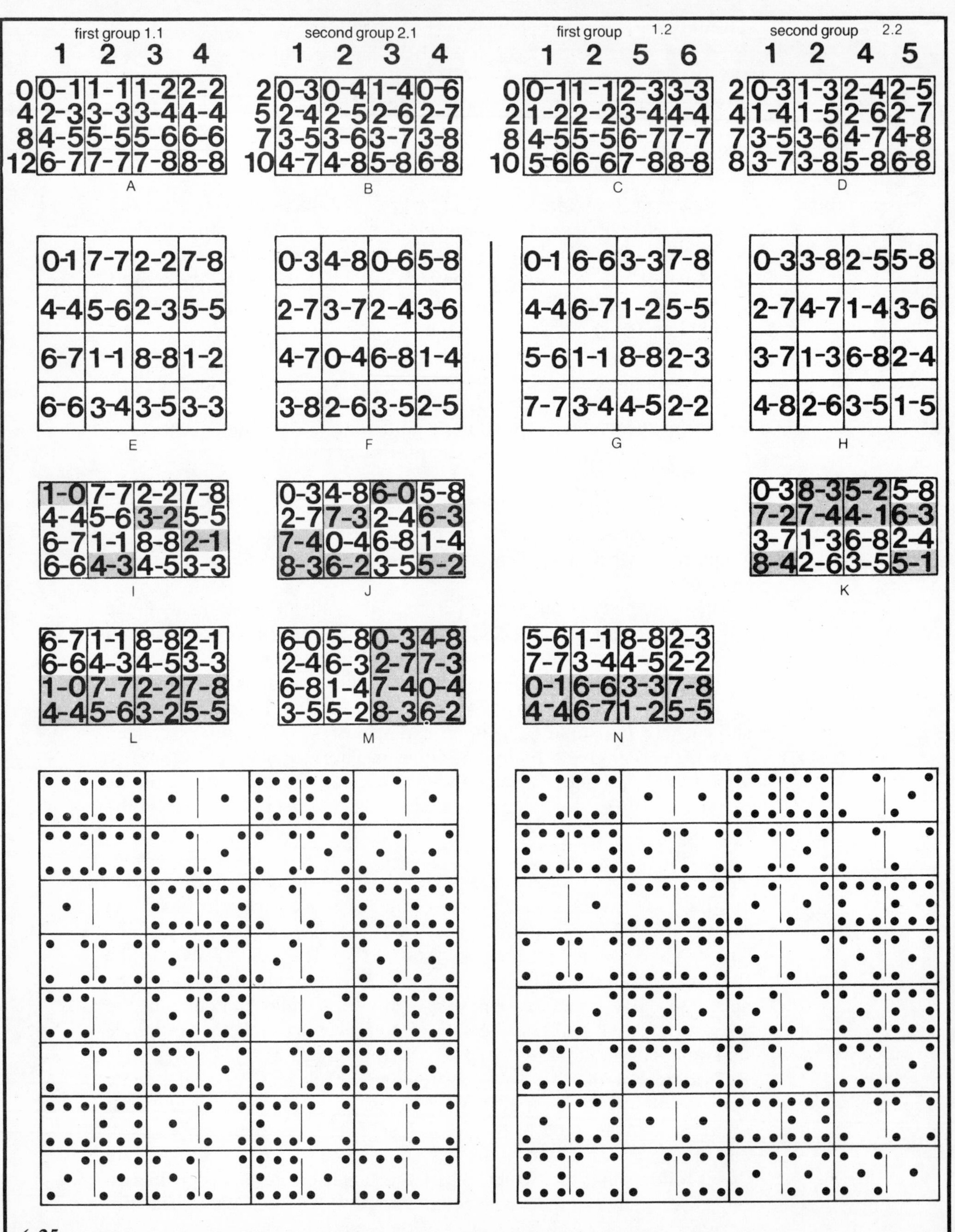
first group 1.1
1 2 3 4
0 0-1 1-1 1-2 2-2
4 2-3 3-3 3-4 4-4
8 4-5 5-5 5-6 6-6
12 6-7 7-7 7-8 8-8
A
second group 2.1
1 2 3 4
2 0-3 0-4 1-4 0-6
5 2-4 2-5 2-6 2-7
7 3-5 3-6 3-7 3-8
10 4-7 4-8 5-8 6-8
B
first group 1.2
1 2 5 6
0 0-1 1-1 2-3 3-3
2 1-2 2-2 3-4 4-4
8 4-5 5-5 6-7 7-7
10 5-6 6-6 7-8 8-8
C
second group 2.2
1 2 4 5
2 0-3 1-3 2-4 2-5
4 1-4 1-5 2-6 2-7
7 3-5 3-6 4-7 4-8
8 3-7 3-8 5-8 6-8
D
0-1 7-7 2-2 7-8
4-4 5-6 2-3 5-5
6-7 1-1 8-8 1-2
6-6 3-4 3-5 3-3
E
0-3 4-8 0-6 5-8
2-7 3-7 2-4 3-6
4-7 0-4 6-8 1-4
3-8 2-6 3-5 2-5
F
0-1 6-6 3-3 7-8
4-4 6-7 1-2 5-5
5-6 1-1 8-8 2-3
7-7 3-4 4-5 2-2
G
0-3 3-8 2-5 5-8
2-7 4-7 1-4 3-6
3-7 1-3 6-8 2-4
4-8 2-6 3-5 1-5
H
1-0 7-7 2-2 7-8
4-4 5-6 3-2 5-5
6-7 1-1 8-8 2-1
6-6 4-3 4-5 3-3
I
0-3 4-8 6-0 5-8
2-7 7-3 2-4 6-3
7-4 0-4 6-8 1-4
8-3 6-2 3-5 5-2
J
0-3 8-3 5-2 5-8
7-2 7-4 4-1 6-3
3-7 1-3 6-8 2-4
8-4 2-6 3-5 5-1
K
6-7 1-1 8-8 2-1
6-6 4-3 4-5 3-3
1-0 7-7 2-2 7-8
4-4 5-6 3-2 5-5
L
6-0 5-8 0-3 4-8
2-4 6-3 2-7 7-3
6-8 1-4 7-4 0-4
3-5 5-2 8-3 6-2
M
5-6 1-1 8-8 2-3
7-7 3-4 4-5 2-2
0-1 6-6 3-3 7-8
4-4 6-7 1-2 5-5
N

6.25

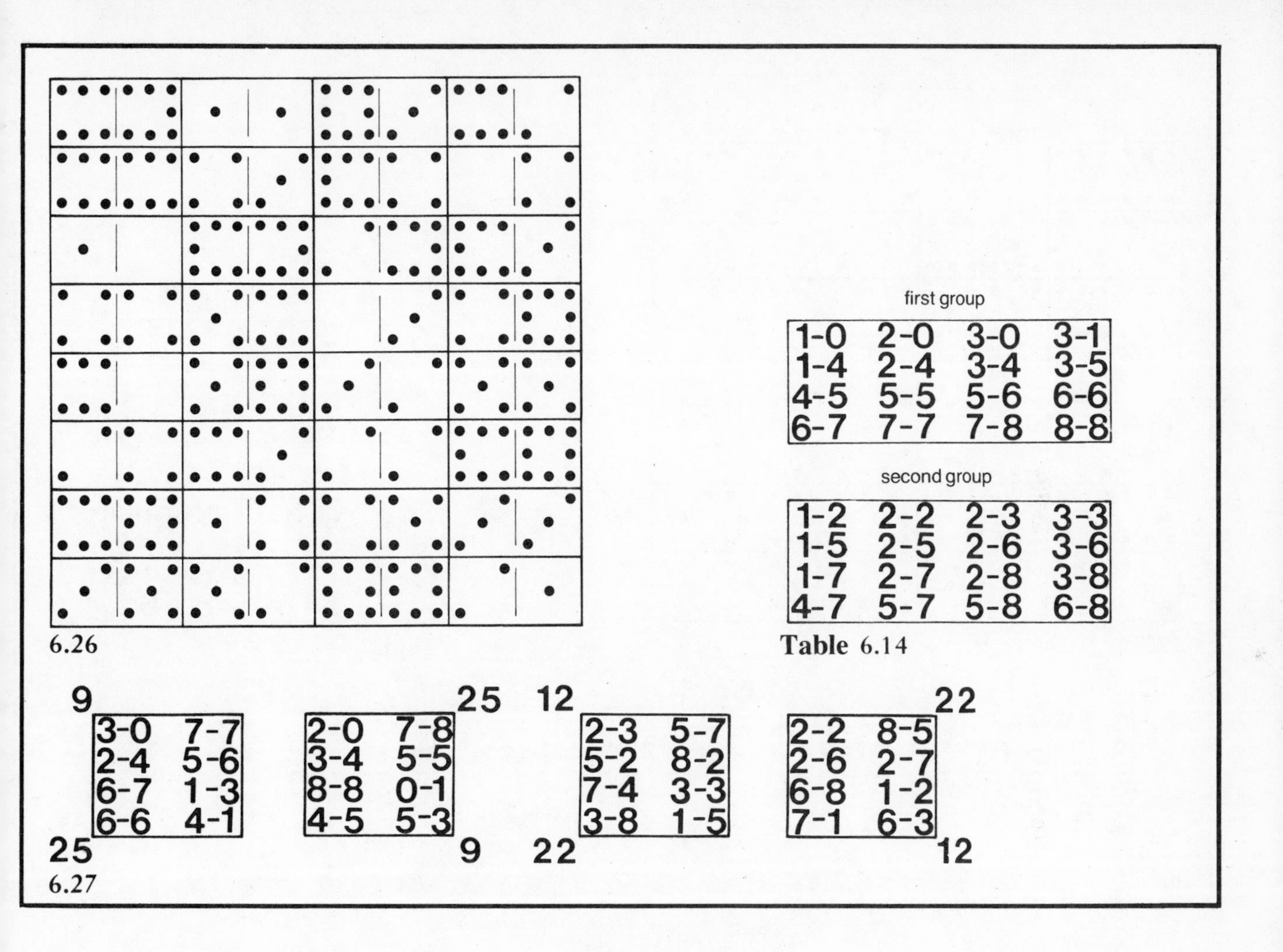

6.26

first group

1-0	2-0	3-0	3-1
1-4	2-4	3-4	3-5
4-5	5-5	5-6	6-6
6-7	7-7	7-8	8-8

second group

1-2	2-2	2-3	3-3
1-5	2-5	2-6	3-6
1-7	2-7	2-8	3-8
4-7	5-7	5-8	6-8

Table 6.14

9
3-0 7-7
2-4 5-6
6-7 1-3
6-6 4-1
25
25
2-0 7-8
3-4 5-5
8-8 0-1
4-5 5-3
9
12
2-3 5-7
5-2 8-2
7-4 3-3
3-8 1-5
22
22
2-2 8-5
2-6 2-7
6-8 1-2
7-1 6-3
12

6.27

And since the twice two squares can be formed in two ways while retaining the orientation of their stones, the total number of non-equivalent magic squares that can be built from the top rectangle is no less than $2 \times 2^7 \times 2^7 = 2^{15} = 32{,}768$.

In both rectangles the two inside rows can be exchanged (or the two outside, which amounts to the same thing). The half rectangles remain semi-magic, but the sum of the dots on the diagonals becomes in the first case 16 + 18 and in the second case for the one half 15 + 19 and for the other 13 + 21. The number of magic squares that can be formed from the rectangle thus modified is $2^{14} = 16{,}384$, bringing the total to almost 50,000!

Even this large number does not exhaust all possibilities. It must be doubled again. The halves of the modified first rectangle can always be combined with the halves of the unmodified second and the halves of the unmodified first with that of the modified second. This brings the total to 98,304 magic squares, all of them capable of being laid out with thirty-two stones, grouped in a certain way in two rectangles with no other tricks than the usual exchanging of rows and columns, reversing, and turning (example 2.68).

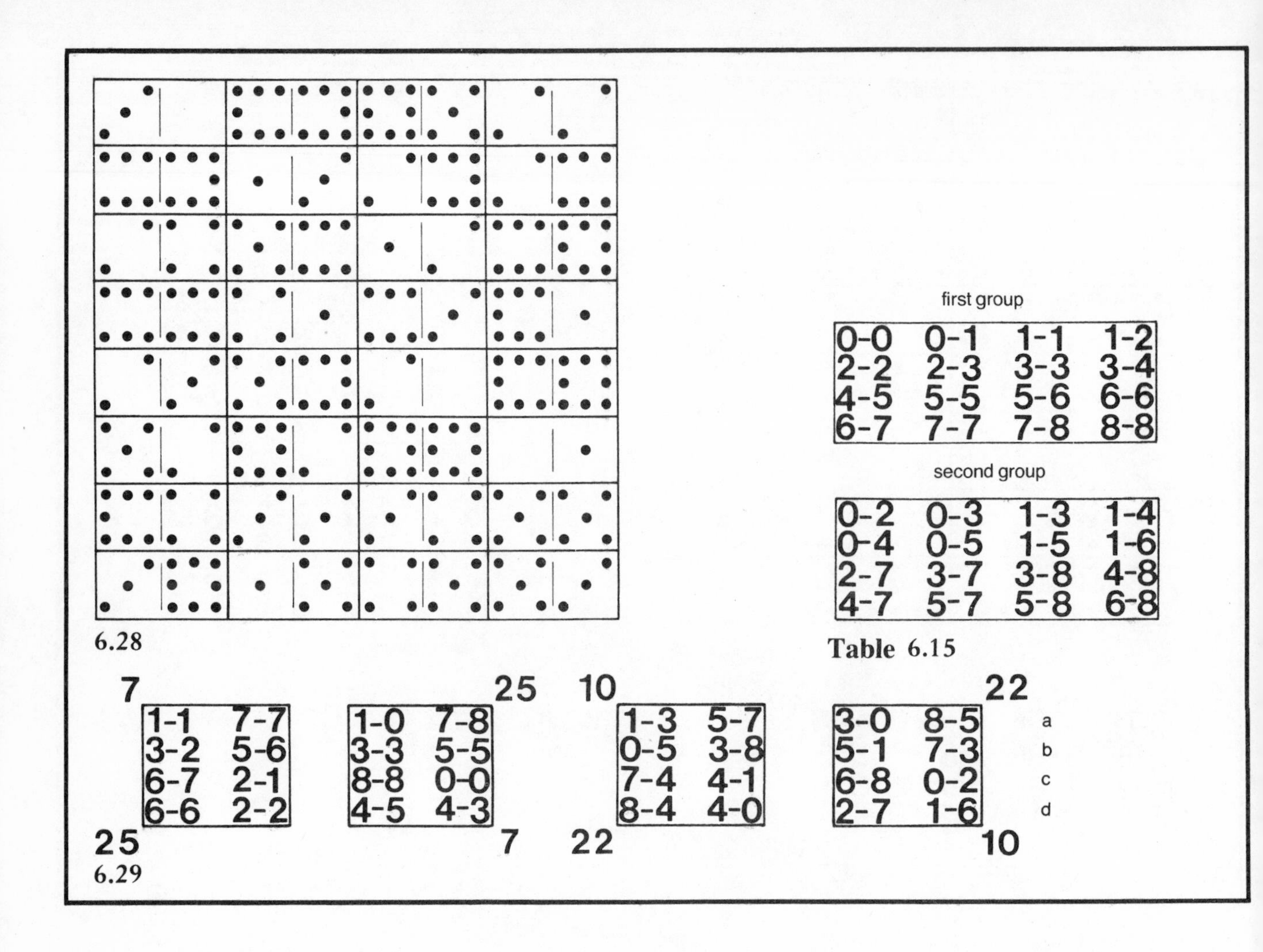

7
25
1-1 7-7
3-2 5-6
6-7 2-1
6-6 2-2
1-0 7-8
3-3 5-5
8-8 0-0
4-5 4-3
7
10
22
1-3 5-7
0-5 3-8
7-4 4-1
8-4 4-0
22
10
3-0 8-5
5-1 7-3
6-8 0-2
2-7 1-6
a
b
c
d

6.28

6.29

first group

0-0	0-1	1-1	1-2
2-2	2-3	3-3	3-4
4-5	5-5	5-6	6-6
6-7	7-7	7-8	8-8

second group

0-2	0-3	1-3	1-4
0-4	0-5	1-5	1-6
2-7	3-7	3-8	4-8
4-7	5-7	5-8	6-8

Table 6.15

This large number can be surpassed by the total number of magic squares that can be laid out in the given way from the following selection of stones:
Place to one side the stones:
0–6, 0–7, 0–8, 1–7, 1–8, and 2–8;
2–4, 2–5, 2–6, 3–5, 3–6, and 4–6;
in addition to the 4–4.

The remaining thirty-two stones are divided into two groups (table 6.15). After exchanging the left and right half of the two top rows, two pairs of semi-magic squares develop (example 6.29).
In each semi-magic square the sum of the dots on the rows and the columns is 16. Squares of the eighth order made from these squares will have 32 as the magic sum.

We consider first the squares of the first group. In both double columns of a square there are two squares which on their ends have dots differing only by one. If these two stones are both turned a half turn, the columns will keep the same number of spots. There are four possibilities:

A. as shown in example 6.29;
B. the stones are turned in both the left and the right columns;
C. the stones are turned only in the left columns;
D. the stones are turned only in the right columns.

There are a number of permutations of the rows possible whereby the semi-magic character of the left and the right squares is maintained. In general, the number of spots on the diagonals of a square will change, but their total must remain 32. The number of permutations is greater for C and D than for A and B. The semi-magic characteristics always remain if the left and the right double columns are exchanged. Through turning the stones this exchange loses meaning as it yields only equivalent squares.

In the squares of the second group no stones can be turned; nevertheless, many permutations of the rows are possible, as is the exchanging of the double columns, which in this group do not yield an equivalent form.

In table 6.16 the permutations of the rows reading from top to bottom are shown by letters; the exchanging of the columns are shown from left to right by numbers. In the squares of example 6.29 the sequence of the rows is abcd and of the columns 1–2.

For both groups the table contains the diagrams of the nonequivalent squares that can be made by the exchanges described above, divided according to the number of dots on their diagonals. The table also indicates the number of ways, including their equivalent figures, two suitable squares can be placed in opposite squares of the magic square. There are, moreover, three cases in which the same number of eyes appears on the diagonals of squares from both the first and the second group. In such cases, squares of a group can form a rectangle against which a rectangle comprised of squares of the other group has been placed to complete the magic square. The table shows the number of ways similar rectangles can be formed in which two figures must be divided along the parallel diagonals that have the same number of dots intersecting.

The rectangles can be placed horizontally in the magic square. The squares then lie next to each other. However, vertical placing is also possible by which the squares then lie one above the other. Because of the previously discussed orientation of the stones, these placements do not have the same value.

Sum of the diagonals	first group											second group						
	left square				right square				number of placements			left sq.		right sq.		number of placements		
—	A 1-2	B 1-2	C 1-2	D 1-2	A 1-2	B 1-2	C 1-2	D 1-2	in opposite sqs.	in adjacent sqs.		1-2	2-1	1-2	2-1	in opposite sqs.	in adjacent sqs.	
26 - 6	—	—	b a d c	a b c d	—	—	b a d c	a b c d	2^5	—	—	—	—	—	—	—	—	—
25 - 7	a b c d b a d c	a b c d b a d c	b a c d a b d c	b a c d a b d c	a b c d b a d c	a b c d b a d c	b a c d a b d c	b a c d a b d c	2^9	2^9	2^9	b a c d	a b d c	a b d c	b a c d	2^5	2^5	2^5
24 - 8	—	—	a b c d	b a d c	—	—	a b c d	b a d c	2^5	2^5	2^5	b a d c a c b d	a b c d b d a c	b a d c a c b d	a b c d b d a c	2^7	2^7	2^7
22 - 10	—	—	—	—	—	—	—	—	—	—	—	a b c d b d a c	b a d c a c b d	a b c d b d a c	b a d c a c b d	2^7	—	—
21 - 11	—	—	—	—	—	—	—	—	—	—	—	a b d c	b a c d	b a c d c b a d	a b d c a d c b	2^6	—	—
19 - 13	—	—	—	—	—	—	—	—	—	—	—	c a b d	a c d b	c a b d a d b c a d c b	a c d b b c a d c b a d	3.2^5	—	—
18 - 14	—	—	a c b d	b d a c	—	—	a c b d	b d a c	2^5	—	—	—	—	—	—	—	—	—
17 - 15	a c b d b d a c	a c b d b d a c	a c d b c a b d b c a d a d c b	a c d b c a b d a d b c c b a d	a c b d b d a c	a c b d b d a c	a c d b c a b d	a c d b c a b d	3.2^8	3.2^8	3.2^8	a c d b a d c b c b a d	c a b d a d c b c b a d	a c d b	c a b d	3.2^5	3.2^5	3.2^5
16 - 16*	—	—	b d a c	a c b d	—	—	b d a c	a c b d	2^6	—	—	—	—	—	—	—	—	—
								total	45.2^5						total	17.2^5		

*These squares are magic

Table 6.16

By taking all these factors into consideration, the number of non-equivalent magic squares that can be formed from the selected stones can be discovered.
The number formed by placing the squares of one group

in opposite quadrants:	$2 \times 17 \times 45 \times 2^5 =$	1,566,720
in adjacent quadrants:	$2 \times 2 (2^{14} + 2^{12} + 9 \times 2^{13}) =$	376,832
		1,943,552

or almost 2,000,000.

11. Completely Magic and Compound Magic Squares of the Eighth Order

Are there, among the abundance of magic squares of the eighth order, hidden ones which are also completely magic? This is indeed the case, and it is relatively easy to discover them.
In every magic square that is formed in the manner discussed above, the sum appears not only on the main diagonal but also on the broken diagonals that consist of 4 + 4 cells. This follows directly from the characteristic of the component squares that the total sum of dots on their diagonals is the same as the magic sum.

In each of these squares imagine a diamond drawn that, as discussed on page 92, once again has definite characteristics. The number of eyes on the four sides of the diamond equal the magic sum; there are two pairs of sides on which half the sum appears. If rectangles which go together are placed in opposite quadrants of the magic square, it is possible by correct use of their equivalent forms in some cases to form a configuration such as is shown in example 6.30. In this configuration, all broken diagonals that have 2 + 6 cells total the magic sum.

Care must be taken that the broken diagonals, consisting of 3 + 5 and 1 + 7 cells, also total the magic sum. It is sufficient for one of these two cases to achieve this; we choose therefore the diagonal with 1 and 7 cells.

Two squares belonging to the same group are placed in opposite quadrants with due regard to the requirements for the formation of the diagonals of 2 + 6 cells.

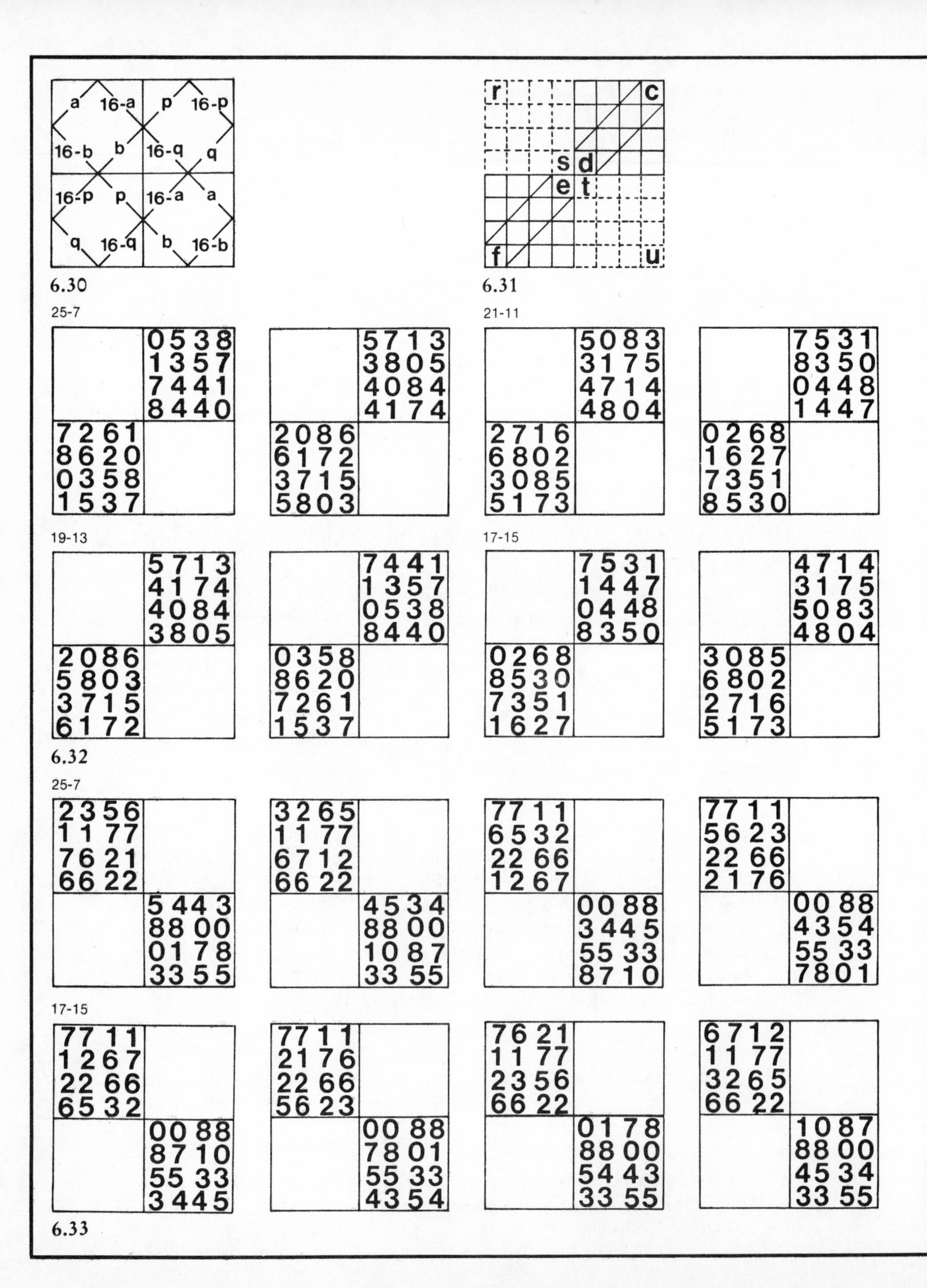

6.30

6.31

6.32

6.33

As the figure (example 6.31) shows, the values of $r + t$ and $s + u$, which are necessary in order to complete the number of dots on the two diagonals of 1 + 7 cells, then develop. These values must be found by the correct choice of two squares of the other group that on opposite corners have r and s and t and u dots.

These squares must at the same time be such that they both have the magic sum on the two crossing diagonals of 1 + 7 cells as shown above and fit in the scheme of the diagonals that consist of 2 + 6 cells.

We examine the square that has 32 as a magic sum and is composed of squares that have an uneven number of dots on their diagonals. From the second groups of these squares eight suitable combinations may be written in the desired manner in opposite squares in two directions, namely on an upward slanting or downward slanting diagonal. This last makes no real difference as the diagonals belong to magic squares formed by exchanging the left and the right halves with each other. We hold for the squares of the second group placement on the upward diagonal (example 6.32).

All these combinations yield that $r + t = s + u = 7$. The value of $c + e = d + f = 9$. Eight combinations from the first group are hereby in agreement if they are written in the direction of the downward slanting diagonal (example 6.33).

Sixty-four completely magic squares are formed by joining, one of which is shown (example 6.34).

The number of squares is doubled by exchanging a pair of opposite squares—it is unimportant which—and doubled again by the exchanging of the left and the right halves as of the top and the bottom part, making a multiple of eight. Moreover, two opposite squares can be turned 90 degrees at the same time; this can be applied to one group, to the other group, or for both. From this it follows that the number of completely magic squares that can be formed from the combinations is $64 \times 8 \times 4 =$ 2,048.

Further examination does not lead to other combinations that form completely magic squares. Within the approximately one-and-one-half million magic squares in which the component squares are placed diagonally the proportion of completely magic is 1 to 765. This does not include completely magic squares formed from others by rotation of rows and columns. The placement of the stones entails that the columns can be changed only by two at the same time. Moreover, the changing of the rows and columns in so far as this entire square is concerned is already accounted for. The total number of completely magic squares that can be arranged in the previous formation from the chosen stones is therefore $4 \times 2 \times 2{,}048 = 16{,}384$.

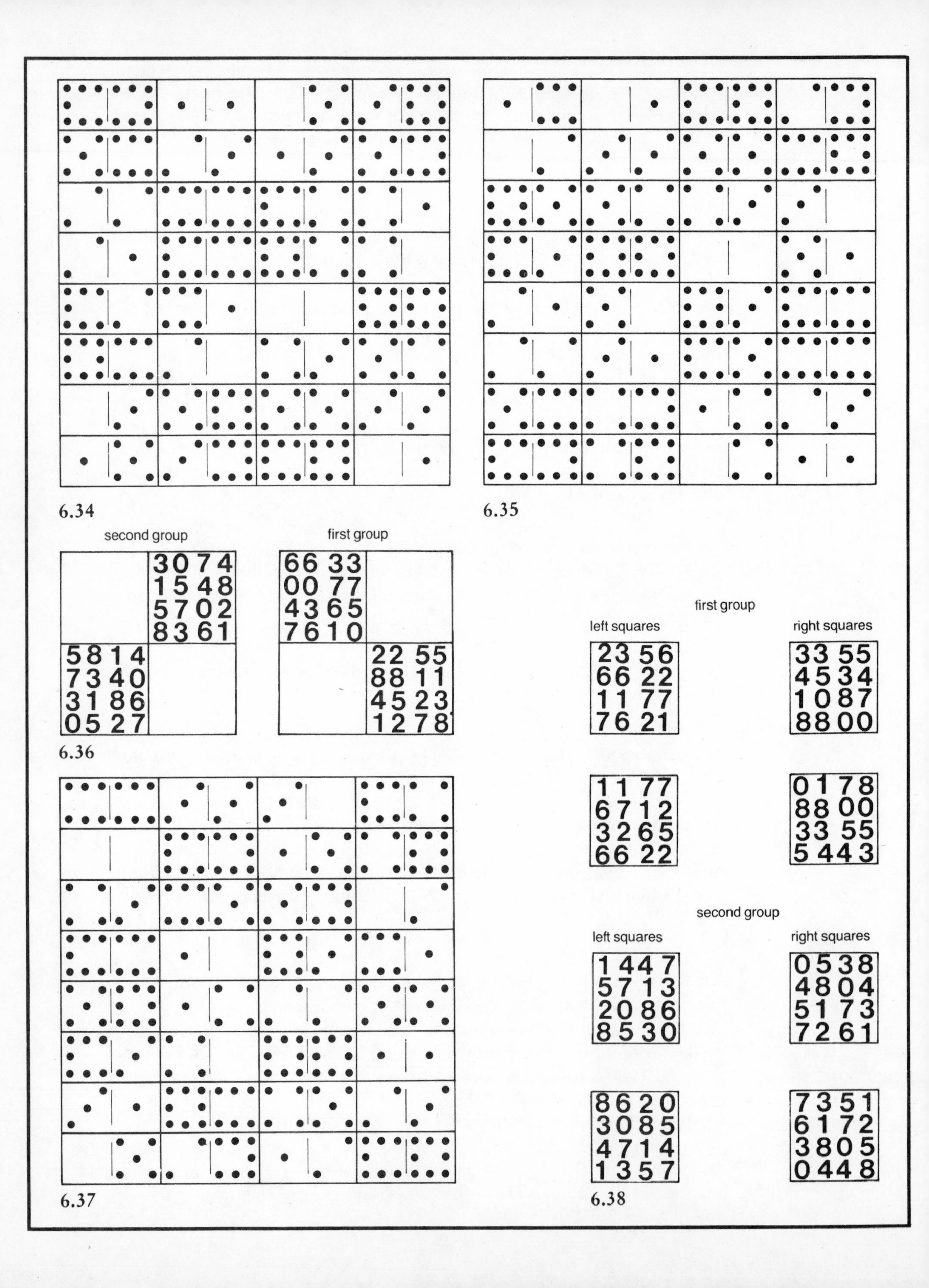

6.34

6.35

6.36

6.37

6.38

In table 6.16 the squares with the possibility of formation into completely magic squares are underlined; squares belonging together have the same type of underlining.

The squares are very regularly divided on the table and fall into no more than four permutations of their rows. In a magic square that has undergone any of the above-mentioned transformations, however, there is little to discover from this regularity. Occasionally a new regularity appears as in example 6.35 in which all diagonals of the squares have sixteen dots. On the other hand, the rows here are no longer magic.

Despite their large number, the magic squares discussed above are still not all that can be formed from the chosen thirty-two stones.
We have the half of the bottom row in the addition table exchanged in order to arrive at semi-magic squares that are easy to handle and offer many convenient possibilities. From the unaltered addition table there are also squares in which the rows alternated totals of 14 and 18 and the columns 15 and 17. From this, magic and even completely magic squares can be formed such as in the example shown (example 6.36).
These combinations yield: $c + e = d + f = r + t = s + u = 8$.
We will leave it at one example (example 6.37) because a complete working out would still not bring us to the end. Both groups of chosen stones can still be placed in two other addition tables (according to example 6.11 on page 93), thereby opening up a new range of possibilities.

Finally, we shall speak briefly of still another type of magic square that can be arranged with the chosen stones. Once two rows are exchanged in the semi-magic squares of the second group shown in example 6.29 they are formed into two magic squares on which the sum of the eyes of all the rows, all the columns, and the diagonals is 16. By rotation of two rows and two columns at the same time a second set of squares develops that is also magic.
Four magic squares of the first group are also discovered (see table 6.16).
Since two squares can be placed next to or across from each other in three ways, $3 \times 2 \times 2^6 \times 2^6 = 3 \times 2^{13}$ magic squares of the eighth order can be built from adjacent squares (example 6.38).

All these squares are *compound magic* because the squares that form them are themselves also magic.
Further examination shows that the left and right squares of the first group have by twos the same sums on the half columns. Left squares of the two groups have the same sums on the half rows in the same way. In the first case a double row and in the second case a double column can be exchanged. From this develops two new squares. This brings the total of compound magic squares to $3^2 \times 2^{13} = 73{,}728$.

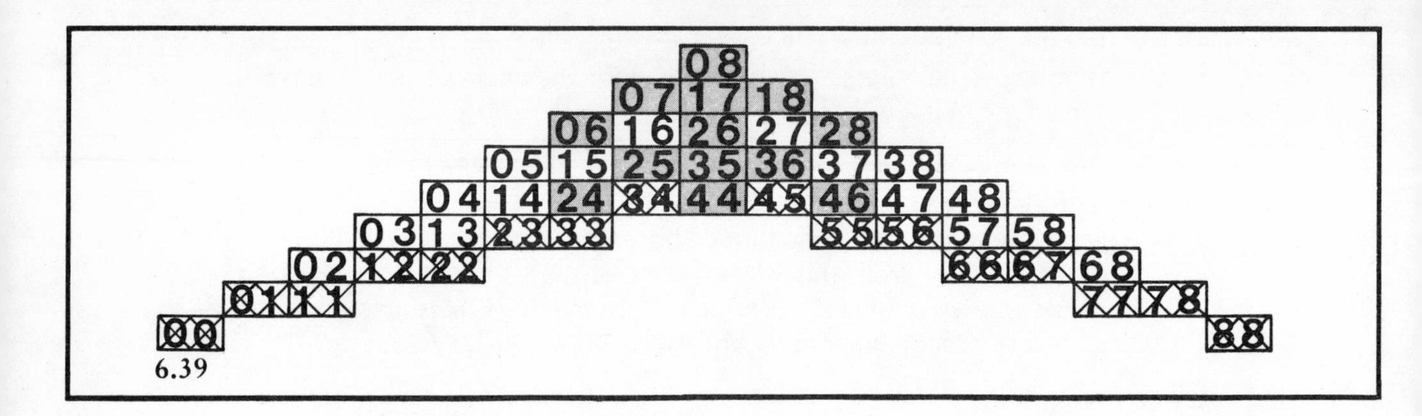

6.39

The last choice from the game seems to be a fortunate one. It is interesting to see how the chosen and discarded stones are divided over the set. To see this, a pyramid of complementary stones is arranged as discussed on page 6 (example 6.39).

The result is surprising. The unused stones—shown with a darker tint—are the ones in the middle column (that have their complement on their own halves) and four pairs on both sides in perfect symmetry, like two halves of an apple.

The groups of the chosen stones lie in conspicuous places. The bottom stones of the columns—arched—form the first group; the remaining the second.

VII Rectangles

1. The Rectangle of Seven by Eight

The problem is to arrange the twenty-eight stones of a domino game (n = 6) in a rectangle of seven by eight so that the four half stones with the same number of dots are in a row. All solutions must be given. Mirror images are counted as equivalents of one and the same solution.
These puzzles, discussed minutely by SCHUH, must be brought to a solution by a number of steps taken one after the other. In order to begin, we must divide the rectangle into fourteen smaller rectangles of one by four half stones.
This can be done in thirteen ways (that is 2n + 1) (example 7.1). In one of these, all the rectangles lie horizontally; in six cases four rectangles are vertical and ten horizontal; in still another six cases there are eight vertical and six horizontal rectangles. Further, the outlines of the twenty-eight stones must be drawn within the rectangle so that there are no duplicates and not more than seven doubles. Figure A does not succeed because in the left as well as the right half there are at least seven doubles. In figure B on the left, at least five, and on the right, seven doubles are necessary, so this figure is also unsatisfactory. Numbers C, D, E, F, H, I, K, and L must also be rejected for the same fault of too many doubles. There remain only three figures in which the stones can be shown without immediate objections. There are figures G, M, and N which must be more closely examined (example 7.2).

In the case of N, the outlines of the stones can be drawn in two ways in the diagram. If one fills in the number of dots of the doubles at will, as is done in the left example, then it appears that by further filling in one quickly runs aground. In the right diagram, the seven doubles cannot be filled in without using the duplicate stones. Case N, therefore, does not lead to a solution. Case G permits only one outline of the stones. Once the numbers of dots of the seven doubles are filled in at will it is established for three of the remaining seven rectangles which numbers must be filled in. This is especially true for f since the stones f−3, f−5, c−2, g−4 and g−6 require that f ≠ 2, ≠ 3, ≠ 4, ≠ 5, and ≠ 6. Thus f can only = 0 or 1. In a similar way we find that: g ≠ 3, ≠ 4, ≠ 5, and ≠ 6; c ≠ 0, ≠ 1, ≠ 2, ≠ 3, ≠ 5.
If f = 0, b ≠ 0, ≠ 1, ≠ 2, ≠ 3, ≠ 4, and ≠ 5, then b = 6; a ≠ 0, ≠ 2, ≠ 3, ≠ 4, ≠ 5, therefore a = 1.
There remain the possibilities c = 4 and g = 2, which exclude each other because of the stones c−2 and g−4.
If f = 1, g = 0 or 2. From g = 2 come the stones 2−6 and 2−4 by which no value for c remains. Therefore g = 0.
Since d = 0, = 1, = 3, = 4, and = 6, d = 2 or d = 5. This last is impossible, however, because the stone f–5 = 1–5 is impossible. Therefore d = 2.
The diagram can be completed from this point in three ways if we bear in mind that the stone 5 − 6 is already used (example 7.2).
In the case of M, the outline of the stones can be written in twelve

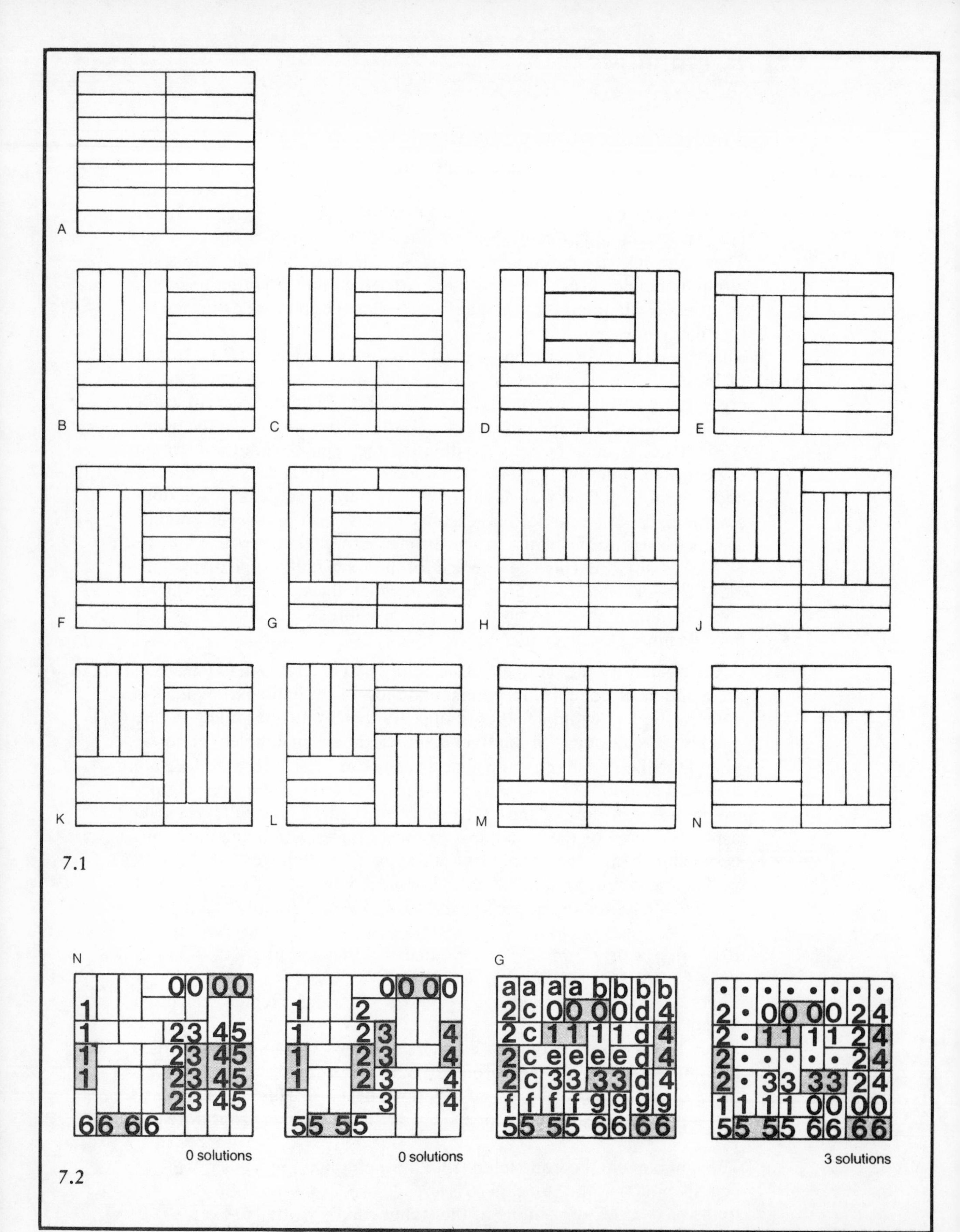
A
B
C
D
E
F
G
H
J
K
L
M
N
7.1

N
0 0 0 0
1
1 2 3 4 5
1 2 3 4 5
1 2 3 4 5
2 3 4 5
6 6 6 6
0 solutions
0 0 0 0
1 2
1 2 3 4
1 2 3 4
1 2 3 4
3 4
5 5 5 5
0 solutions
G
a a a a b b b b
2 c 0 0 0 0 d 4
2 c 1 1 1 1 d 4
2 c e e e e d 4
2 c 3 3 3 3 d 4
f f f f g g g g
5 5 5 5 6 6 6 6
2 0 0 0 0 2 4
2 1 1 1 1 2 4
2 2 4
2 3 3 3 3 2 4
1 1 1 1 0 0 0 0
5 5 5 5 6 6 6 6
3 solutions
7.2

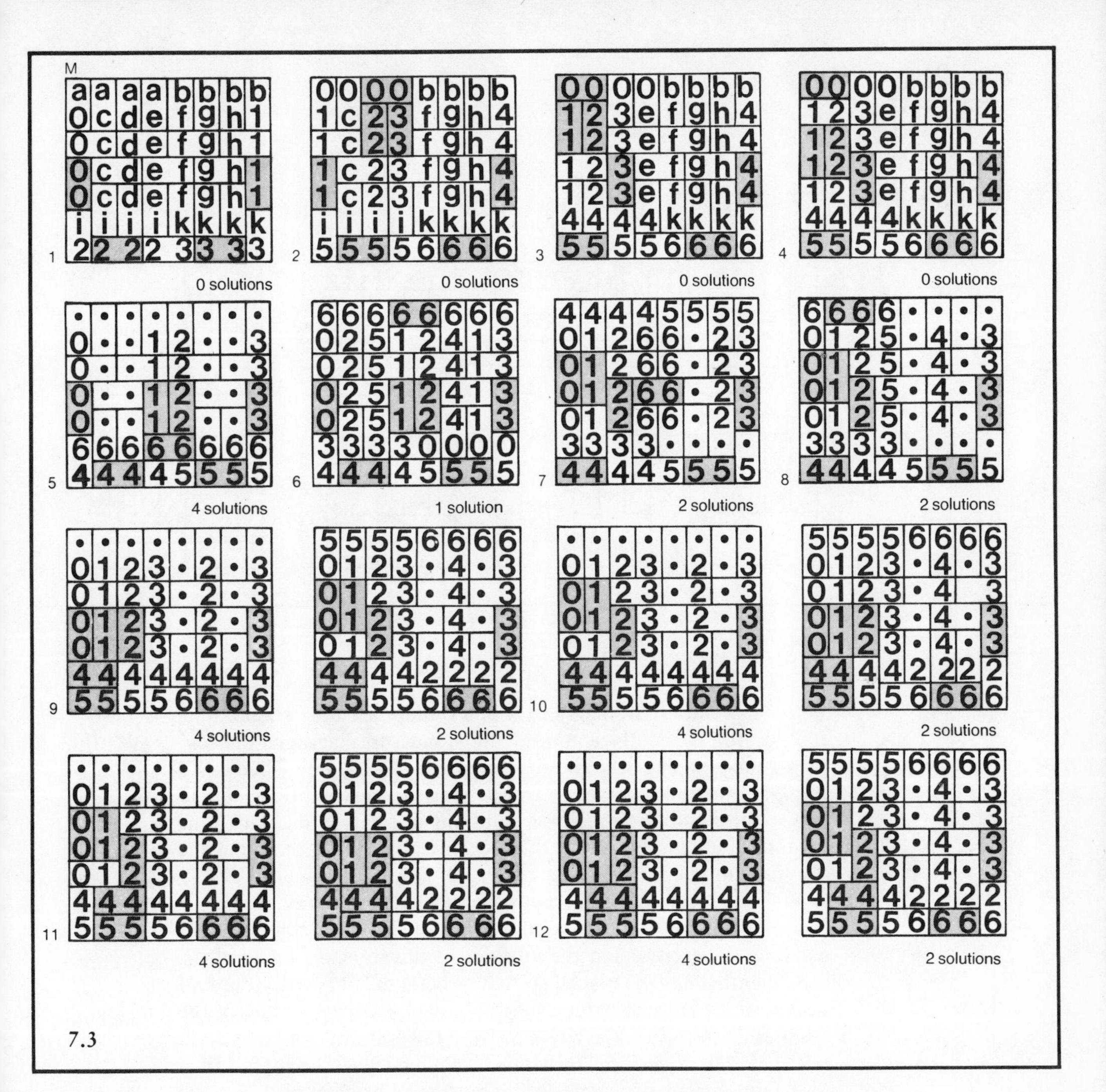

7.3

different ways in the rectangle (example 7.3). In the first (diagram 1), there will be only four doubles. The stone e − f can be a fifth double, but the last two doubles cannot be filled in without using duplicate stones. This diagram has no solution.

The second diagram of case M also has no solution. In this c can = 4 or = 6 only. If c = 4, then there remains no value for i; if c = 6, then i = 4 and the stone 6 − k must be the 6–3. This, however, is impossible due to the stones f − k and f − 3.

In diagrams 3 and 4 there is only one value for i possible, namely i = 4. Further filling in leads to a dead end, so these diagrams also

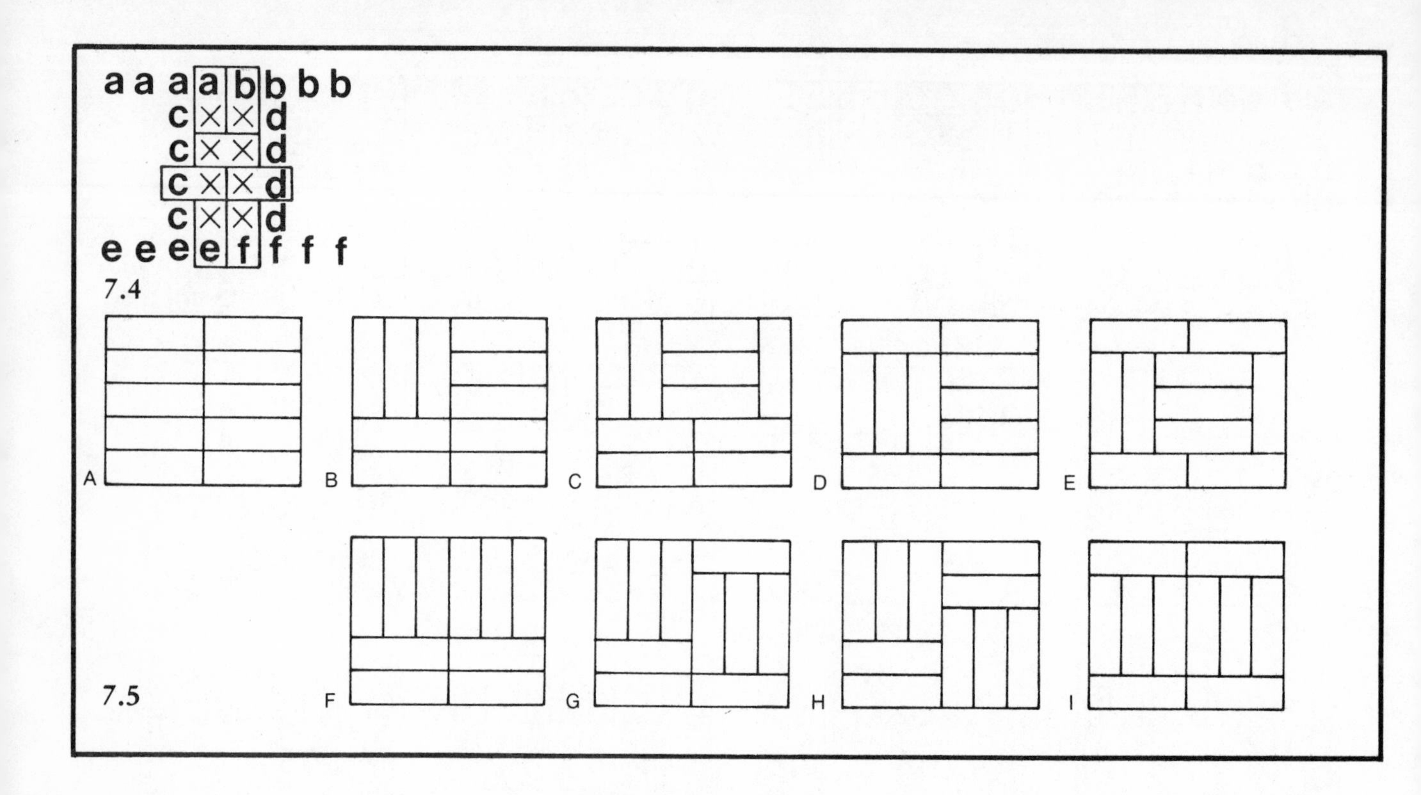

have no solutions. In diagrams 5 and 6 there are only six possible doubles due to the placement of the stones. In diagram 5 the seventh double is placed in the row one from the bottom. Then a = 4 and b = 5 or the reverse. Each of these two possibilities leads to two solutions—therefore, four solutions in total. In diagram 6 the seventh double is placed in the top row. It appears then that the row one up from the bottom can have only the numbers 3 and 0, whereby the rectangle can only be completed in one way.

Also in diagrams 7 and 8 the placement of the seven doubles does not follow directly from the outlines of the stones. In diagram 7, the seventh double is placed so that a rectangle of two by four half stones with the same number of dots develops. This yields for the number on the left in the row one from the bottom: i = 0, = 1, = 2, = 4, = 5, = 6, therefore i = 3. Thus it follows that a = 4 or 5. If a = 5, it follows that the stone to the bottom right must be 5–3 as no other 5 is more suitable; this value for a is out of the question. Therefore a = 4, b = 5, and h = 2. There are then two arrangements possible.

In diagram 8 i can only = 3, from which it follows that e = 5. This diagram also has two solutions. In both g = 4.

Diagrams 9, 10, 11, and 12 can be discussed together. The number 3 can be placed in only one way: e = 3. The numbers 2 and 4 can be filled in in two ways. In the first 0 and 1 as well as 5 and 6 can be filled in in two ways; this leads to four solutions. In the second way a = 5, and b = 6 and only 0 and 1 can be exchanged; this yields two solutions. In total, diagrams 9 to 12 each have six solutions.

The total number of different true solutions of the entire puzzle is 3 + 33 = 36. Among these are two in which a rectangle of two by four half stones develops with eight times the same number of dots, namely the two solutions of diagram 7. These solutions can be found by reasoning that the adjacent figure (or an equivalent thereof) is required, which can be classified only in case M (example 7.4).

2. The Rectangle of Five by Six

It is desired that the set with double four as the highest stone be used to form a rectangle of five by six half stones in which three half stones with the same number of dots are repeatedly placed in a row. Part of the rectangle must be comprised of two rectangles of two by three half stones in which the same number of dots appear six times. All solutions must be given. Mirrored figures are considered one solution.

This is a problem that must also be divided into a number of successive puzzles.
The first consists in the dividing of the rectangle into ten smaller rectangles of one by three. This can occur in nine ways (that is 2n + 1) as in example 7.5.
In one method all the rectangles lie horizontally, in four others there are three vertical and seven horizontal and in the last group of four only six vertical and four horizontal.
It must be determined then whether it is possible to draw the outlines of the fifteen stones in the figure without using identical stones or more than five doubles. Cases A and H are eliminated because they do not meet these conditions.
In the remaining cases, the stones can be filled in in one or more ways.

It is an endless task to track down all the ways to arrange these stones. There are certainly more than 140, and the number of solutions to which these lead is certainly a thousand. Hence it becomes necessary to limit the problem by requiring that the diagram of two rectangles of two by three have six total dot numbers the same. The requirement that the same rectangles must appear in the diagram is an insufficient limitation. The next step then must also be limited. The question is, how, from the stones x–x, x–a, x–b, x–c, and x–d, can a rectangle of two by three half stones with a total of x dots be formed. It must also be stated how the groups can join to the remaining part of the enclosed rectangle. We shall call such a rectangle of two by three with its junctions a constellation. The possible constellations are shown in one of their equivalent figures (example 7.6). The third step is to discover to what extent a constellation fits into one or more of the diagrams B to G and I. This examination can be done most easily by placing a piece of transparent paper over the constellations with drawings in the same scale successively of the diagrams B–G and I. If the constellation fits a diagram, its six rectangles and the six rectangles from the underlying diagram will be completely covered. By turning and inverting the transparent paper, all the equivalent figures can be examined.

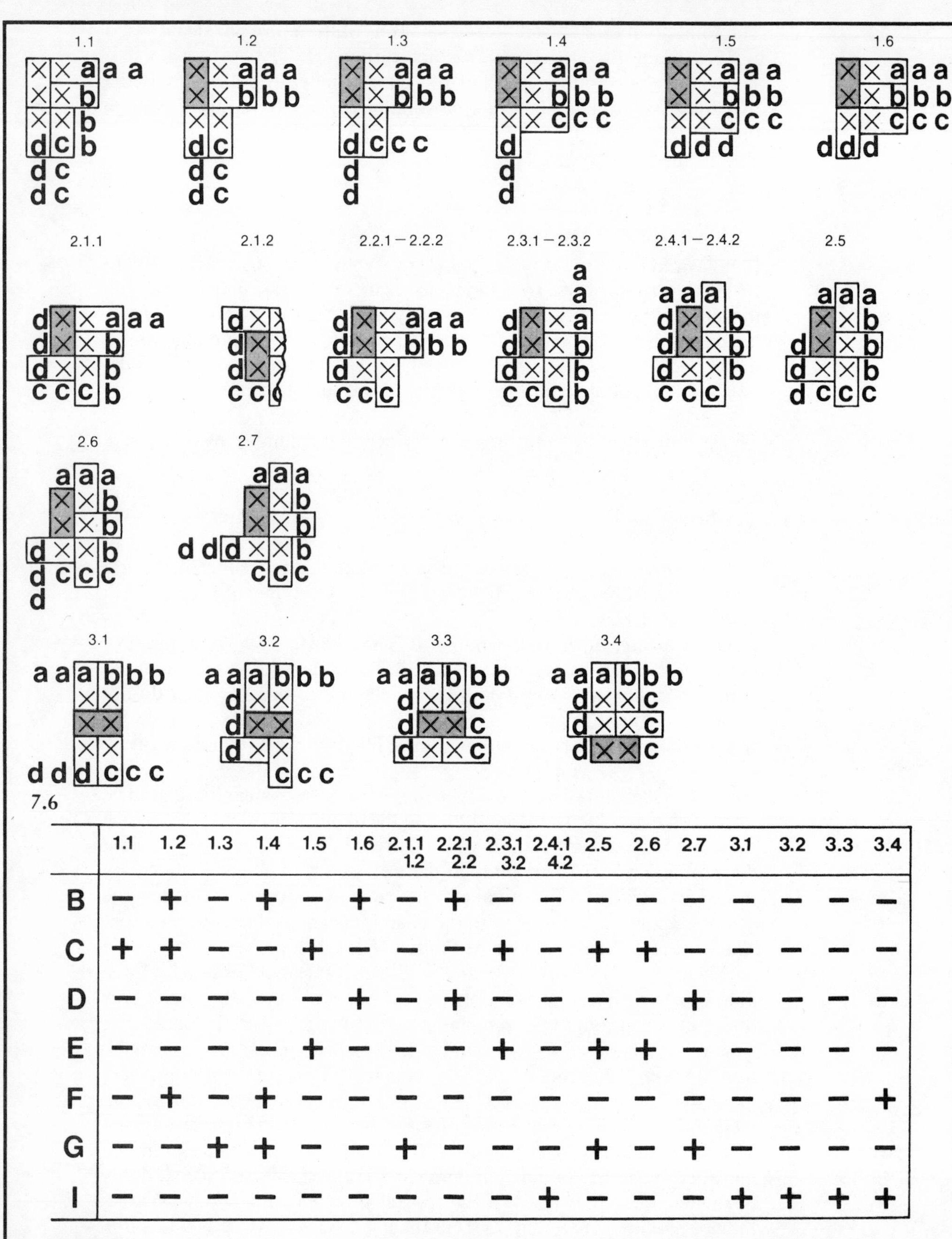

7.6

	1.1	1.2	1.3	1.4	1.5	1.6	2.1.1 1.2	2.2.1 2.2	2.3.1 3.2	2.4.1 4.2	2.5	2.6	2.7	3.1	3.2	3.3	3.4
B	–	+	–	+	–	+	–	+	–	–	–	–	–	–	–	–	–
C	+	+	–	–	+	–	–	–	+	–	+	+	–	–	–	–	–
D	–	–	–	–	–	+	–	+	–	–	–	–	+	–	–	–	–
E	–	–	–	–	+	–	–	–	+	–	+	+	–	–	–	–	–
F	–	+	–	+	–	–	–	–	–	–	–	–	–	–	–	–	+
G	–	–	+	+	–	–	+	–	–	–	+	–	+	–	–	–	–
I	–	–	–	–	–	–	–	–	–	+	–	–	–	+	+	+	+

Table 7.1

If agreement is found between the constellation and a part of the underlying diagram, it is not necessary in this third step to consider whether this agreement can be followed to a solution (with one rectangle of two by three).
The constellations can be divided into three groups. The first four of group 1 can only be arranged in the diagram so that double x is placed in a corner on a long side. 1.5 can also be so placed, with the exception of case H which has no solution. If the double of 1.5 is not already in a corner on the short side of the diagram it also offers possibilities.
Constellation 1.6 and the constellations of group 2 are arranged so that double x is placed in the interior of the diagram. The first four constellations of group 2 have a variation that, however, has no effect on the possibilities for arrangement of one or more of the cases B–G and I.
The third group can only be arranged so that double x is across the short axis of the diagram. This is possible only in I and for 3.4 in F. The result of the third step is shown in table 7.1.
In each of the cases B–G and I, the constellations can be classified in a number changing from three to six.

The next step, the fourth, is the most difficult. It must be determined if constellations that are possible in a certain case within the frame of the diagram can be combined mutually or with themselves. For this examination, further fruitful use can be made of drawings of the constellations on transparent paper. If two constellations fit within one diagram, the rectangles of two by three cannot overlap each other either entirely or in part. One or more rectangles of one by three may be completely covered. If this is the case, however, combining the two constellations is possible only when the placement of the individual stones in the covered parts also agrees. Constellations that are entirely separate should apparently be able to be combined, but this is not the case. The special placement of group 3 means that constellations belonging to that group can be joined neither with themselves nor with any others. This group will not be discussed further. The following combinations are possible:

case	*combinations*
B	1.2 + 1.5
C	1.1 + 2.4; 1.1 + 2.5 and 1.2 + 2.5
F	1.2 + 1.2 and 1.4 + 1.4
G	1.3 + 2.7; 1.4 + 2.5; 2.1.1 + 2.5 and 2.1.2 + 2.5
I	2.4 + 2.4

The final and decisive step is the testing of whether or not the above combinations can indeed be laid out.

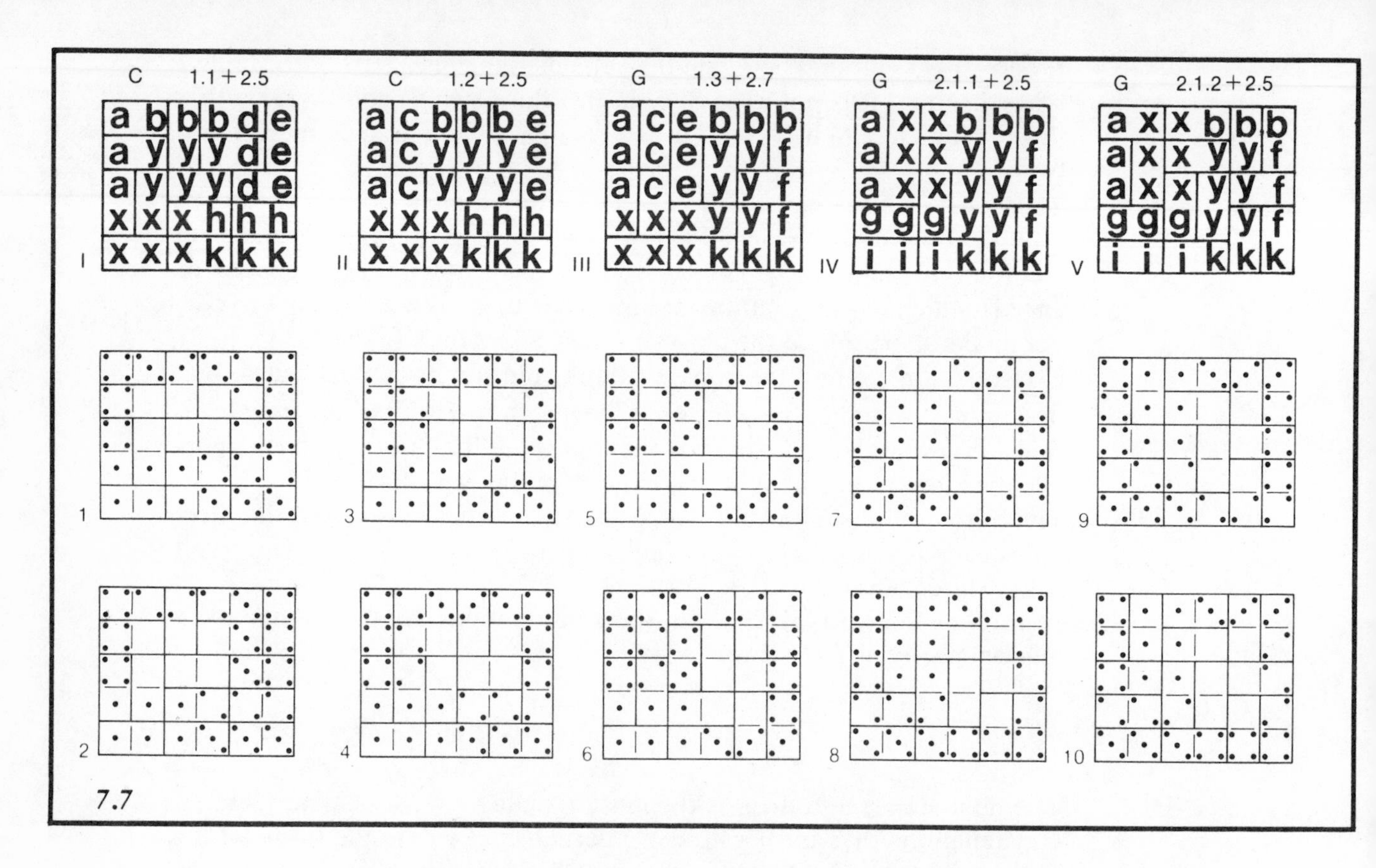

7.7

The combinations in the cases of B, F, and I do not lead to a solution because they require identical stones or too many doubles. This is also true of the combination 1.1 + 2.4 in case C. The combination 1.4 + 2.5 in case G fails because only four doubles appear.

Five combinations remain, two in case C and three in case G, each with two solutions, as shown (example 7.7).

In the set form the puzzle has ten solutions. By exchanging the dots a total of $10 \times 5! = 1{,}200$ solutions can be developed.

VIII Classifications (Arrangements)

1. Rectilinear Classifications

. . . ce problème fort difficile qui semblait rebelle à toutes les méthodes d'investigation.
Edouard Lucas, 'Récréations Mathématiques,' Volume IV

1. Introduction

The question of the number of ways in which the stones of a normal domino set can be placed one after the other according to the usual manner of play with the same number of dots joining kept many minds busy during the second half of the last century. In 1871 there appeared a discussion of this in fifty-eight quarto pages and LUCAS rightly made public his objections to such a long-winded method of work. He, however, had to admit the correctness of the conclusions after he confirmed these by a much simpler method.

For a domino set in which double four is the highest stone ($n = 4$), the problem is scarcely worthy of the name. It is solved by writing all possibilities symmetrically, as is done in table 8.1.
The game is simplified by at first putting the doubles aside.
For the formation of the table, there must first be chosen the number of dots with which it should begin. This choice is made from five possibilities. If this number remains the same, then the first stone is chosen from four, the second from three possibilities. The further working out of the table yields 44 series. The total number of classifications is $5 \times 4 \times 3 \times 44 = 2{,}640$.
In the complete table, every series appears in one and also the opposite direction. The found number therefore includes series which read from left to right as well as from right to left. Though the same, these are regarded as being different.
The doubles must now be added to the series. One double can be placed before as well as behind the chain and at the same time in one place in the chain. The other doubles can be placed in two places in the chain. The addition of the doubles means, therefore, that the found number must be multiplied by 3×2^4.
The total number of right classifications is therefore:

$$48 \times 2{,}640 = 126{,}720,$$

if classifications which have the same order from left to right as from right to left are counted as different.

LUCAS gave another method of solution. He starts from the game without doubles and further frames what he calls the "elementary" classification from which, by permutation of the elements 0, 1, 2, 3, and 4, all others can be arranged.

0	0−1	1−2	2−0	0−3	3−1	1−4	4−2	2−3	3−4	4−0
							4−3	3−2	2−4	4−0
					3−2	2−4	4−1	1−3	3−4	4−0
							4−3	3−1	1−4	4−0
					3−4	4−1	1−3	3−2	2−4	4−0
						4−2	2−3	3−1	1−4	4−0
				0−4	4−1	1−3	3−4	4−2	2−3	3−0
							3−2	2−4	4−3	3−0
					4−2	2−3	3−1	1−4	4−3	3−0
							3−4	4−1	1−3	3−0
					4−3	3−2	2−4	4−1	1−3	3−0
						3−1	1−4	4−2	2−3	3−0
			2−3	3−0	0−2	2−4	4−1	1−3	3−4	4−0
							4−3	3−1	1−4	4−0
					0−4	4−1	1−3	3−4	4−2	2−0
						4−3	3−1	1−4	4−2	2−0
				3−1	1−4	4−0	0−2	2−4	4−3	3−0
							0−3	3−4	4−2	2−0
						4−2	2−0	0−3	3−4	4−0
								0−4	4−3	3−0
						4−3	3−0	0−4	4−2	2−0
								0−2	2−4	4−0
				3−4	4−0	0−2	2−4	4−1	1−3	3−0
						0−3	3−1	1−4	4−2	2−0
					4−1	1−3	3−0	0−2	2−4	4−0
								0−4	4−2	2−0
					4−2	2−0	0−4	4−1	1−3	3−0
							0−3	3−1	1−4	4−0
			2−4	4−0	0−2	2−3	3−4	4−1	1−3	3−0
							3−1	1−4	4−3	3−0
					0−3	3−1	1−4	4−3	3−2	2−0
						3−4	4−1	1−3	3−2	2−0
				4−1	1−3	3−0	0−4	4−3	3−2	2−0
							0−2	2−3	3−4	4−0
						3−4	4−0	0−3	3−2	2−0
								0−2	2−3	3−0
						3−2	2−0	0−4	4−3	3−0
								0−3	3−4	4−0
				4−3	3−0	0−4	4−1	1−3	3−2	2−0
						0−2	2−3	3−1	1−4	4−0
					3−1	1−4	4−0	0−3	3−2	2−0
								0−2	2−3	3−0
					3−2	2−0	0−3	3−1	1−4	4−0
							0−4	4−1	1−3	3−0
		1−3								
		1−4								
	0−2									
	0−3									
	0−4									
1										
2										
3										
4										

Table 8.1

I	01 2 0 3 1 4 2 3 4	XII	01 2 3 1 4 0 3 4 2
II	01 2 0 3 1 4 3 2 4	XIII	01 2 3 1 4 2 0 3 4
III	01 2 0 3 2 4 1 3 4	XIV	01 2 3 1 4 2 0 4 3
IV	01 2 0 3 2 4 3 1 4	XV	01 2 3 1 4 3 0 2 4
V	01 2 0 3 4 1 3 2 4	XVI	01 2 3 1 4 3 0 4 2
VI	01 2 0 3 4 2 3 1 4	XVII	01 2 3 4 0 2 4 1 3
VII	01 2 3 0 2 4 1 3 4	XVIII	01 2 3 4 0 3 1 4 2
VIII	01 2 3 0 2 4 3 1 4	XIX	01 2 3 4 1 3 0 2 4
IX	01 2 3 0 4 1 3 4 2	XX	01 2 3 4 1 3 0 4 2
X	01 2 3 0 4 3 1 4 2	XXI	01 2 3 4 2 0 3 1 4
XI	01 2 3 1 4 0 2 4 3	XXII	01 2 3 4 2 0 4 1 3

Table 8.2

If one writes the number of dots of a right classification in the usual way from left to right, two joined pairs emerge from each number except for the first and the last. If each pair is shown by one number and the last number (which is the same as the first) is placed aside, then each classification is represented by a series of ten numbers. In such a series the numbers 0, 1, 2, 3, and 4 each appear twice. If the first and the last numbers of the series are also considered as neighbors, each number stands once and no more than once next to each of the remaining.
By agreement, we can call the first number 0, the second 1. The first stone then becomes 0–1. The following number is shown by 2. The first three numbers of an elementary classification then are always 0, 1, 2.
The fourth number can be either identical to the first or a new number represented by 3. Continuing in this way, twenty-two series are shown in table 8.2.

If one turns one of the sequences of numbers in one of the above lists and renumbers it in the arranged way, one naturally returns to one of the notations of the table. Two cases must, however, be excepted. In one case the renumbered notation is the same as the one which is replaced; LUCAS calls this a symmetrical solution. In the second case another notation develops; LUCAS calls such a solution asymmetrical.

There are six symmetrical notations, namely I, IV, XI, XVI, XX and XXII. The asymmetrical notations II, V, VI, IX, X, XII, XVII, and XVIII have respectively as opposites III, VII, VIII, XIII, XV, XIV, XXI, and XIX.

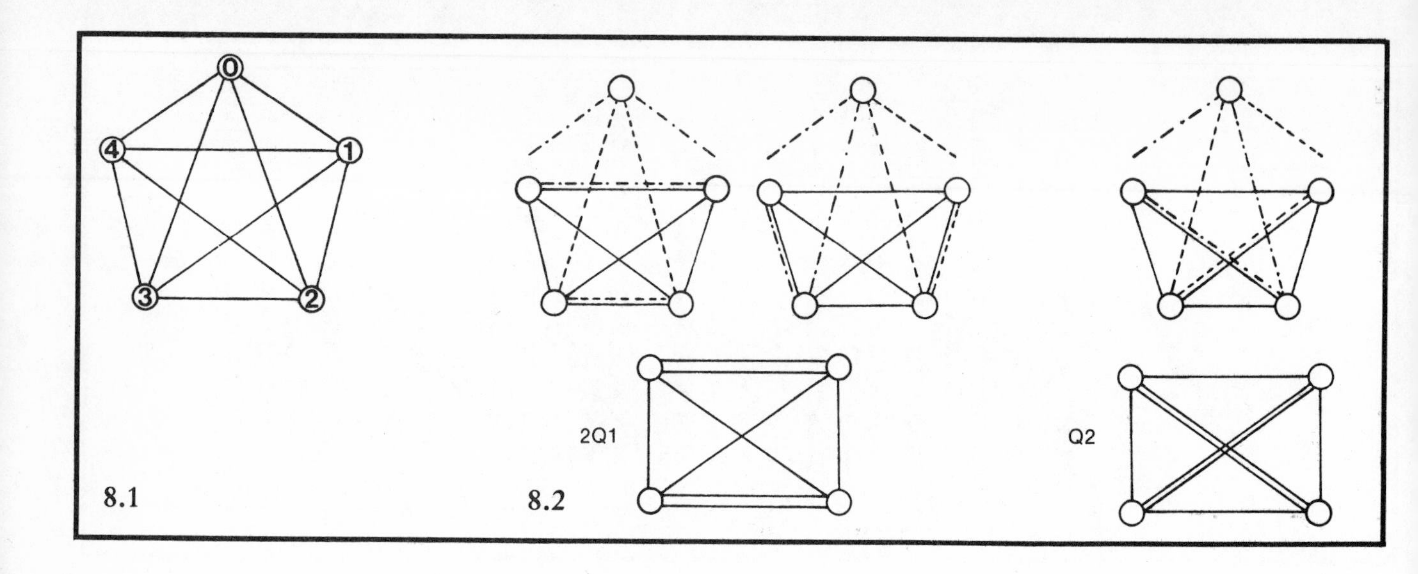

8.1 8.2

The number of permutations of five elements is $1 \times 2 \times 3 \times 4 \times 5 = 5! =$ 120. Each symmetrical notation has 120 different classifications—each asymmetrical and its opposite 240 different classifications. In total there are $[6 + (2 \times 8)]\ 120 = 2{,}640$ classifications.
The set with the doubles can be classified in $2{,}640 \times 48 = 126{,}720$ ways if, again, classifications in which stones in the same sequence from left to right as from right to left are considered as different.

1.2. General Method of Solution

One of LUCAS's correspondents, LAISANT, pointed out an elegant way of solving the problem. A domino game from which the doubles are removed can, if the highest number of dots is = 2n and therefore even, be represented by the lines joining the points of the corners of a polygon with 2n + 1 corners. For the sake of convenience a regular, at least symmetrical, polygon is chosen.
Such a figure is called a *network* and, because in each corner an even number of lines, 2n, meets, an *even network*. An even network can be gone through in a closed path; that is to say we can imagine that the point of a pencil, beginning at a corner, runs through all the lines of the network (all the connecting lines from corner to corner) once and not more than once and ends at the point of departure. The pencil may touch the same corner two or more times.
The set in which 2n = 4 is, without doubles, represented by the sides and the diagonals of a regular pentagon (example 8.1) whose corners are numbered 0, 1, 2, 3, and 4. The line that, for example, joins the corners 0 and 3, represents the stone 0–3, and so forth. The number of ways in which this set (without doubles) can be arranged in a closed ring is the same as the number of times that all the lines of the pentagon can be gone through in a closed path.
The problem is in this way brought back to the determination of the number of closed paths.

TARRY has found a splendid and simple solution. TARRY calls the lines of the network "roads" *(allées)* and uses the term "dead end" *(impasse)*, by which he means a line that returns to its own point of departure. Further, he says the following:

a. If a dead end is removed from a network, the number of closed paths of the thus reduced network multiplied by the number of roads that emerge from the corner belonging to the dead end is the same as the number of closed paths of the original network. The other dead ends that are joined to the same corner must be counted as two roads. Let N be the number of paths through which the reduced network can run and 2n the number of roads emerging at the corner point at which the dead end is placed, then the number of paths of the original network is the same as N × 2n. The proof of this theory is easy to see. Each of the paths, N, that are possible in the reduced network passes n times the corner of the dead end. In one of these passages—it doesn't matter which—the path can be interrupted in order to cross the dead end, which crossing is possible in two directions. After that the path continues in the normal way. From this it follows that each of the N paths of the reduced network yields 2n paths of the original.

b. If in the corner H of an even network without dead ends and having a total of k corners, 2n roads meet, these roads can in 1 × 3 × 5 × 7 × . . . . × (2n–1) ways be divided into n groups of two, or into n pairs. If, in such a division, each pair of roads is replaced by a new road between the two corners that are connected with H by these roads, then a new smaller network develops with (k–1) corners. In the exceptional case that both roads lead to the same corner, they are replaced by a dead end at the corner. If this is carried out for each division, then a total of 1 × 3 × 5 × 7 × . . . . × (2n–1) reduced networks develops.

It is again not difficult to see that the number of closed paths through which the original network can run is the same as the total of the closed paths in the 1 × 3 × 5 × 7 × . . . . × (2n–1) reduced network. A certain number of paths in the original network belongs to each of the above divisions, namely the paths in which, as corner H is passed repeatedly, the entering and leaving roads agree with one of the n groups of two roads forming the division. This number of paths doesn't change if such a pair of paths is replaced by a new connecting path or by a dead end. And it is clear that in all the divisions all paths of the original network are represented.

For instance, example 8.2 shows all the crossings of the pentagon in three four-cornered figures. The four roads that meet in the top corner can be combined into two pairs in 1 × 3 ways. The one pair is shown by a straight line, the other by a broken line. By the replacement of each

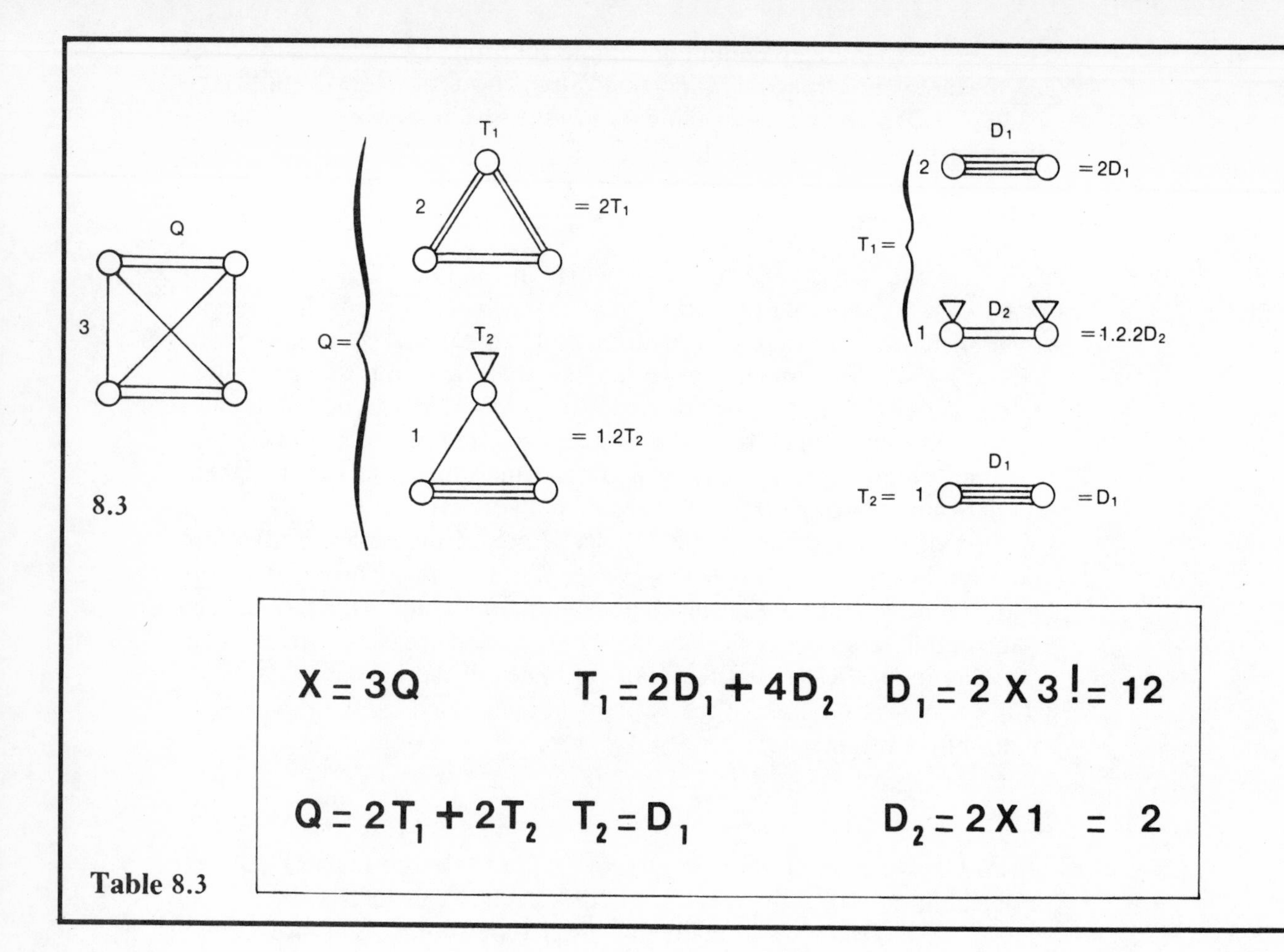

8.3

Table 8.3

pair with a new joining, two four-cornered figures Q1 with a double road along the two parallel sides and one four cornered figure Q2 with a double path along both diagonals develop.

The number of paths in the pentagon (X) is then the same as the sum of 2 $\times$ the number of paths in Q_1 and the number of paths in Q_2 or $X = 2Q_1 + Q_2$.

By continuing the reduction of the number of corners and thereby the removal of the dead ends one finally arrives at a number of parallel lines which run between the two last remaining corners. If 2n paths are between these points, then the number of paths in this simplified network is the same as 2x (2n–1)! if a distinction is made in the direction in which the lines run.

1.3. Application to the Set with n = 4

Example 8.3 shows further work with the pentagon from the set without doubles and n = 4 as the highest number of dots. The difference between Q_1 and Q_2 is disregarded because both forms have the same continuation. Two networks have the same number of paths if the corners of the one agree, taken one at a time, with the corners of the second network; that is, if the number of divisions of the roads that lead from a chosen corner is the same in both networks. This rule makes it possible to represent two different but in this respect agreeing figures by a single figure. In this way, the figures Q_1 and Q_2 can be shown by one figure Q because in both Q_1 and Q_2 four roads—two single roads and one double—extend from each corner.

In example 8.3 a dead end is shown by an isosceles triangle standing on one corner. Above each figure is a classification number. Similar figures are indicated by the same number. The number on the left of the figure is that which can be obtained by the reduction of the corners of the preceding figure. On the right of each figure (in the following example in a given case under it) is calculated the number of times the paths which can go through the figure after the removal of the dead ends must be taken into consideration. This number of paths is shown by the classification number.
These lead to table 8.3.

The total number of closed paths which run through the pentagon is $X = 3 \times 2\ (32 + 12) = 264$. This is therefore also the number of ways in which the game without doubles can be classified in a ring.

Each of the five doubles can be added in two places in this ring. In order to arrive at the rectilinear classification the complete game can be broken down into ring form by each of the fifteen stones. It follows that the number of rectilinear classifications is $15 \times 2^5 \times 264 = 126{,}720$, if a distinction is made according to the direction in which the stones are arranged.

1.4. Application to Larger Sets

For figuring the number of ways in which the normal domino game with double six as the highest stone can be classified rectilinearly, it is best to follow TARRY's method, as this is most manageable. Other methods are too unwieldy for this and larger sets.

The game without doubles is arranged along the sides and diagonals of a regular seven cornered figure. The working out is done in the following way (see example 8.4, which is borrowed from TARRY):

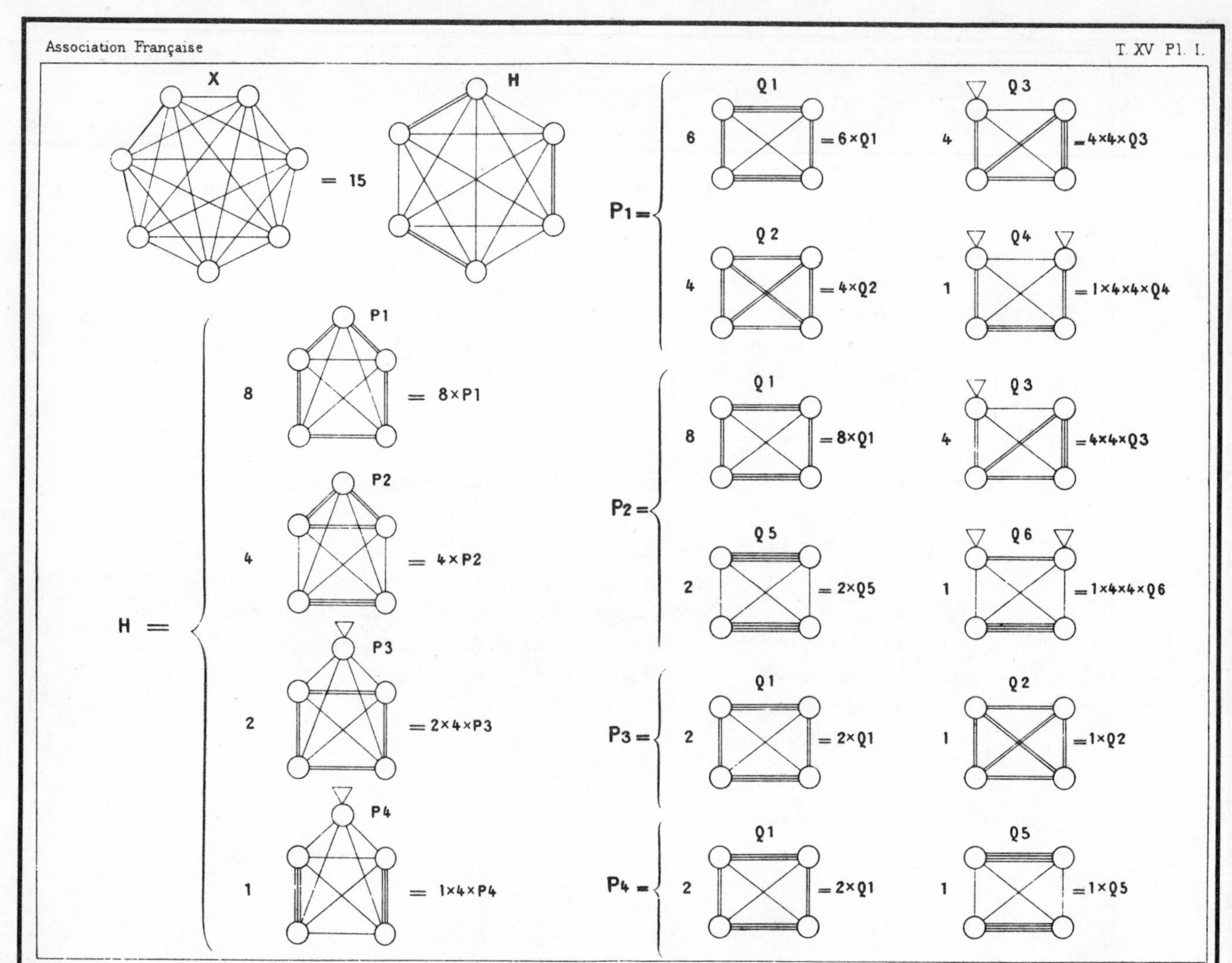

8.4

$X = 15\,H$
$H = 8\,P_1 + 4P_2 + 8P_3 + 4P_4$

$P_1 = 6Q_1 + 4Q_2 + 16Q_3 + 16Q_4$
$P^2 = 8Q_1 + 16Q_3 + 2Q_5 + 16Q_6$
$P_3 = 2Q_1q + Q_2$
$P_4 = 2Q_1 + Q_5$

$Q_1 = 6T_1 + 24T_2 + 48T_3$
$Q_2 = 8T_1 + 24T_2 + 64T_4$
$Q_3 = 2T_1 + 4T_2$
$Q_4 = 2T_2 + 4T_3$
$Q_5 = 48T_2 + 24T_5$
$Q_6 = 2T_2 + 2T_5$

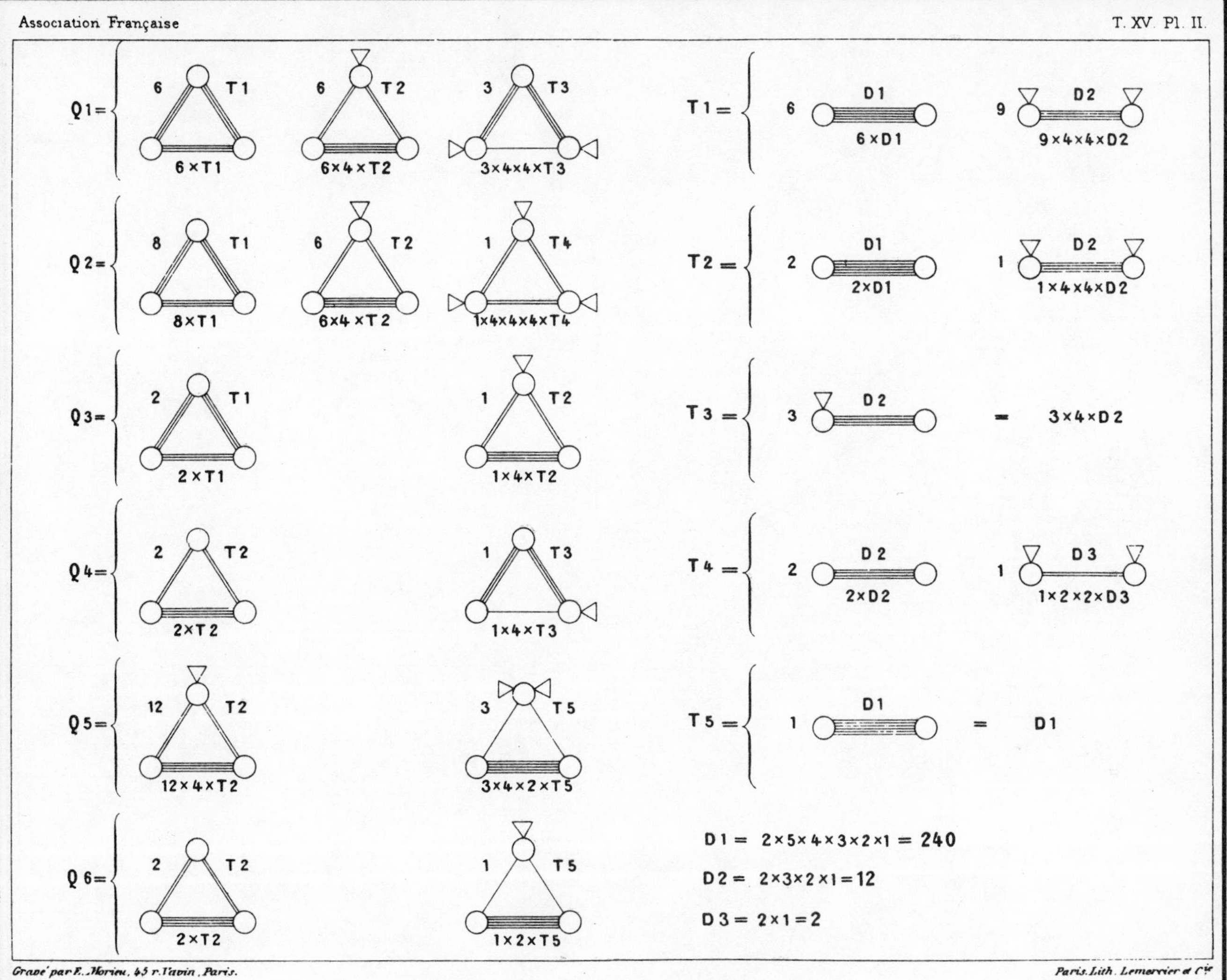

TARRY — PROBLÈME DES DOMINOS

8.4

$T_1 = 6D_1 + 144D_2$
$T_2 = 2D_1 + 16D_2$
$T_3 = 12D_2$
$T_4 = 2D_2 + 4D_3$
$T_5 = D_1$

$D_1 = 240$; $D_2 = 12$; $D_3 = 2$.

The number of classifications forming rings is:
129,976,320;
the number of rectilinear classifications of the complete game is 28×3^7 times as many, or:

7,959,229,931,520.

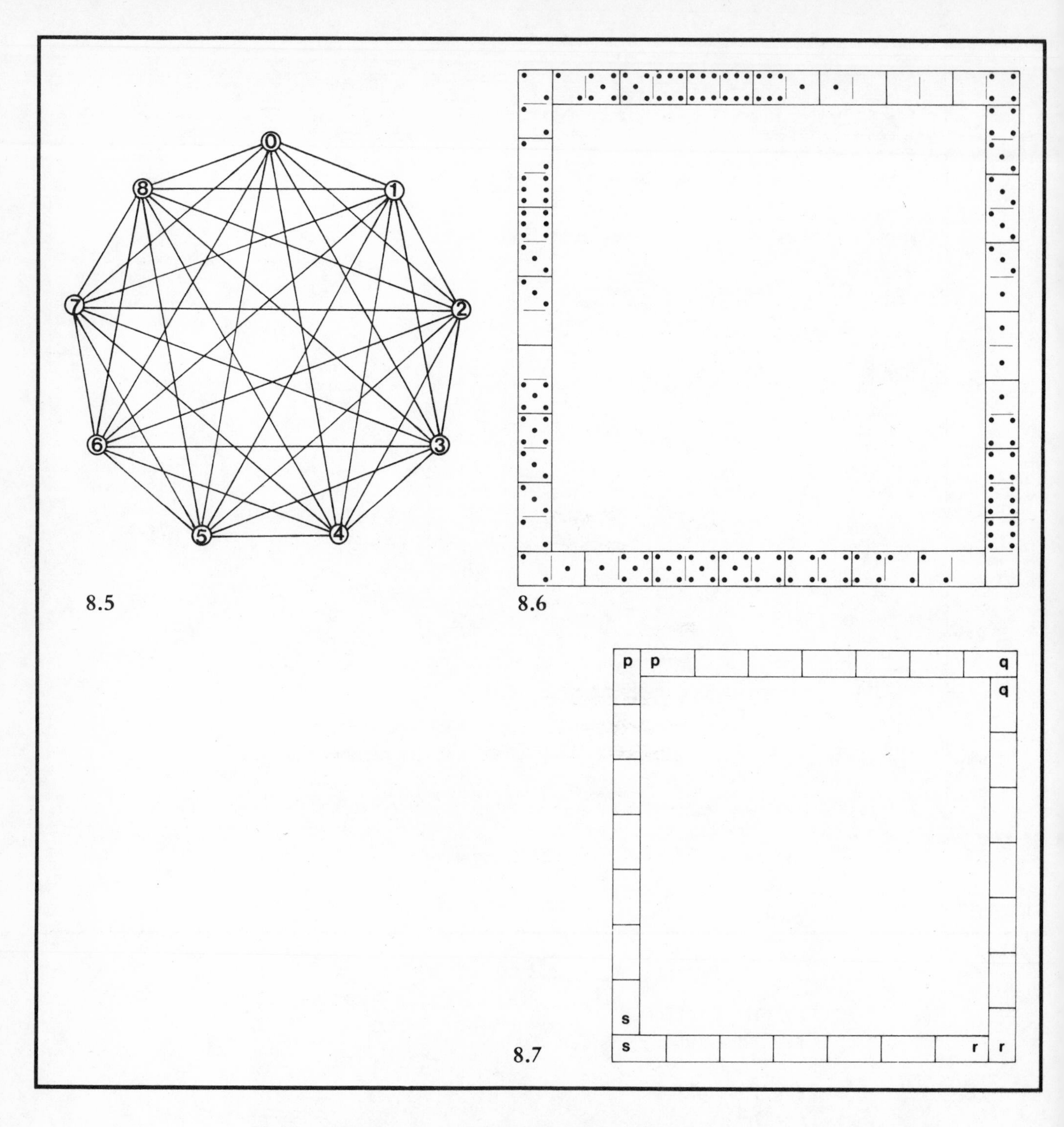

8.5

8.6

8.7

Using the same method TARRY has figured the number of closed paths in the regular nine cornered figure (example 8.5) to be:

911,529,057,021,235,200.

This number must be multiplied by 45×4^9 in order to get the number of rectilinear classifications of the game with double eight as the highest stone.

S	p+q+ +r+s	p	q	r	s	S	p+q+ +r+s	p	q	r	s
42	0	–	–	–	–	46	16	6	6	4	0
								6	6	0	4
43	4	–	–	–	–			6	4	6	0
								6	6	2	2
44	8	4	4	0	0			6	2	6	2
		4	0	4	0			6	4	4	2
		4	2	2	0			6	4	2	4
		4	2	0	2			4	6	2	4
		2	4	0	2						
						47	20	–	–	–	–
45	12	5	5	1	1						
		5	1	5	1	48	24	–	–	–	–
		5	3	3	1						
		5	3	1	3						
		3	5	1	3						

Table 8.4

2. Classification in a Square

DUDENEY gives the illustrated figure (example 8.6) in which the stones, arranged in the normal manner with 0 joined to 0, 1 to 1, and so forth, are formed into a square frame. This frame has the characteristic that the sum of the dots on each of the four sides is the same, namely forty-four.

The figure is only one of many solutions of the problem of arranging the stones in a square whose sides have the same number of dots. The solution permits a number of variations. On the left side of the row stones 2–2 and 3–2 can be exchanged as can stones 2–6 and 3–2 and 3–0 and 5–3. Similar exchanges are possible on the right and the bottom.

If the numbers of dots in the corner sections of the frame are shown with p, q, r, and s as in the schematic figure (example 8.7) and the sum of the dots of a side with S, then

$$4S = 168 + p + q + r + s,$$

from which it follows that $p + q + r + s$ is a multiple of four.

Furthermore, p, q, r, and s cannot all have the same value as then the double could only be placed in three corner sections.

If S is even, p, q, r, and s must also be even. If S is uneven, then p, q, r, and s are also uneven.

If there are solutions which, by turning, develop into one and the same solution, then the combinations of S, p, q, r, and s noted in table 8.4 are possible.

Each of these possibilities can be worked out to a large number of solutions. There is little reason to go over them.

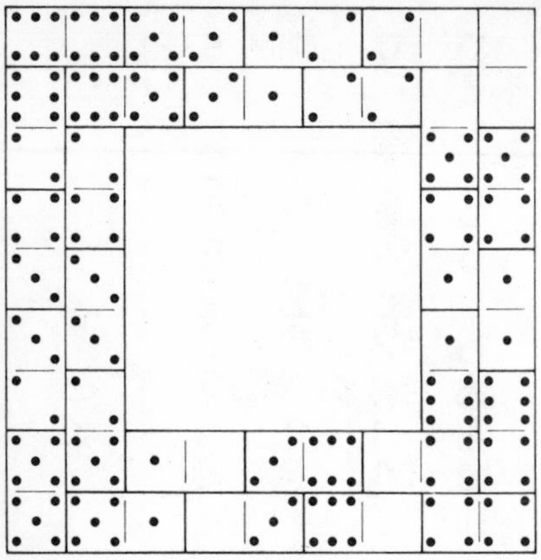

8.8

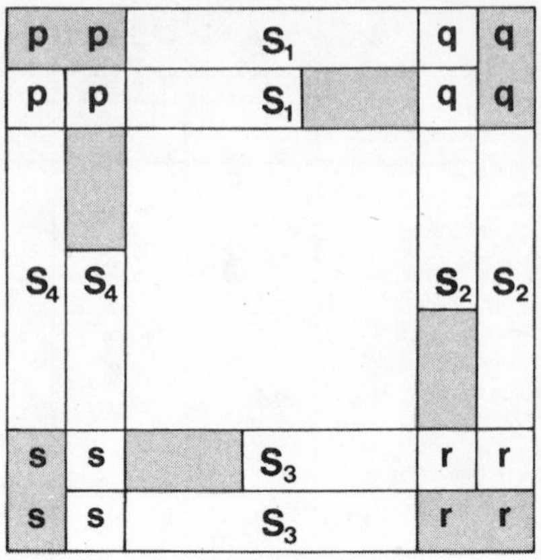

8.9

	p	S_1	q	S_2	r	S_3	s	S_4	p
a	0	2+3+5+6+6	1	0+3+4+5+6 0+3+5+5+5	2	0+1+4+4+5	3	1+2+4+5+6 1+2+5+5+5	0
b	0	2+3+5+6+6	1	0+2+4+4+6 0+2+4+5+5	3	0+1+4+4+5	2	1+3+5+5+6 1+3+4+6+6	0
c	0	1+3+5+5+6 1+3+4+6+6	2	0+1+4+4+5	3	0+2+4+4+6 0+2+4+5+5	1	2+3+5+6+6	0
d	0	1+3+4+6+6 1+3+5+5+6	2	0+3+4+5+6 0+3+5+5+5	1	0+2+4+4+6 0+2+4+5+5	3	1+2+5+5+5 1+2+4+5+6	0
e	0	1+2+5+5+5 1+2+4+5+6	3	0+2+4+4+6 0+2+4+5+5	1	0+3+4+5+6 0+3+5+5+5	2	1+3+4+6+6 1+3+5+5+6	0
f	0	1+2+4+5+6 1+2+5+5+5	3	0+1+4+4+5	2	0+3+4+5+6 0+3+5+5+5	1	2+3+5+6+6	0

Table 8.5

3. Classification in a Square with Double Sides

The following puzzle (example 8.8) is laid out in the Austrian manner in which the stones are joined not against the ends but along the long side. They can then be formed into a square with double sides.
In the example, there is a double on the outside of each corner. This gives the figure a great regularity. Four halves with the same number of dots are placed at each corner.

The object is to form a similar figure (example 8.9) with a double at each of the four corners and the three doubles in three of the four places on the inside sections shown in the above sketch such that each side contains the two dot numbers that appear in the corners opposite and such that the sum of the dots for each side is the same and, respectively, as small as possible or as large as possible.

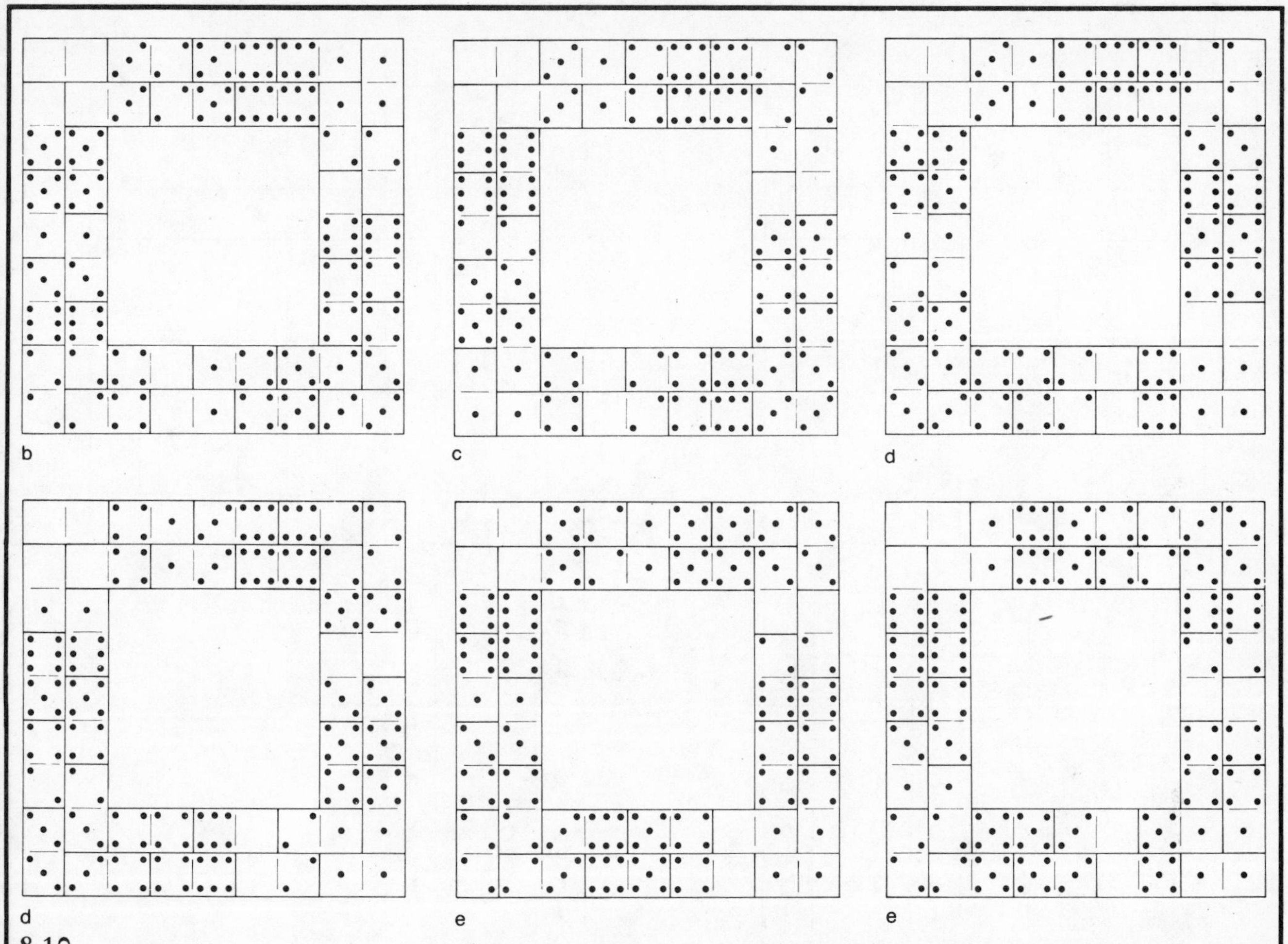

b c d

d e e

8.10

All solutions are asked. Solutions that are formed by turning are considered as the same solution.
If the sum of the dots on each side interior and exterior = 2S, and the numbers of spots on the four corners are represented by p, q, r, and s (p, q, r, and s are all four different) then is $8S = 168 + 4(p + q + r + s)$ or $S = 21 + \frac{p + q + r + s}{2}$.
The smallest sum of p, q, r, and s $= 0 + 1 + 2 + 3 = 6$ and the largest $6 + 5 + 4 + 3 = 18$. From this it follows that the smallest value of S is 24 and the largest is 30.

A. The sum of the dots on a side is as small as possible: S = 24

There are six truly different ways in which the number of dots p, q, r, and s can be divided among the four corners. Once it is known which value is placed at each corner it is then known for each side how many dots the 2 x 5 half stones in between must total.
Of the number of dots on these ten half stones, 2×2 are already known,

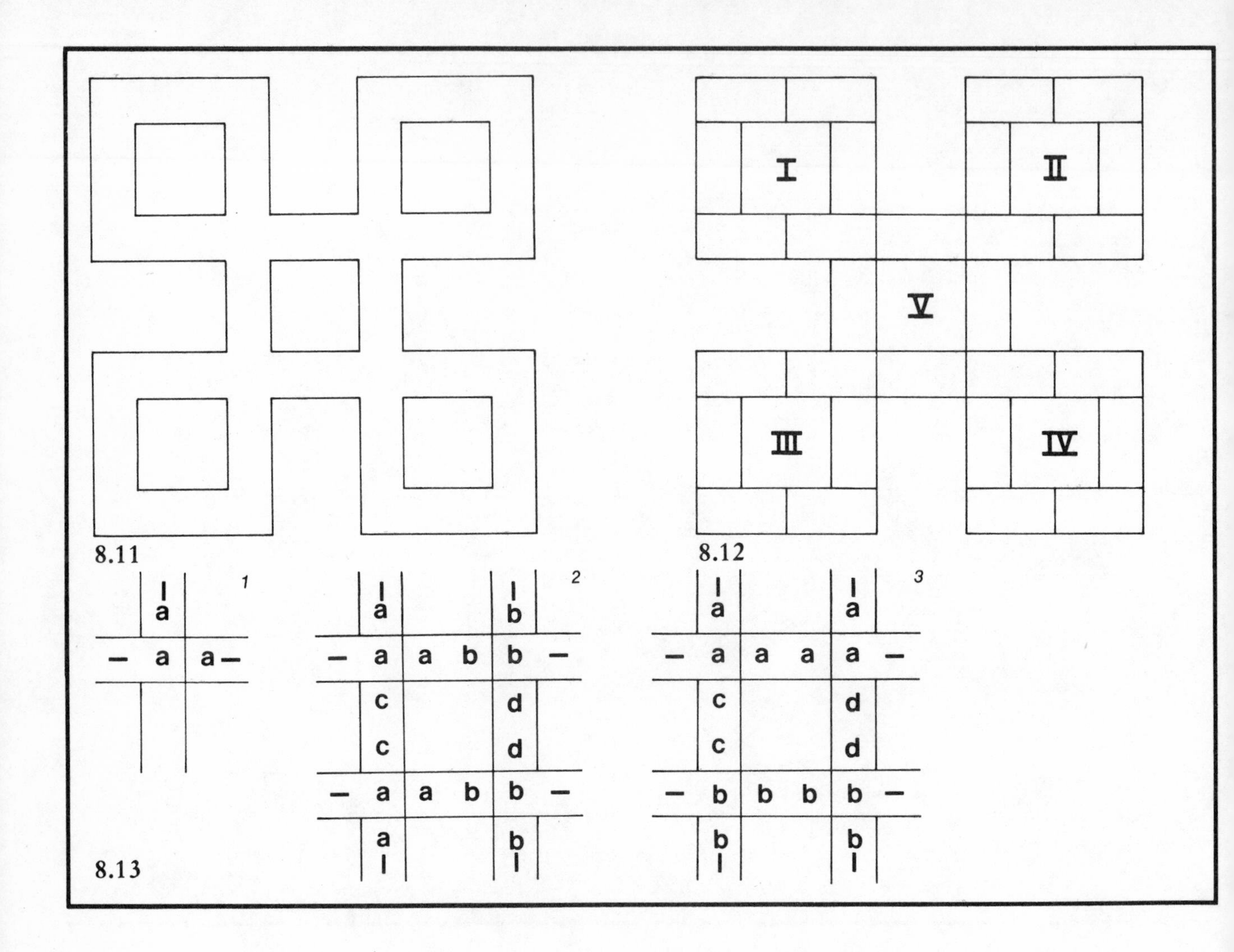

as they must be the same as the two numbers on the corners of the opposite side. The 2 × 3 remaining must be chosen so that S is the right value.

Leaving aside for the time being the sequence of the numbers, we can combine the possibilities as in table 8.5.
The half stones that form twice S_1, S_2, S_3, and S_4, must contain zero, one, two, or three dots four times and four, five, or six dots eight times.

At the same time, it must be possible to place double four, double five, and double six.
Case a does not meet these requirements. The underlined section of case b, in which the double four can be placed in S_2 and also in S_3, does. If double four is placed in S_2, the 4–6 must also be placed at the same time since this stone can go nowhere else. Because the 0-1 must go in S_3, S_2 contains the 0-2 and S_1 begins on the left with 0-3. From this come two solutions differing only in the placement of the stones 4-0, 0-1, and 1-4 in S_3.

If double four is in S_3, no solution is possible. Case c leads to a solution if double four is in S_2. From this solution a second can be developed by placing the stones 4-0, 0-2, and 2-4 in S_3. In case d, two connected solutions of the same type are found if the double five is placed in S_4 and two others if the double is placed in S_2. Accordingly, case e has two solutions with double five in S_1 and two with double five in S_3.
Case f has no solutions.

The puzzle with the smallest sum of the dots on each side has twelve solutions. Six of them are shown above. The other six can be formed from there by shifting three stones (example 8.10).

B. The sum of the dots on a side is as large as possible: S = 30.

This puzzle also has twelve solutions which can be formed from A in a simple manner by exchanging each number of dots with its complement to six. 6 is used in place of 0, 5 in place of 1, 4 in place of 2, and the reverse.

4. Classification by Five Connected Squares

The problem is to arrange the domino stones as shown in example 8.11 so that:

1. going around from one outward corner to another, the stones are joined as in the normal game—that is to say, with the same number of dots meeting. The doubles are not placed crosswise. If a double is bordered in the direction of movement on both sides by a pair of half stones with the same number of eyes, this double forms an independent pair;
2. the sum of the eyes in each of the five squares is the same.

All solutions are requested.

If equivalent figures are not considered as independent solutions, the stones can be placed in only one way, as illustrated (example 8.12). The four crossing points take the form of example 8.13 figure 1 or an equivalent position. At each crossing point, three half stones with the same number of dots appear. Since the number of half stones with the same number of dots is even, there must be a second crossing point with three times the same number of dots. This leads to the solution to the central square of figures 2 and 3.
The solution of figure 2 is impossible as two stones are a – b.

Let the sum of the dots in square = S, then it follows:
$5S = 168 + 2(a + b)$
from which it follows:

$5S = 170$,	or $S = 34$,	$a + b = 1$;
$5S = 180$,	or $S = 36$,	$a + b = 6$;
$5S = 190$,	or $S = 38$,	$a + b = 11$.

	a	b	c	d	e	f
1	0	6	1	5	2	4
2	0	6	2	4	1	5
3	1	5	0	6	2	4
4	1	5	2	4	0	6
5	2	4	0	6	1	5
6	2	4	1	5	0	6

Table 8.6

001566	*4*	013356	*1, 2, 3, 4*	112356	*1, 2, 3, 4, 5, 6*
002466	*6*	013446	*1, 2, 3, 4, 5, 6*	112446	
002556		013455	*1, 2, 3, 4, 5, 6*	112455	*5*
003456	*1, 2, 3, 4, 5, 6*	022356	*1, 2, 3, 4, 5, 6*	113346	*2, 5*
011466		022446	*1*	113445	
011556	*2*	022455		122346	*1, 2, 3, 4, 5, 6*
012366	*1, 2, 3, 4, 5, 6*	023346	*1, 2, 5, 6*	122355	
012456	*1, 2, 3, 4, 5, 6*	023355	*2, 5*	122445	*3*
		023445	*1, 2, 3, 4, 5, 6*	123345	*3, 4, 5, 6*

Table 8.7

$S = 34$ and $S = 38$ are not satisfactory because:

$S = 34: c + d = \frac{34 - 4}{2} = 15,$

$S = 38: c + d = \frac{38 - 44}{2} = -3.$ Both sums are impossible.
From this it follows that $S = 36$ and $a + b = 6$, which means that $c + d = 6$. The sum of the third pair of dots which is not $= 3$ must then also be 6. Table 8.6 gives a survey of all possible cases. It should be noted that the values of a and b can be mutually exchanged just as can those of c and d and of e and f.
Each of the four outside squares consists of six pairs of half stones with the same number of dots. If each pair is shown by one number representing the number of dots—regardless of the sequence—each outside square can be shown by a series of six numbers with the sum $= \frac{1}{2} S = 18$.
In such a series the same number may not appear more than twice and the sequence cannot be made from three pairs of the same numbers. If these conditions are not satisfied, the square cannot be laid out. For the same reason, the series requires that for the given values of a, b, c, and d:
2 times a, 2 times b, 2 times c and 2 times d, not paired, can be united or combined in one and the same series with two times another number;
in each series at least 1 time a or 1 time b must appear.
While observing these conditions twenty-six series can be shown that

	1	2	3	4	5	6
	abcdef	abcdef	abcdef	abcdef	abcdef	abcdef
	061524	062415	516024	154206	426015	245106
Possible series with ee						
abeeff	022446	011556	522441	100665	411552	200664
bceef3	122346	112356	223461	003465	113562	003564
abdee3			502236			
acdee3						
acee33					411336	
bdee33		113346				
with 33						
abcd33	013356	023346	503361	123345	403362	213354
abef33	023346	013356	523341	103365	413352	203364
acff33		023355				
bdff33					033552	
acee33					411336	
bdee33		113346				
with ff						
abeeff	022446	011556	522441	100665	411552	200664
adeff3	023445	013455	502344	102366	401355	201366
abcff3	013446					
bcdff3			034461			
acff33		023355				
bdff33					033552	
remaining, only a						
acddf3	013455	023445	500346	122346	400356	211356
accef3				103446		
aacde3					440136	
aacef3						220356
only b						
bccde3	112356	122346	023661	023445	013662	013554
bddef3				022365		
bbcdf3					035622	
bbdef3						013644
a and b						
abcdef	012456	012456	502461	102465	401562	201564
aabdf3	003456	003456	550341	112365	440352	221364
abbce3	012366	012336	523611	103455	413622	203544
abccf3		022356				
abdde3		013446				

Table 8.8

are given in table 8.7 with mention of the six cases they serve. It appears that six series are eliminated.

From the possible series from the given a, b, c, and d, combinations of four must be formed so that such a combination:

has 3 times a, 3 times b, 3 times c, 3 times d and 4 times the other numbers;

has a place for the three doubles that cannot be used in the middle square;

has all the possible pairs from the domino stones.

Since the eight equivalent forms are considered one and the same solu-

Table 8.9

		1	2	3	4	5	6
		abcdef	abcdef	abcdef	abcdef	abcdef	abcdef
		061524	062415	516024	154206	426015	245106
1	bceef3	122346	112356	223461	003465	113562	003564
	abcd33	013356	023346	503361	123345	403362	213354
	adeff3	023445	013455	502344	102366	401355	201366
	abcdef	012456	012456	502461	102465	401562	201564
2	abeeff	022446	011556	522441	100665	411552	200664
	abef33	023346	013356	523341	103365	413352	203364
	acddf3	013455	023445	500346	122346	400356	211356
	bccde3	112356	122346	023661	023445	013662	013554
3	bceef3		112356				
	acff33		023355				
	abdde3		013446				
	abcdef		012456				
4	bdee33		113346				
	adeff3		013455				
	abccf3		022356				
	abcdef		012456				
5	abeeff			522441			
	abcd33			503361			
	bcdff3			034461			
	acdee3			502236			
6	acdee3			502236			
	abef33			523341			
	bcdff3			034461			
	abcdef			502461			
7	abeeff				100665		
	abcd33				123345		
	bddef3				022365		
	accef3				103446		
8	bceef3					113562	
	bdff33					033552	
	aacde3					440136	
	abcdef					401562	
9	acee33					411336	
	bdff33					033552	
	abcdef					401562	
	abcdef					401562	

tion, it is a matter of indifference which of the two suitable values are given to a and which to b.

This leads in a corresponding way to the values that are suitable for c and d.

By choosing in the six possible cases the values of a and b and of c and d as given at the head of table 8.8, the series can be brought to as small as possible a number shown by letters. The adding up of the combinations then is simplified. At the same time it must be remembered that in combinations containing two of the series:

abeeff,	abdee3	and bdee33	the stone c–e is missing;
abeeff,	abeff3	and bdff33	the stone c–f is missing;
abeeff,	bceef3	and acee33	the stone d–e is missing;
abeeff,	abcff3	and acff33	the stone d–f is missing.

The combinations shown in table 8.9 can be added together.
There are nine combinations possible. Two of these cover all six cases. In order to see to what extent they lead to a solution, only one case must be more closely examined. If one or more solutions to the examined case is found, the solutions of the remaining five cases can be discovered by exchanging the dots.
The remaining seven combinations each apply only to one case.

For a solution of combination *1* in case 1, it can be taken as a starting point that the common corner of the squares I and V has a 0 and that square I is occupied by the series 013356. Thus will be established which series goes in square II and which two series in III or in IV.
Because double three must be put in square I, the number of dots there can be classified in $\frac{4!}{2} = 12$ ways. The two classifications having the same sequence if the one is read in a clockwise direction and the other counterclockwise are considered as one for the time being. Because of the formation of the series that must appear in III or IV, the 0-3 and the 3-5 must be placed in squares I or II.
There are thirty-six solutions for case I and 4 x 36 solutions following from these in cases 2 – 6.

Combination *2* has no solutions, nor does combination 9.

The number of solutions of *3.2* is strictly limited by the small number of possibilities in series 013446 without placing the unusable double 4. There are eight solutions.

A similar limitation gives combination *4.2* ten solutions.

In combinations *5.3* the series 522441 must have the 2-4 and the 5-4 and, furthermore, must contain two doubles. This combination has twelve solutions.

Just as *1,* combinations *6.3* has thirty-six solutions.

In combination *7.4,* the series 123345 must have the 2-4 and the 5-4 in addition to double three; because of the absence of double two, the series 022365 has the 2-5; and, for a corresponding reason, the series 103446 has the 1-4. There are eight solutions.

In combination *8.5* the series 401562 must have 4-2 and 4-5 while in the series 440136 the 4-3 must appear. This combination has sixteen solutions.

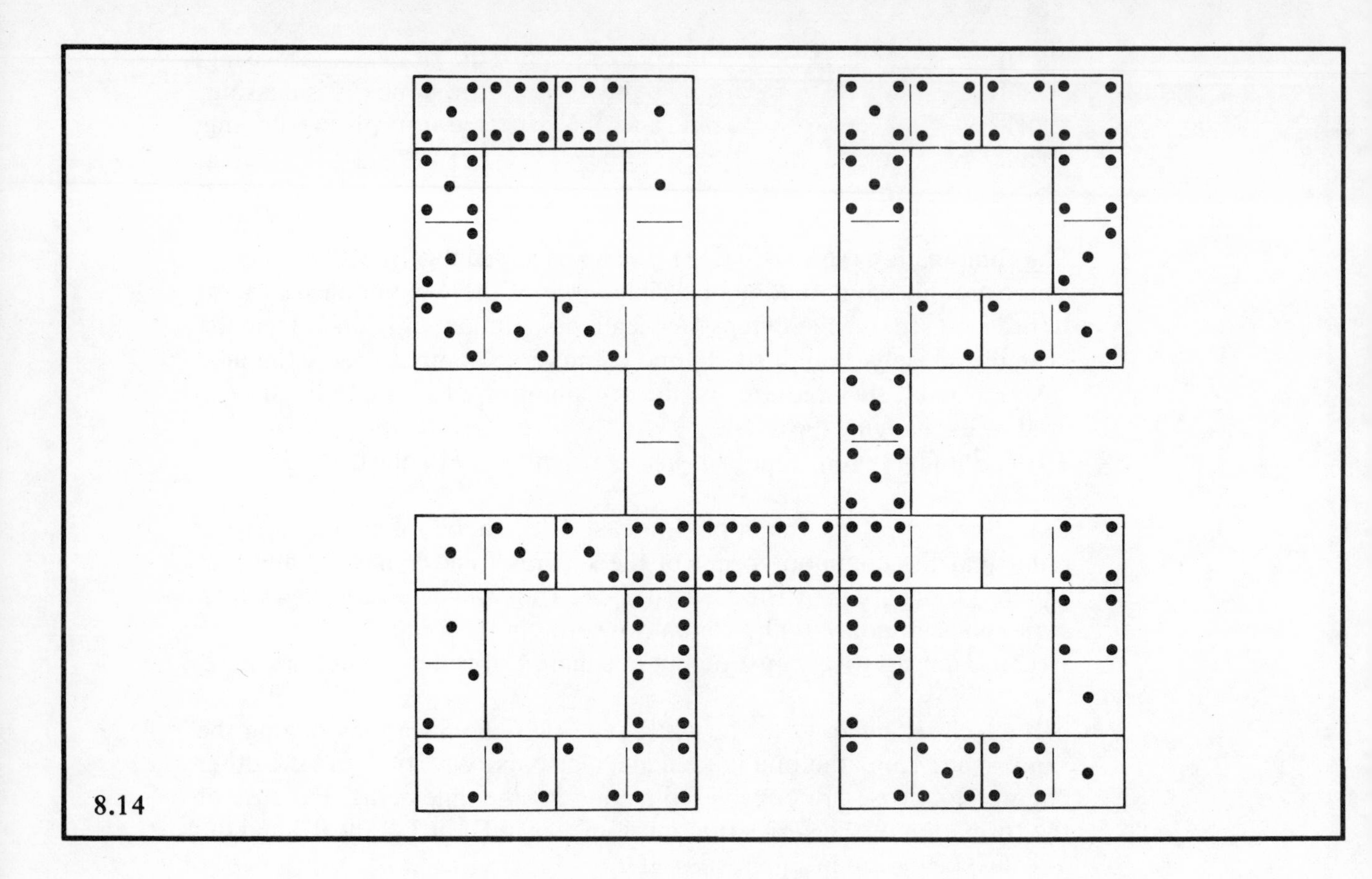
8.14

There are a total of 36 + 8 + 10 + 12 + 36 + 8 + 16 = 126 independent solutions (example 8.14). In all solutions the stones in each square including the middle one can be placed in two directions by turning. From this develop 2^5 variations.
In the solutions for combinations 1–7 the squares I and II, III and IV, and I and IV can be exchanged. This gives 2^3 variations.
In the solutions of *8*, the squares I and II can be exchanged as can II and IV. Square II can be joined to V in two ways at the common corner. For this there are also 2^3 variations.
The total number of solutions is: $(126 + 5 \times 36)2^8 = 78{,}336$.

With games of larger scope, similar diagrams can be laid out. If the highest stone is the double n–n, the figure consists of $\frac{1}{2}n + 2$ squares that have $n - 2$ corners and each n^2 dots, provided n is even. In this instance, also, the number of possibilities to be examined is so large that the desire to find a complete solution is lost. Example 8.15 gives an illustration of this type of problem.

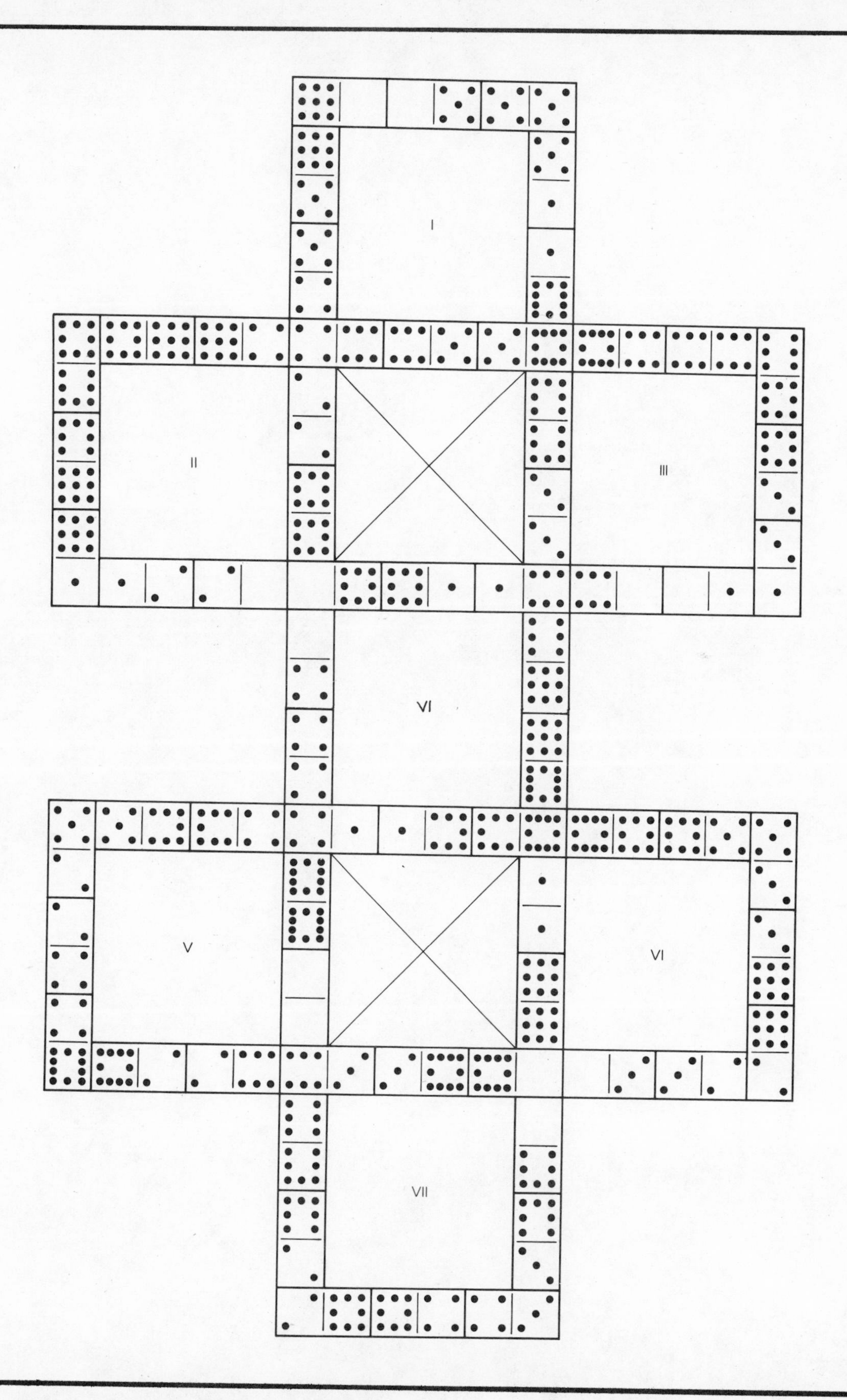

8.15

Bibliography

1. Encyclopedia Britannica, Vol. VII, 1957, i.v. 'Dominoes'
2. BRETHOUWER, D.H.G., *Domineren en Nossen,* Van Goor Zonen, den Haag
3. ARMANINO, D.C., *Dominoes,* McKay Co., New York, 5th Printing, 1967
4. ARMANINO, D.C., *Popular Domino Games,* McKay Co., New York, 2nd printing, 1965
5. FRANK, THEA, *Roulette, Domino, Puff,* Gerstenberg Verlag, Hildesheim, 1952
6. BECK, FRITZ, *Domino in vielen Spielarten,* Adelbert Pechan, Wien, 1960
7. KRAITCHIC, MAURICE, *Mathematical Recreations,* Allen & Unwin, London, 5th Impr., 1955
8. LUCAS, EDOUARD, *Récréations mathématiques,* Gauthier-Villars et Fils, Paris, 2me Ed., T. II 1896, T. IV 1894
9. English Edition, *The Master Book of Mathematical Puzzles and Recreations,* Dover Publications, Inc., New York, 1969
10. DRIEL, M.J. VAN, *Oneven toovervierkanten zijn geen puzzles,* Versluys, Amsterdam, 1931
11. DUDENEY, H.E., *Amusements in Mathematics,* Dover Publications Inc., New York, 1958
12. EULER, L., *Recherches sur une nouvelle espèce de quarrées magiques,* Verh. Zeeuwse Genootschap der Wetensch., IX, 1782, pp. 85-239
13. BERGHOLT, E., "Magic of sixteen cells," *Nature, 83,* March-June 1910, p. 368
14. FRÉNICLE, B., *Table générale des Quarrez de Quatre,* Mém. de l'Acad. Roy. d. Sc., contenant les ouvrages adoptez par cette Acad. avant son Renouvellement en 1699, T. II, Amsterdam, 1736
15. ANDREWS, W.S., *Magic Squares and Cubes,* Dover Publications Inc., New York, 1960
16. REISS, M. "Evaluation de nombre de combinaisons desquelles les 28 des d'un jeu au domino sont susceptibles d'après la règle de ce jeu," *Annali di Matematica pura ed applicata,* V 1871, pp. 63-120
17. TARRY, G., *Geometrie de situations,* Comptes rendus de l'Ass. franc. pour l'avancement des sciences, XV, 1886, p. 49-53.

Afterword

Survey of Quadrilles to Be Made from the Normal Game

Between the quadrille with ten corners and that with twenty-four corners lie many others. Anyone trying to track them down, however, finds himself entangled with the many variations that threaten to hinder the survey. Many quadrilles, for instance, can be changed by taking out a certain group of stones from the figure and rearranging them. In this way a series of quadrilles can develop from one, and a good survey must clearly indicate the connection of such a series.
The listing of possible quadrilles, therefore, is preceded by a systematic summary of the variations, each with a number. There are three types of variations:

V_1 — V_3, consisting of five stones including two doubles;
V1.1 — V6.3, consisting of nine stones, including three doubles;
W1 and W2, consisting of seven stones, including three doubles.

Both of the first mentioned types can appear without regard to the number of corners. The third type is only found in figures with sixteen or more corners.

In the list the quadrille or one of the quadrilles with the smallest number of corners is chosen as the standard. The different variations are shown in the fifth column with their numbers. The notation $V_2|V_1$ means that on the left side the figure shows the variation V_2, on the right side variation V_1. Similarly, the notation $\frac{V_2}{V_1}$ refers to the top and bottom of a figure. The number preceding the variation indicates how many corners the particular quadrille has.
Furthermore, another variation appears a few times when two stones lying next to each other in the interior of a figure are each accounted for in the list.
Finally, the table includes the quadrilles that develop when two sections of a figure change places. Usually when one quadrille changes into another a double is exchanged with a group of stones. In the discussion of the twenty-four-cornered figure, examples are given. Occasionally there is an exchange in the center, as in quadrilles 12.1 and 12.2.
Figures that have no solutions are not given in the table, even though the outlines of the stones can be shown without more than seven doubles or identical stones appearing.

Table A1 gives the total number of quadrilles divided according to their outline, including the variations that are in the survey and the number of solutions.

number of corners	number of quadrilles	number of solutions
10	1	14
12	8	126
16	10	100
	46	347
18	50	278
20	39	189
22	8	41
24	20	91
	182	1186

Table A1

Systematic Survey of Variations

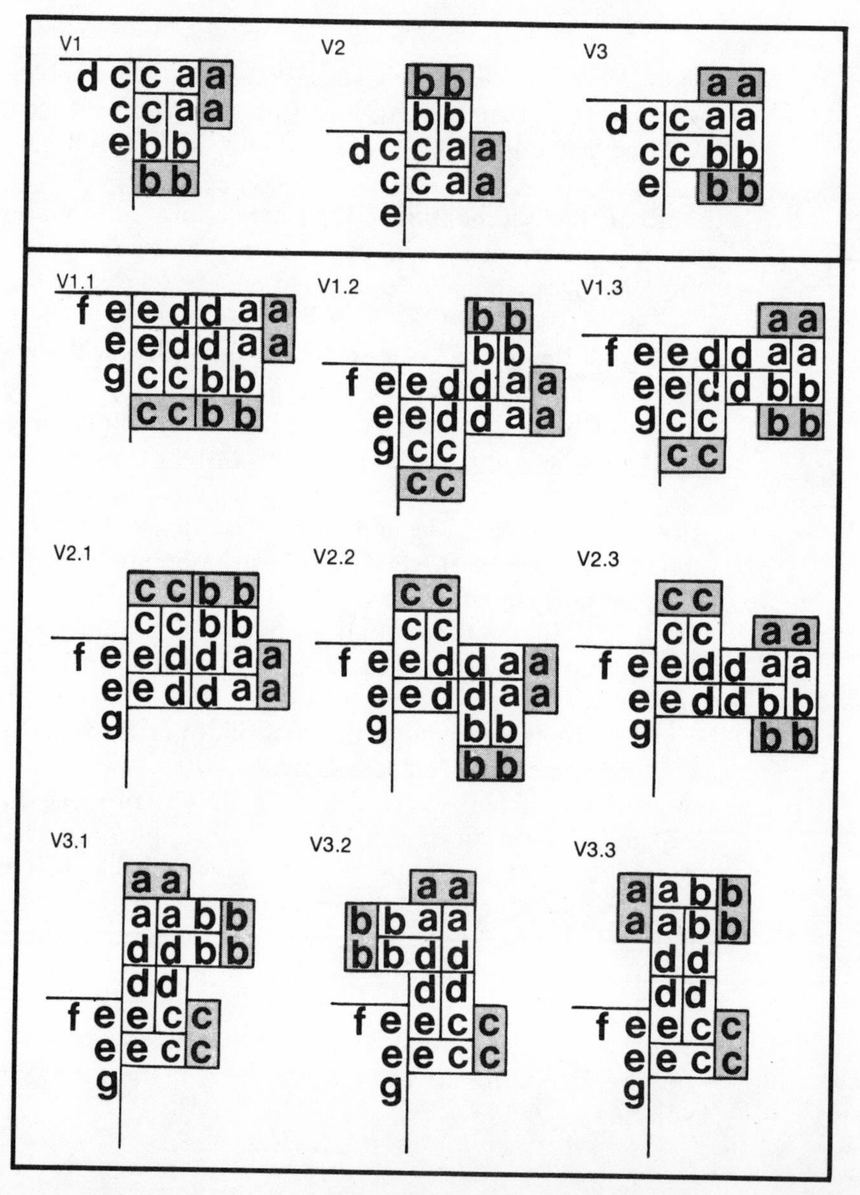

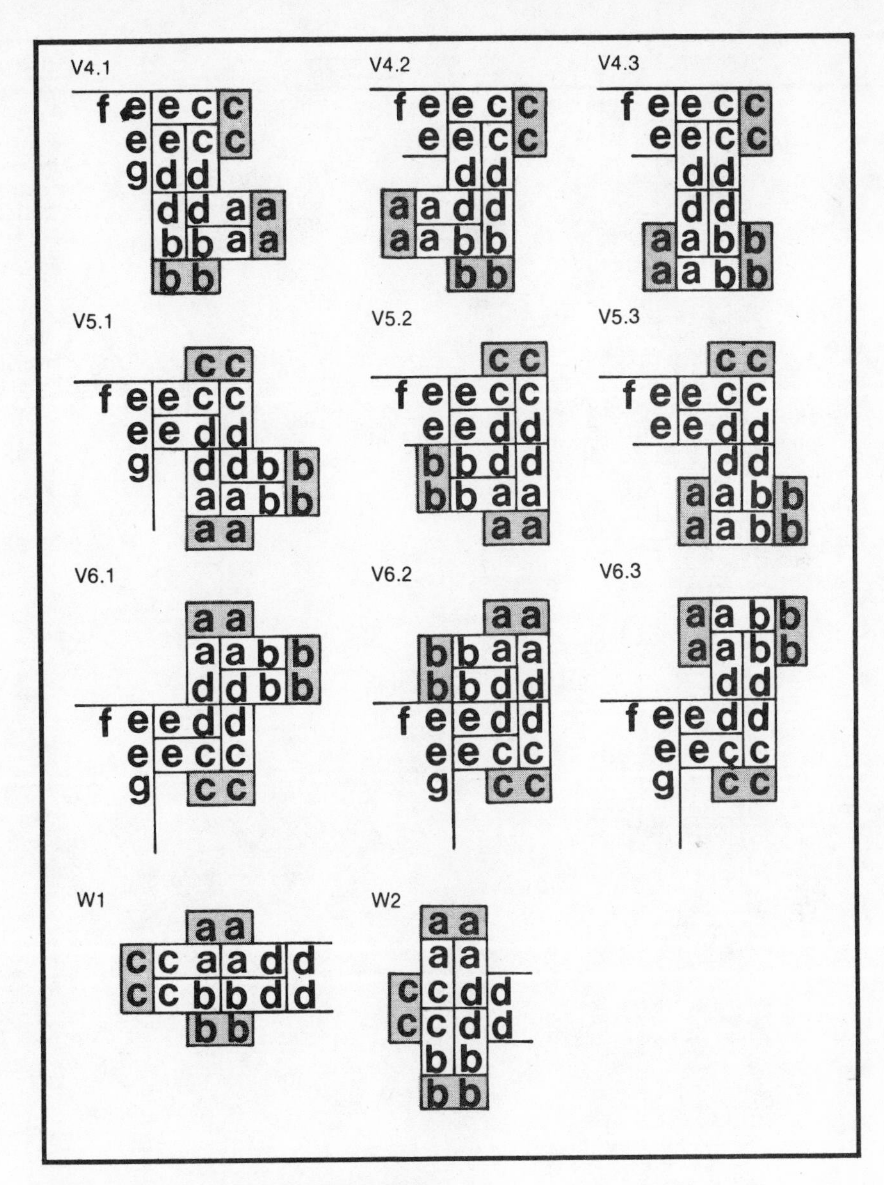

Survey of Quadrilles

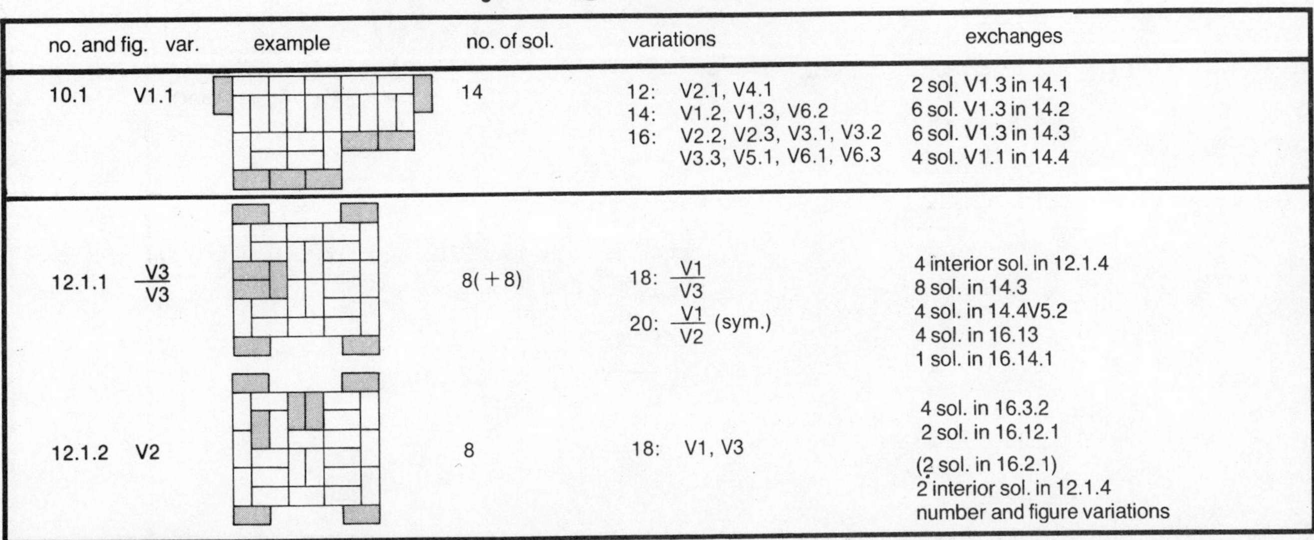

no. and fig.	var.	example	no. of sol.	variations	exchanges
10.1	V1.1		14	12: V2.1, V4.1 14: V1.2, V1.3, V6.2 16: V2.2, V2.3, V3.1, V3.2, V3.3, V5.1, V6.1, V6.3	2 sol. V1.3 in 14.1 6 sol. V1.3 in 14.2 6 sol. V1.3 in 14.3 4 sol. V1.1 in 14.4
12.1.1	V3/V3		8(+8)	18: V1/V3 20: V1/V2 (sym.)	4 interior sol. in 12.1.4 8 sol. in 14.3 4 sol. in 14.4V5.2 4 sol. in 16.13 1 sol. in 16.14.1
12.1.2	V2		8	18: V1, V3	4 sol. in 16.3.2 2 sol. in 16.12.1 (2 sol. in 16.2.1) 2 interior sol. in 12.1.4 number and figure variations

no. and fig.	var.	example	no. of sol.	variations	exchanges
12.1.3	V1|V2		4(+4)	18: V1|V1, V1|V3 20: V2|V1, V3|V3 (sym.) V2|V3	2 interior sol. in 12.8.4 2 sol. in 14.5.2 4 sol. in 16.2.2 2 sol. in 16.3.3 1 sol. in 16.12.2
12.1.4			14		4 interior sol. in 12.1.1 2 interior sol. in 12.1.2 2 interior sol. in 12.1.3
12.2.1			11(+11)		8 interior sol. in 12.2.2 2 interior sol. in 12.2.4 and - 5 3 interior sol. in 12.2.3
12.2.2			8		8 interior sol. in 12.2.1 2 interior sol. in 12.2.4 and - 5
12.2.3			3		3 interior sol. in 12.2.1
12.2.4			2		2 interior sol. in 12.2.1, - 2 and - 5
12.2.5			2		2 interior sol. in 12.2.1, - 2 and - 4
12.3			8		3 sol. in 12.4
12.4			3		3 sol. in 12.3 number and figure viarations
12.5.1			22	2 solutions to vary with 12.5.2 9 sol. in the adjacent form which is identical to 10.1 - V4.1	2 sol. via 10.1V4.1 in 14.1
12.5.2			2	to vary with 12.5.1	

no. and fig.	var.	example	no. of sol.	variations	exchanges
12.6		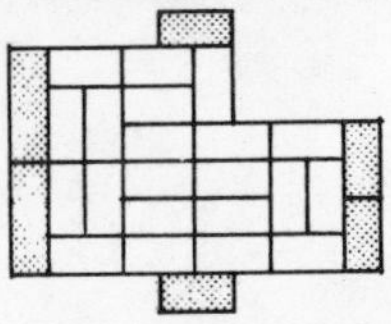	3		
14.1	$\frac{V1}{V3}$	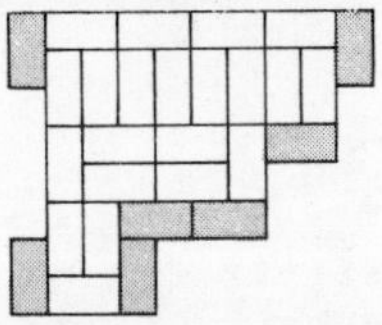	4	16: $\frac{V2,\ V3,\ V1}{V3\ \ V3\ \ V1}$ 18: $\frac{V2,\ V3}{V1\ \ V1}$	2 sol. $\frac{V1}{V1}$ in 10.1V1.1 2 sol. via 10.1V4.1 in 12.5.1
14.2	$\frac{V1}{V3}$	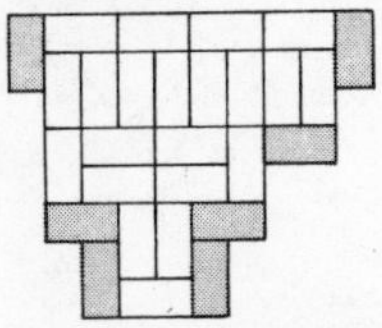	12	16: $\frac{V2,\ V3}{V3\ V3}$	6 sol. in 10.1V1.3
14.3	$\frac{V1}{V3}$	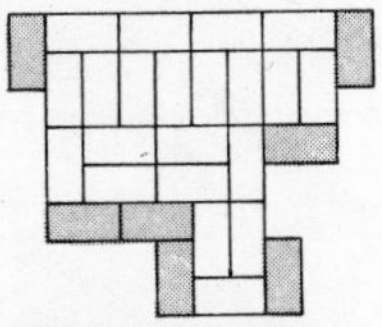	12	16: $\frac{V2,\ V3,\ V1}{V3\ \ V3\ \ V2}$ 18: $\frac{V2,\ V3}{V2\ \ V2}$	6 sol. in 10.1V1.3 8 sol. in 12.1.1
14.4	V1.1	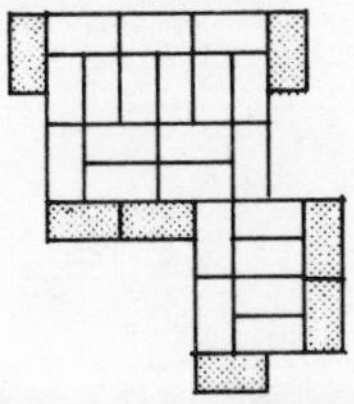	4	14: V5.2 16: V5.1., V5.3, V6.1 18: V1.2, V1.3, V3.1, V3.2, V4.1, V4.2, V4.3	4 sol. in 10.1 4 sol. in 12.1.1 4 sol. via 10.1V4.1 in 12.5.1
14.5.1	V1.1	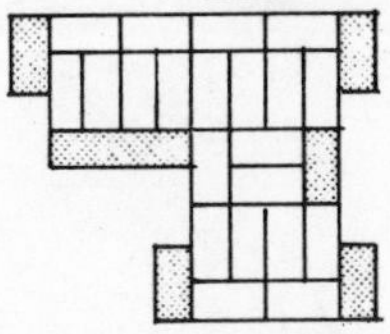	2	16: V2.1, V4.1 18: V1.2, V1.3, V6.2 20: V2.2, V2.3, V3.1, V3.2 V3.3, V5.1, V6.1, V6.3	2 sol. in 16.2.2
14.5.2	V1.1	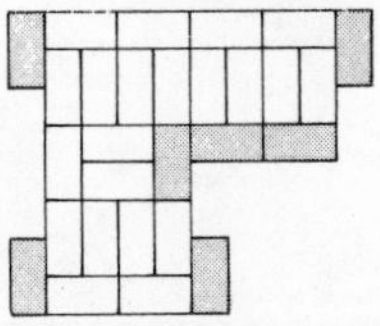	2	as 14.5.1	2 sol. in 12.1.3 2 sol. in 16.2.2
14.5.3	V1	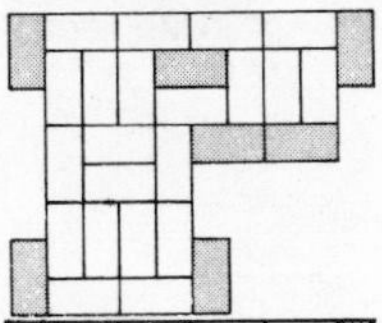	4	18: V2, V3	4 sol. in 16.2.1
14.5.4	outline V1.1	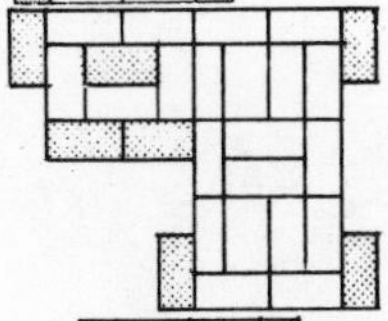	6	16: outline V2.1	6 sol. in 16.19 and - 20 6 sol. in 18.8 and - 9
14.6	V1	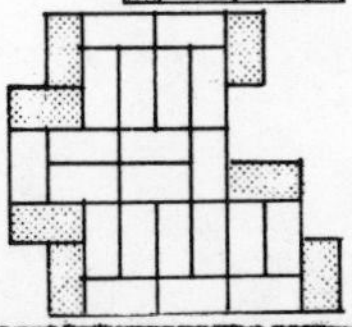	8	16: V2, V3 identical with 14.5.1V4.1 1 solution to vary with 16.3.1	

no. and fig.	var.	example	no. of sol.	variations	exchanges
16.1		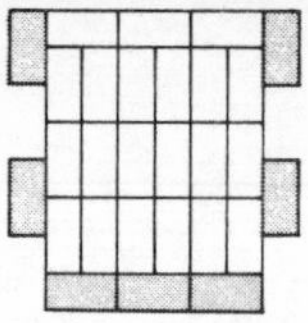	1(+1)		
16.2.1	V1	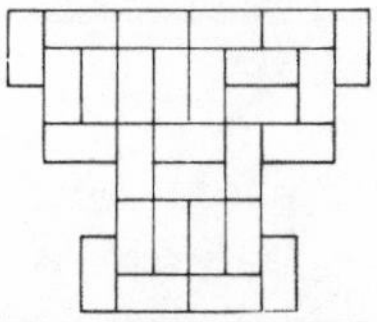	6	18: V2, V3	2 sol. in 12.1.2 4 sol. in 14.5.3
16.2.2	V2|V1	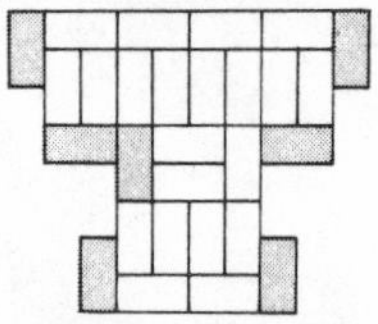	4	18: V1|V1, V3|V1, V2|V2 V2|V3 20: V1|V2, V3|V3 (sym.)	4 sol. in 12.1.3 2 sol. in 14.5.1 2 sol. in 14.5.2
		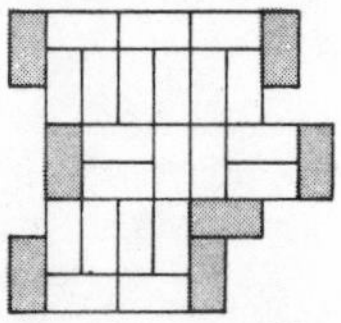	(2)	identical to 14.5.1, V4.1 1 sol. to vary with 16.3	
16.3.1		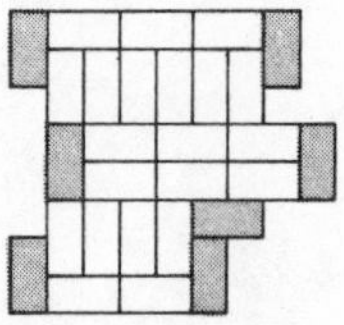	1	to vary with 14.5.1, V4.1	
16.3.2		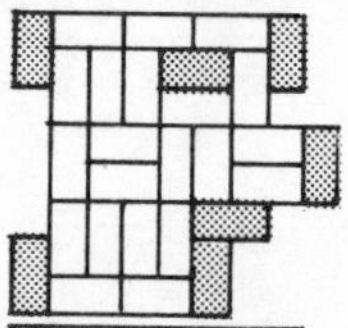	4		4 sol. in 12.1.2 2 sol. in 16.12.1
16.3.3		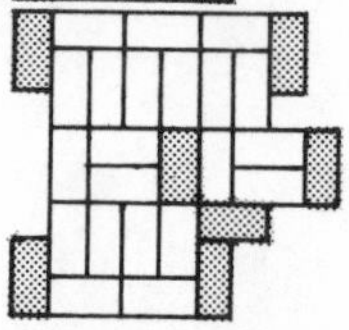	2		2 sol. in 12.1.3 1 sol. in 16.12.2
16.4	V2	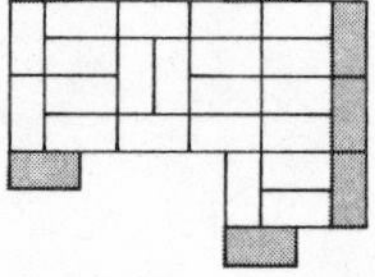	16	18: V1 20: V3	6 sol. in 18.5 and 22.1 4 sol. in 20.4 2 sol. in 20.5
16.5	V3	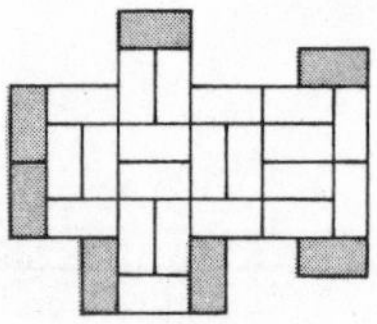	3		
16.6	V1	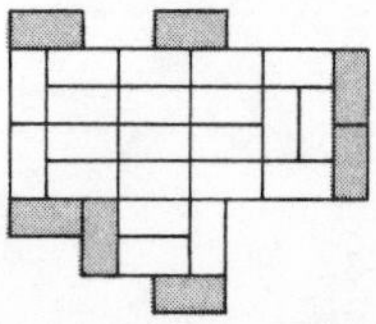	6	18: V2 20: V3	2 sol. in 20.6

no. and fig.	var.	example	no. of sol.	variations	exchanges
16.7.1	W2	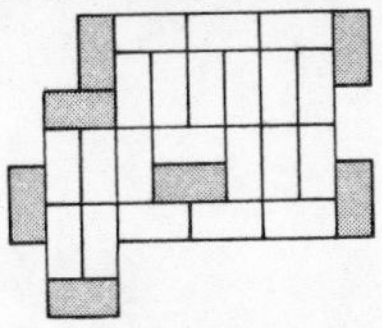	2	20: W1	2 sol. in 16.9.2
16.7.2	W2	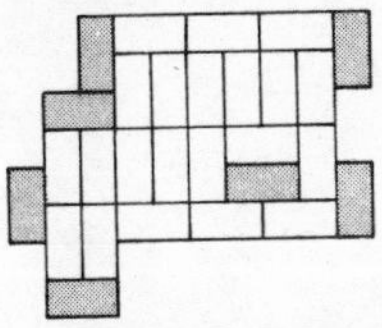	2	20: W1	
16.8.1		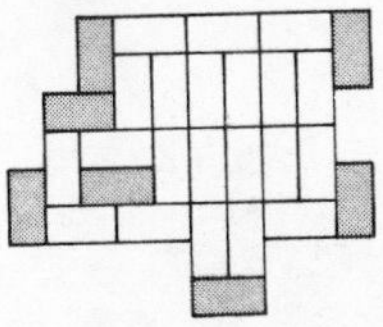	1		in 16.9.1
16.8.2	V1	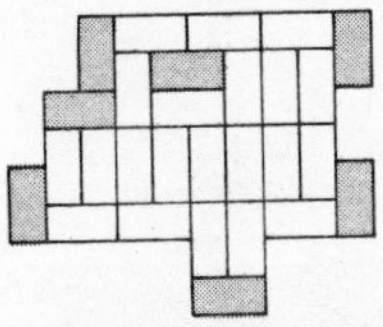	2	20: V2, V3	2 sol. in 16.9.3
16.9.1		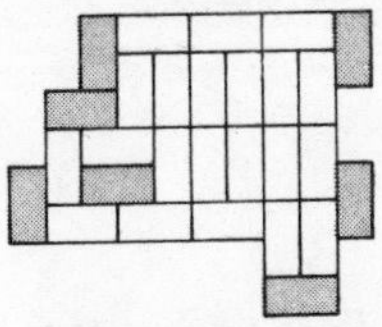	3		1 sol. in 16.8.1
16.9.2	V1	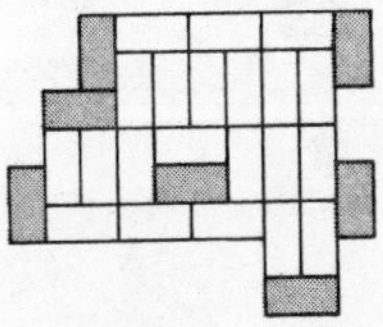	4	20: V2, V3	2 sol. in 16.7.1 2 sol. in 16.10.2 4 sol. in 20.9.3
16.9.3	V1	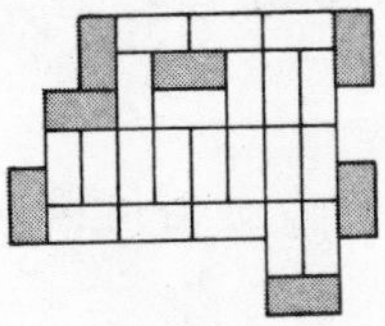	4	20: V2, V3	2 sol. in 16.8.2
16.10.1		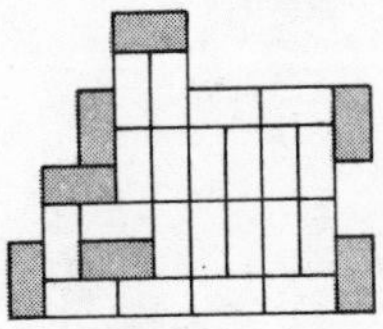	2		1 sol. in 16.11.1
16.10.2	V1	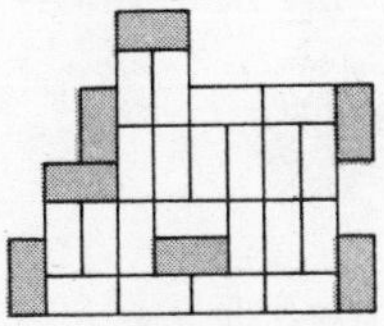	2	20: V2, V3	2 sol. in 16.9.2 2 sol. in 20.9.1
16.10.3	V1	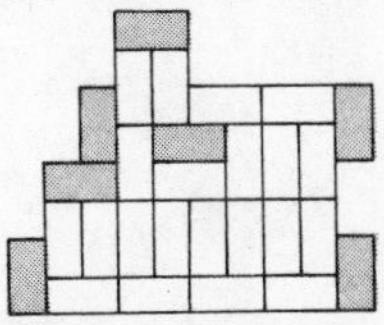	4	20: V2, V3	4 sol. in 16.11.2 2 sol. in 20.9.2

no. and fig.	var.	example	no. of sol.	variations	exchanges
16.11.1		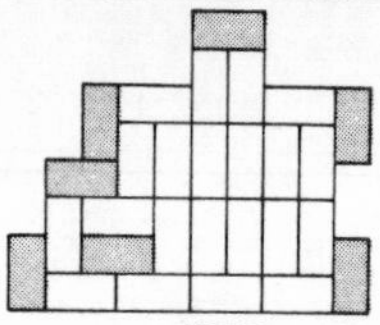	1		in 16.10.1
16.11.2	V1	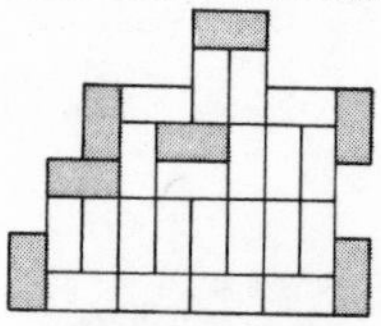	4	20: V2, V3	4 sol. in 16.10.3 2 sol. in 20.8
16.12.1		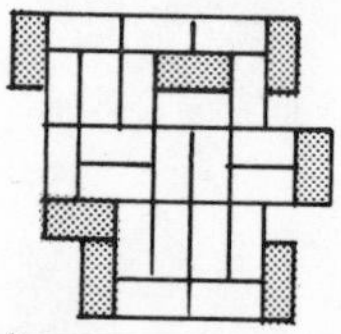	2		2 sol. in 12.12 2 sol. in 16.3.2
16.12.2		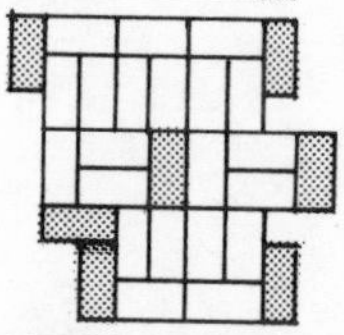	1		1 sol. in 12.1.3 1 sol. in 16.3.3
16.13		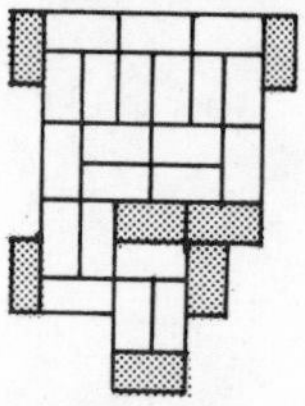	4		4 sol. in 12.1.1
16.14.1		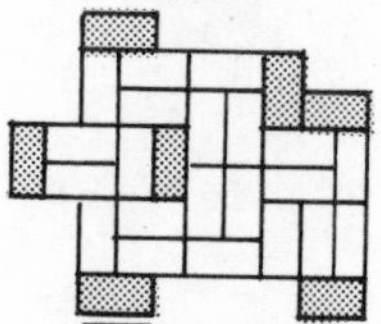	1		1 sol. in 12.1.1
16.14.2		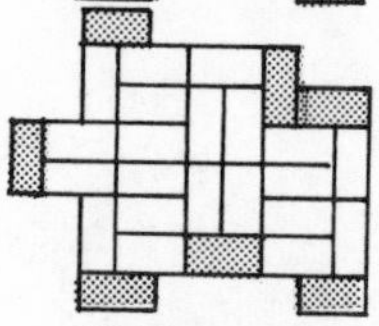	1		1 sol. in 16.15
16.15		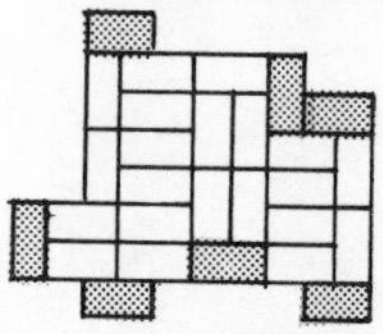	2		1 sol. in 16.14.2
16.16	V1	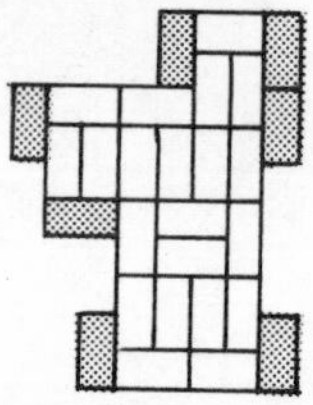	6	18: V2, V3	2 sol. in 16.17 4 sol. in 18.6

no. and fig.	var.	example	no. of sol.	variations	exchanges
16.17	V1	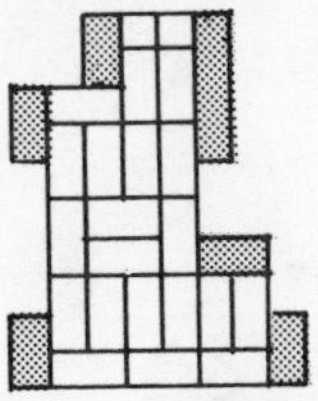	8	18: V2, V3	2 sol. in 16.16 2 sol. in 16.18 4 sol. in 18.7
16.18		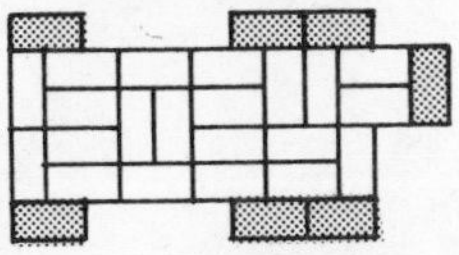	2		2 sol. in 16.17
16.19		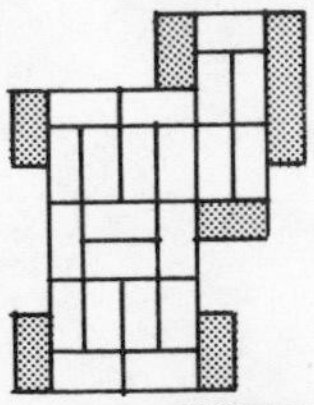	6		6 sol. in 14.5.4 6 sol. in 16.20 6 sol. in 18.8 and -9
16.20		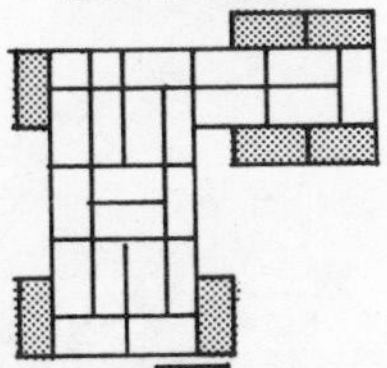	6		6 sol. in 14.5.4 6 sol. in 16.19 6 sol. in 18.8 and - 9
16.21.1		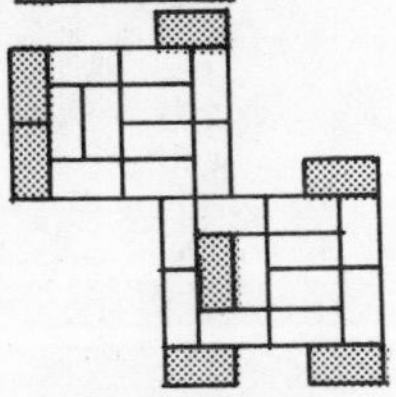	2		2 sol. in 18.10.1
16.21.2		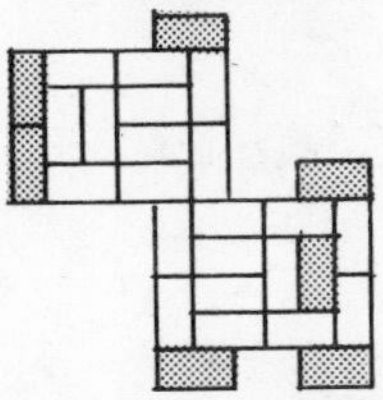	2		2 sol. in 18.10.2
16.22		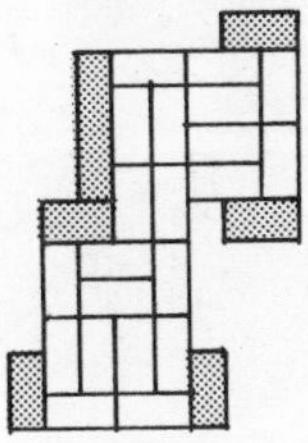	2		2 sol. in 16.23
16.23		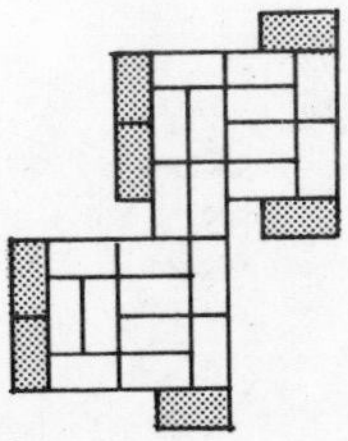	2		2 sol. in 16.22

no. and fig.	var.	example	no. of sol.	variations	exchanges
18.1		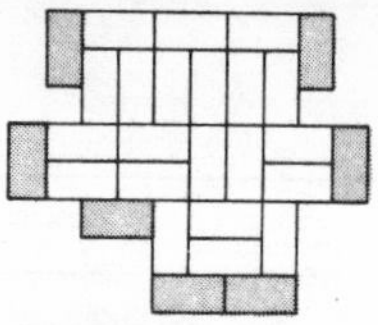	4		
18.2		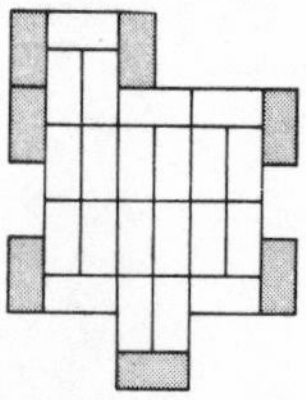	1		in 18.3
18.3		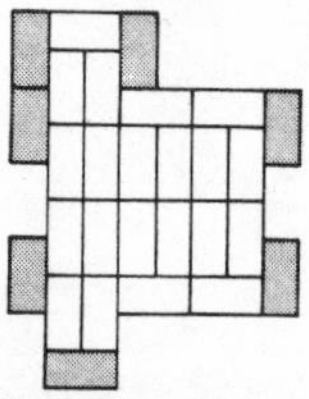	1		in 18.2
18.4		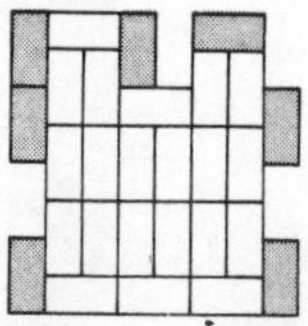	2		1 sol. in 22.4
18.5	W2	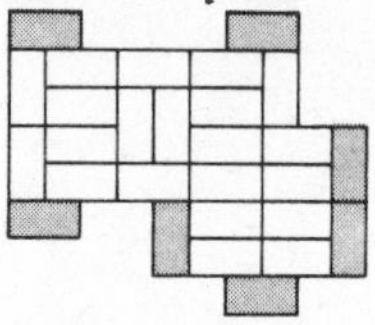	10	24: W1	6 sol. in 16.4 4 sol. in 18.11 10 sol. in 18.12 10 sol. in 22.1
18.6	V3	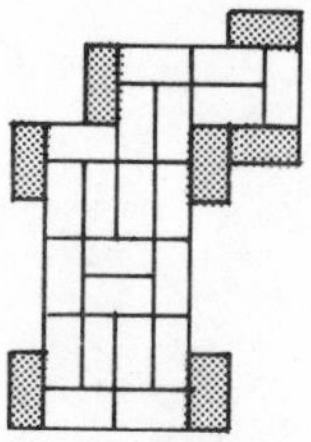	4	20: V2	4 sol. in 16.16
18.7	V1	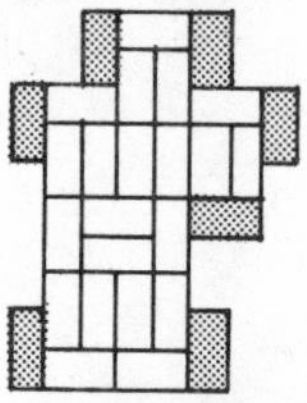	4	18: V3	4 sol. in 16.17
18.8		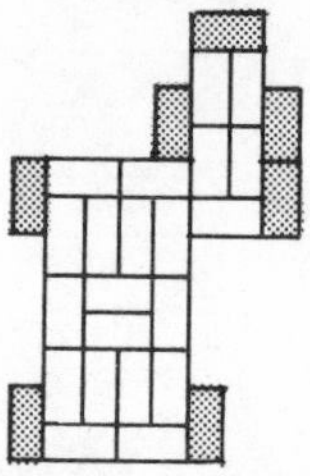	6		6 sol. in 14.5.4 6 sol. in 16.19 and -20 6 sol. in 18.9

no. and fig. var.	example	no. of sol.	variations	exchanges
18.9	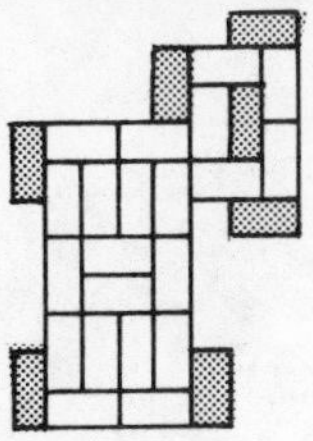	6		6 sol. in 14.5.4 6 sol. in 16.19 and - 20 6 sol. in 18.8
18.10.1	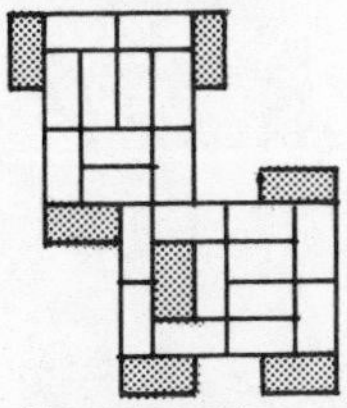	2		2 sol. in 16.21.1
18.10.2	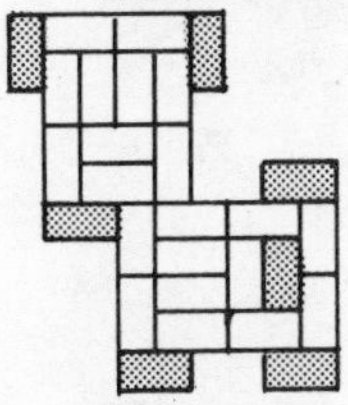	3		2 sol. in 16.21.2
18.11	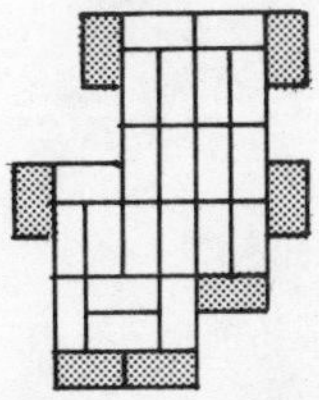	4		4 sol. in 18.5 W2
18.12	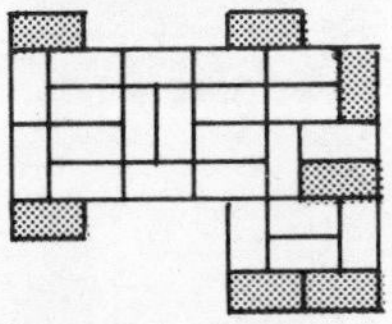	10		10 sol. in 18.5 10 sol. in 22.1
18.13	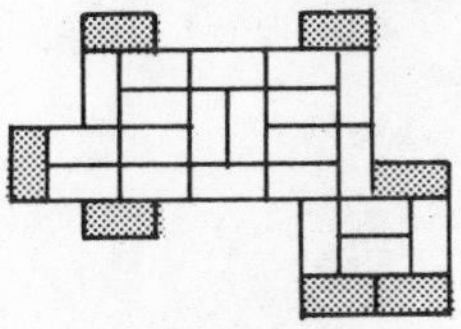	6		6 sol. in 22.2
18.14	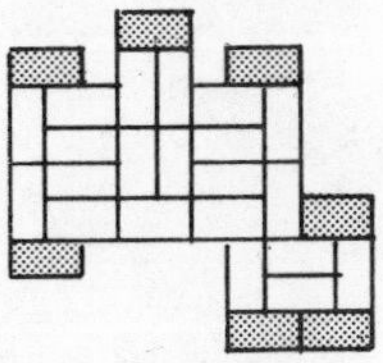	4		4 sol. in 22.3
20.1.1	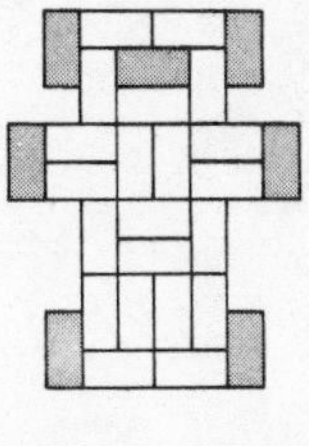	1		1 sol. in 22.4

no. and fig. var.	example	no. of sol.	variations	exchanges
20.1.2	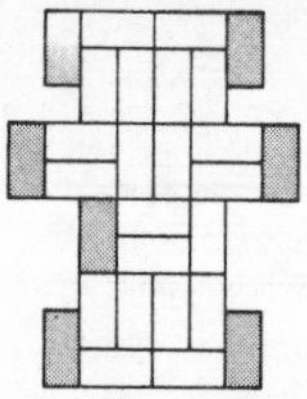	1		
20.2	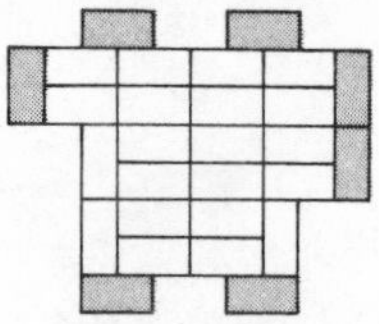	4		2 sol. in 20.3 2 sol. in 24.2
20.3	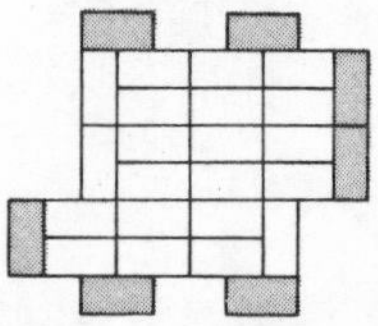	3		2 sol. in 20.2 2 sol. in 24.2
20.4 V3	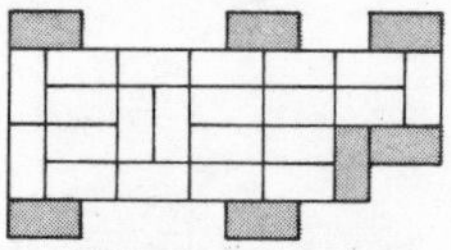	4	22: V2	4 solutions in 16.4
20.5 V2	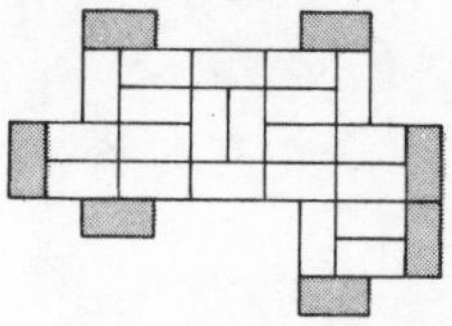	10	22: V1 24: V3	2 sol. in 16.4 4 sol. in 22.2 6 sol. V3 in 24.5
20.6 V3	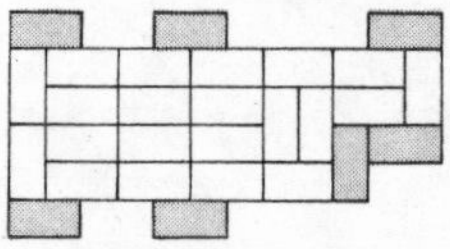	2	22: V2	2 sol. in 16.6
20.7 V2	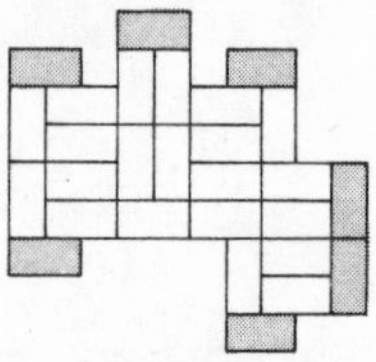	4	22: V1 24: V3	4 sol. V3 in 24.8
20.8 V3	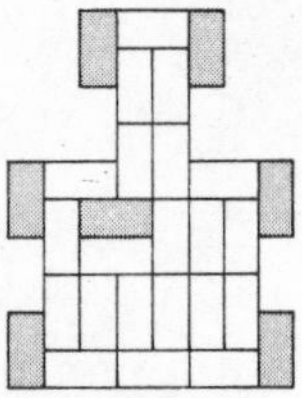	2	20: V1, V2	2 sol. in 16.11.2 2 sol. in 20.9.2
20.9.1 V3	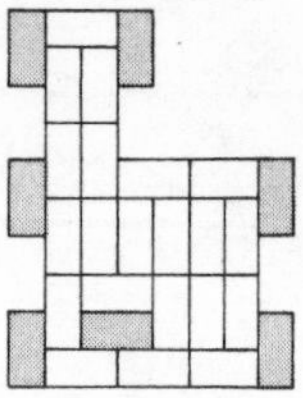	2	20: V1, V2	2 sol. in 16.10.2 2 sol. in 20.9.3

no. and fig.	var.	no. of sol.	example	variations	exchanges
20.9.2	V3	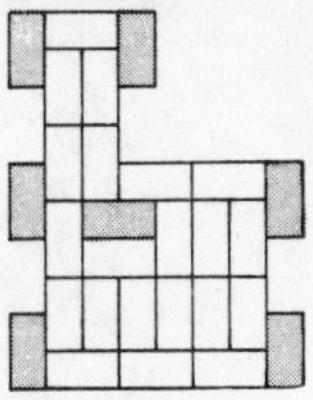	2	20: V1, V2	2 sol. in 16.10.3 2 sol. in 20.8
20.9.3	V3	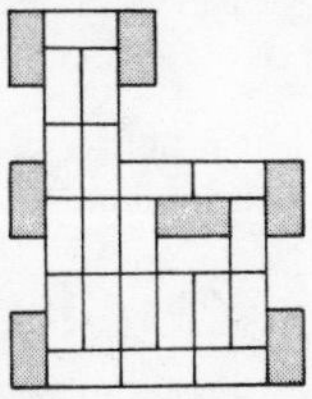	4	20: V1, V2	4 sol. in 16.9.2 2 sol. in 20.9.1
22.1	W2	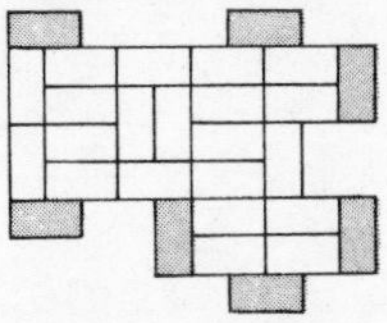	10	24: W1	6 sol. in 16.4 6 sol. in 18.5 and - 12
22.2	W2	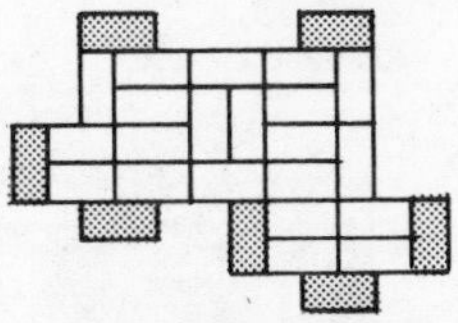	6	24: W1	4 sol. in 18.13 4 sol. in 20.5 2 sol. W1 in 24.3
22.3	W2	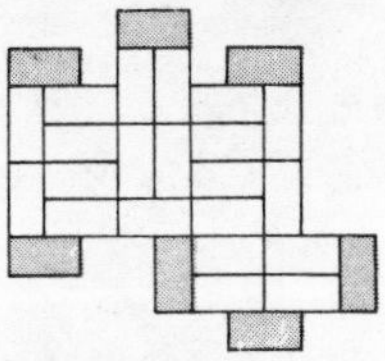	4	24: W1	4 sol. in 18.4 4 sol. W1 in 24.4
22.4		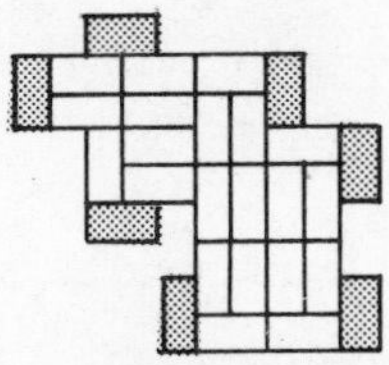	1		1 sol. in 18.4
24.1		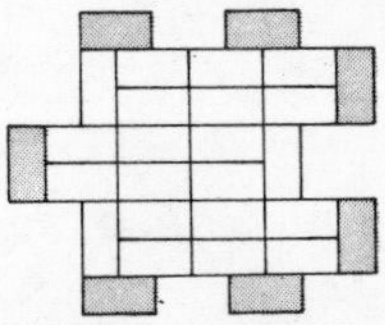	2(+2)		1 sol. in 24.2
24.2		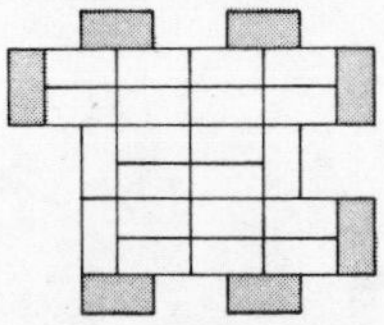	5		2 sol. in 20.2 2 sol. in 20.3 1 sol. in 24.1
24.3	W1	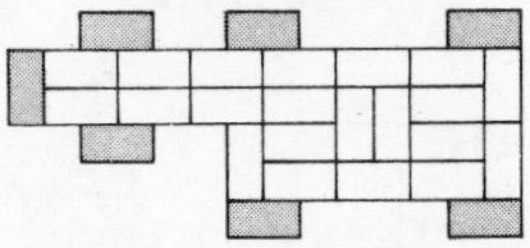	2	24: W2	2 sol. in twenty-four cornered 22.2W1

no. and fig.	var.	example	no. of sol.	variations	exchanges
24.4	W1	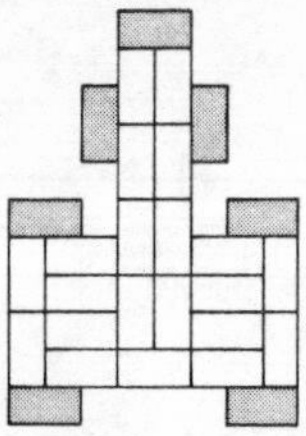	4(+4)		4 sol. in twenty-four cornered 22.3W1
24.5	V3	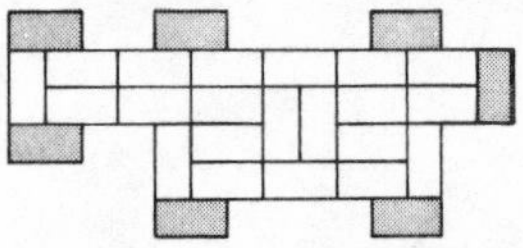	6	24: V1, V2	6 sol. in twenty-four cornered 20.5V3
24.6	V3	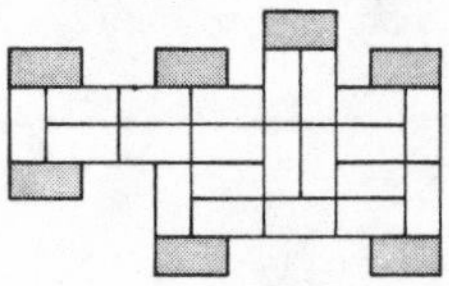	2	24: V1, V2	2 sol. in 24.7
24.7	V3	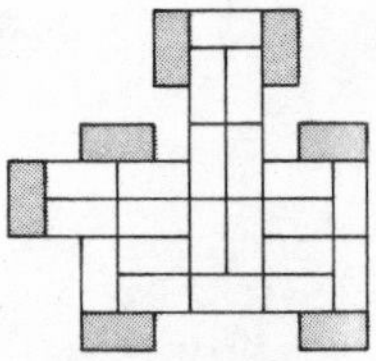	2		2 sol. in 24.6
24.8	V3	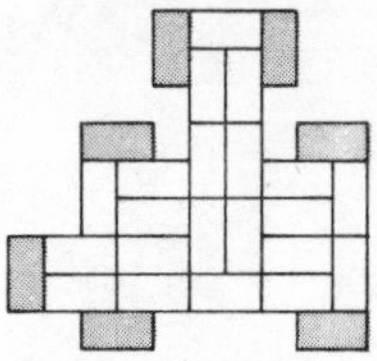	4		4 sol. in twenty-four cornered 20.7V3
24.9	V3	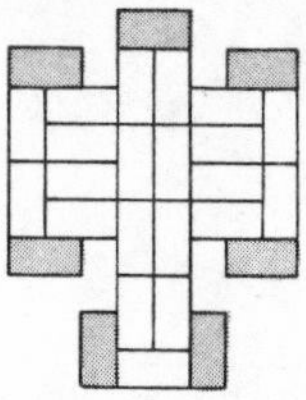	2(+2)